Treatise on Materials Science and Technology

VOLUME 24

Preparation and Properties of Thin Films

TREATISE ON MATERIALS SCIENCE AND TECHNOLOGY

VOLUME 24

PREPARATION AND PROPERTIES OF THIN FILMS

EDITED BY
K. N. TU
and
R. ROSENBERG

IBM Thomas J. Watson Research Center
Yorktown Heights, New York

1982

ACADEMIC PRESS
A Subsidiary of Harcourt Brace Jovanovich, Publishers

New York   London
Paris   San Diego   San Francisco   São Paulo   Sydney   Tokyo   Toronto

6834-6189

ACADEMIC PRESS, INC.
111 Fifth Avenue, New York, New York 10003

United Kingdom Edition published by
ACADEMIC PRESS, INC. (LONDON) LTD.
24/28 Oval Road, London NW1 7DX

LIBRARY OF CONGRESS CATALOG CARD NUMBER: 77-182672

ISBN 0-12-341824-0

PRINTED IN THE UNITED STATES OF AMERICA

82 83 84 85   9 8 7 6 5 4 3 2 1

Contents

PART I. INTRODUCTION

1   Preparation and Property Correlations in Thin Films

K. N. Tu and R. Rosenberg

PART II. VARIATION OF MICROSTRUCTURE OF THIN FILMS

2   Molecular Beam Epitaxy of Superlattices in Thin Films

A. C. Gossard

3   Epitaxial Growth of Silicon Structures—Thermal, Laser-, and Electron-Beam-Induced

S. S. Lau and J. W. Mayer

PART IV. VARIATION OF PATTERN OF THIN FILMS

8   Fabrication and Physical Properties of Ultrasmall Structures

R. B. Laibowitz and A. N. Broers

Contributors

Numbers in parentheses indicate the pages on which the authors' contributions begin.

C. L. BAUER (113), Department of Metallurgy and Materials Science, Carnegie-Mellon University, Pittsburgh, Pennsylvania 15213

ILAN A. BLECH (163), Department of Materials Engineering, Technion-Israel Institute of Technology, Haifa, Israel

A. N. BROERS (285), IBM Thomas J. Watson Research Center, Yorktown Heights, New York 10598

F. COSANDEY (113), Department of Mechanics and Materials Science, Rutgers University, Piscataway, New Jersey 08903

A. C. GOSSARD (13), Bell Laboratories, Murray Hill, New Jersey 07974

TUNG-SHENG KUAN (163), IBM Thomas J. Watson Research Center, Yorktown Heights, New York 10598

R. B. LAIBOWITZ (285), IBM Thomas J. Watson Research Center, Yorktown Heights, New York 10598

S. S. LAU (67), University of California at San Diego, La Jolla, California 92093

J. W. MAYER (67), Cornell University, Ithaca, New York 14850

MASANORI MURAKAMI (163), IBM Thomas J. Watson Research Center, Yorktown Heights, New York 10598

J. M. POATE (213), Bell Laboratories, Murray Hill, New Jersey 07974

R. ROSENBERG (3), IBM Thomas J. Watson Research Center, Yorktown Heights, New York 10598

K. N. TU (3, 237), IBM Thomas J. Watson Research Center, Yorktown Heights, New York 10598

Preface

The thin film is a form of material that finds applications in many modern electronic, magnetic, optical, and energy-related devices. In these applications a detailed understanding of thin-film properties and their dependence on structure, composition, and patterning is indispensable. This volume emphasizes the progress made in the preparation of thin films and the corresponding study of their properties. Full control of film preparation, combined with modern physical analyses, is essential in advancing our knowledge about submicron structures in VLSI electronics and about near-surface phenomena and interfacial properties. We believe that the time has come to introduce these topics to scientists and engineers who are interested in thin films.

We are grateful to Professor Herbert Herman of the State University of New York at Stony Brook and the staff of Academic Press for encouraging us to compile this work, to the contributors for their effort in this serious undertaking, to the management at IBM for support, and to Lorraine Miro and Wessie Wilson for secretarial work.

Part I

Introduction

1

Preparation and Property Correlations in Thin Films

K. N. TU and R. ROSENBERG

IBM Thomas J. Watson Research Center
Yorktown Heights, New York

In order to pursue a systematic thin-film study in the coming era of very large-scale integration (VLSI), where a premium is paid for generation of processes for miniaturization of microelectronic devices, there are in general four critical problem areas to consider. The first is thin-film preparation, the second is thin-film patterning (the fabrication of small structures of micron and submicron dimensions), the third is thin-film characterization (both structure and composition), and the fourth is thin-film properties (their correlation with structure, composition, and pattern). The theme of this volume is to illustrate some of the unique structure–composition–pattern–property correlations.

The capability of controlling thin-film microstructure, composition, and dimension is of increasing importance in thin-film applications. As microelectronics devices are made with denser and denser integration of circuits, the demand for unique and reliable properties of thin films has increased dramatically and many recent improvements have been achieved in the control of microstructure and composition. Consider as an example the case of metallic silicide contacts to Si. We can prepare epitaxial single-crystal, textured, polycrystalline, or amorphous silicide contacts. Then, by using ion implantation, we can introduce various dopants and impurities near the contact interface to influence contact properties such as Schottky barrier height and contact resistance. As the contact area decreases and becomes more shallow, the contact resistance rises rapidly and quickly becomes a limitation on the device performance. In addition to the technological relevance of submicron structures, there are basic scientific studies which are now in the beginning stages using these structures; for example, the use of thin-film weak links in superconductivity studies and the use of long and narrow thin-film lines in conduction localization studies. Hence, it is unique to thin-film research that one can not only correlate structure and composition with properties, but also various patterns with properties.

3

To understand and utilize the correlation between the different phases of thin-film study we must learn the necessary techniques to control thin-film structure and composition and to make the submicron patterns required for specific studies. This volume, following this introductory chapter (Part I), is therefore organized into three parts. In Part II, we emphasize the variation of microstructure of thin films and the study of physical properties of these films. By many techniques we can prepare epitaxial single-crystal thin films or multilayers—a stack of thin films—to form man-made superlattices. Bicrystal, textured, randomly oriented polycrystalline, fine-grained, and amorphous thin films can also be prepared in a controlled manner. Stresses in films and structure-related stress relaxation become important contributions to instability in various device structures such as Josephson tunnel junctions and are treated in detail. In Part III, the emphasis is placed on variation of the composition of thin films and related studies. Because the film thickness is of the order of the ion penetration depth for typical implantation studies, the composition of a thin film can be tailored by ion beam techniques; for example, a small compositional change can be achieved using ion implantation and at the same time a substantial change can be brought about by ion beam mixing. Then, a continuous compositional change can be obtained by codeposition using two *e*-guns whereas a fixed composition of an alloy or compound can be produced by sputtering techniques. A thorough summary of the state of understanding of shallow silicide formation and diffusion barrier effects is included as an example of the complex metallurgical situations that are evolving under the more stringent process requirements of miniaturization. In Part IV, a novel approach to submicron patterning is illustrated as one means of achieving ultrasmall structures and of investigating and utilizing the physical properties associated with such structures.

As we witness increasingly more rapid progress in thin-film studies and applications, it becomes more difficult to prepare a book that will cover the subject completely. For this reason, certain areas have been omitted in this volume, such as the preparation and properties of amorphous thin films and large-area thin films in storage and solar energy applications. Nevertheless, we hope that these and other omissions will have a negligible effect on this volume's modest goal of showing the potential use of thin films in basic and applied studies. In the following, a brief introduction to subsequent chapters is given.

Molecular Beam Epitaxy of Superlattices in Thin Films (Chapter 2)

Interest in the Group III–V semiconductor family has derived largely from the ability to separately manipulate energy band gap and lattice spacing by composition control. This has allowed the fabrication of a multitude of devices utilizing heterojunctions for the control of electron transport, e.g., the double-heterojunction (DH) laser, high-efficiency solar cells, GaAs bipolar transistors, superlattices, and modulation-doped GaAs MESFETs. The author, Gossard, in concentrating on the latter two, illustrates important characteristics of the epitaxial growth process and electron behavior at the heterojunction.

Molecular beam epitaxy (MBE) has become a useful experimental tool for deposition of high-quality pure films and the fabricated superlattice structures described in Chapter 2 were prepared by that technique. The control made possible by MBE was illustrated by the author, who deposited distinguishable layers about 10 Å thick of alternating GaAs and AlGaAs films. A wealth of detail about crystal growth processes may be achieved in studying ultrathin layers. Also, x-ray techniques employed with the superlattice clearly showed compositional variations produced during growth and anneal. Many different ordered superlattice structures are illustrated.

Although the original intent behind fabricating the superlattice was to observe novel electron transport perpendicular to the layers, one of its most interesting applications is the use of the in-plane transport characteristics. In the "modulation-doped" structure, AlGaAs layers are n-doped and intervening GaAs layers are left intrinsic. Because of the difference in conduction-band-edge energy, electrons spill into the GaAs near the interface and these electrons are able to move freely in it since the donor scattering centers are in the AlGaAs. Mobilities as high as 10^5 cm/s have been observed at liquid nitrogen temperatures. Applications of superlattice structures of this type to electronic devices are now being pursued in many laboratories.

The author also points out that because of the relatively thin layers, defects such as misfit dislocations may not form. In addition to improving present devices, such as superlattice lasers instead of the more degradable DH lasers, this could also open opportunities for the use of heterojunctions between materials heretofore considered incompatible because of nonideal lattice matching.

Epitaxial Growth of Silicon Structures—Thermal, Laser-, and Electron-Beam-Induced (Chapter 3)

In Chapter 3, Lau and Mayer explore the details by which amorphous films are transformed into polycrystalline or epitaxial layers by either solid-state thermal or beam annealing techniques. As a consequence of more complex device processing and the need to produce high-quality semiconductor layers at subnormal epitaxy temperatures, this subject has been receiving increased attention in recent years. Unfortunately, because a fundamental understanding of the mechanisms by which films transform has been elusive, a persistent opinion has it that high-quality films cannot be achieved by deposition and regrowth.

Lau and Mayer observe that the differences between deposited and ion-implanted and regrown amorphous silicon are mainly associated with interface contamination and impure films. In the implanted films where no contamination is present, epitaxial layer growth is impeded only if the amorphous layer is doped. With oxygen at the interface of a deposited layer and the substrate, initiation of the epitaxial growth process requires an initial time delay. This becomes important when the time delay is of the order of the incubation time for critical polycrystalline nucleation and growth, as measured by the authors, and the two processes, epitaxy and polycrystal nucleation, become competitive. On clean substrate surfaces, the authors find that deposited films have no delay time and are equivalent in quality to implanted and annealed structures. Also, recrystallization by cw laser scanning will not help the problems caused by interface contamination, but pulsed laser anneal in the regions where the absorption depth is higher than the deposited film thickness, will result in good epitaxial films.

With the teaching of this chapter and the increased availability of high-vacuum equipment and other *in situ* surface cleaning techniques, such as ion beam bombardment, it may be possible to prepare low-temperature high-quality device structures with a wider variety of vertical structures.

Characterization of Grain Boundaries in Bicrystalline Thin Films (Chapter 4)

It has been recognized that many important characteristics of thin-film layers are related to the properties of grain boundaries and interfaces in these layers as well as the intrinsic properties of the materials involved. This is a consequence of the relatively small grain size and high density of boundaries in deposited films. Detailed structure analysis and characterization of grain boundaries are therefore important considerations for the understanding and control of desirable film properties. In Chapter 4, Cosandey and Bauer review the present state of understanding of the detailed atomic configurations in various boundary types, properties associated with boundaries, methods of preparation of desired boundaries, and characterization techniques. Extension of the concepts to layer interfaces and boundaries between dissimilar materials appears to be readily achievable and would be of importance for many practical applications in device environments such as contact reactions, electromigration, and diffusion barriers.

This chapter considers a wide range of boundaries from low-angle to high-angle and specially oriented structures. Geometric and energetic models are reviewed, illustrating dislocation models for low-angle boundaries extending to complex coincidence site configurations involving atomic and rigid-body relaxations. Properties related to the character of the boundaries described are classified as chemical, e.g., solute segregation and second phase formation; kinetic, e.g., nonequilibrium processes such as diffusion; and electrical, e.g., grain boundary scattering of electrons or electromigration.

Fabrication of known boundaries is necessary to begin to develop the type of fundamental information that will move thin-film technology and metallurgical interactions into a more fundamental mode of investigation. To accomplish this, the authors have developed an epitaxial technique in which they deposit metal films onto bicrystal substrates. Detailed study by high-resolution TEM and lattice fringe imaging has resulted in a more systematic verification of the atomistic models than we had before and provides assurance that detailed structure–property relationships are at hand.

Mechanical Properties of Thin Films on Substrates (Chapter 5)

Many degradation modes in electronic devices in which thin films are an integral part are caused by the inability of films to withstand the high stresses resulting from device fabrication procedures. Chapter 5 deals mainly with stress induced by differences in the thermal expansion coefficients of film and substrate, e.g., in soft films like lead, where residual growth stress is low. The authors, Murakami, Kuan, and Blech, attempt to provide detailed descriptions of a biaxial strain model, strain relaxation mechanisms to relieve the stress, and application to understanding the role of grain structure and surface condition in lead alloy films used in Josephson junction devices.

A deformation map is presented in which the dominant strain relaxation mechanism is calculated as a function of stress and temperature. From the map, it was determined that dislocation glide is most important at high stress and at temperatures below room temperature, which would apply, for example, in the Josephson junction case, for cooling to operating temperature (liquid He). On annealing at or above room temperature, diffusional creep is controlling. For the latter case, grain boundary diffusion and volume diffusion give rise to two-stage relaxation. Convincing SEM and TEM evidence is given in support of the predictions of the map.

The complex stress situations that are a result of substrate constraint, film edges, the ability of films to maintain high elastic strains, and the mechanisms by which plasticity occurs are treated extensively in this chapter. As a result, the reader is given an extraordinary insight into film behavior under stress and with proper use of the rate equations this could allow extrapolation of the ideas to other systems and layer configurations.

Ion Beam Modification of Thin Films (Chapter 6)

As device structures have become shallow and the need for selective doping has become more prevalent, ion implantation of the dopant species has evolved as the primary technology for control of dopant distribution in semiconductors. In the process of implantation, many secondary events have been noticed, such as knock-ons of surface layer atoms into the bulk and sputtering of top layers during bombardment. On the whole, these have been considered as unwanted by-products, but recently significant effort has been devoted to utilizing these events to advantage, especially with the advent of high-current-density ion sources.

In Chapter 6, Poate illustrates the use of ion beams to modify the chemistry and structure of films, e.g., in producing metastable alloys, changing surface composition, and interface mixing. The surface composition of an alloy, e.g., PtSi, during implantation or sputtering becomes richer in the heavier element, e.g., Pt_2Si, because of relative sputter yields. It has also been reported that elements normally embedded in a surface layer can be found on the surface after ion bombardment, illustrating possible long-range cascading. As described by Poate, much recent experimentation has been reported that attempts to utilize these observations in creating mixing of multilayer metal films. Not only does mixing occur, but also metastable compositions typical of vapor-quenched films are produced, e.g., complete single-phase solid solutions are formed by bombardment of Ag and Cu layers even though the solid solubility is about 5% Ag in Cu. Formation of metastable metal phases or silicides by this technique, as described in the chapter, might have an application in producing uniform shallow contacts or controlled Schottky barrier heights, where the metal composition affects its electron work function.

Poate also illustrates the direct formation of metastable solid solutions by direct implant, e.g., implantation of Ag into Cu to form metastable single-phase compositions and of W or Ta into Cu substitutional sites (1%), where solubility is normally near zero. Tailoring of metal composition by direct implant or mixing through patterned masking layers may provide a valuable process enhancement for the future.

Thin Alloy Films for Metallization in Microelectronic Devices (Chapter 7)

In considering the difficulties in developing the necessary process enhancements for moving into the VLSI era, by far the most demanding innovations lie in the metallurgical system. As patterns become narrower and device structures shallower, standard processes and metallic components become subject to a host of degradation modes dealing mainly with metal–silicon and metal–metal interactions. Chapter 7 offers the reader a detailed summary of the types of problems workers in the silicon industry have confronted over the years, and describes extremely novel approaches to minimize the various degradation mechanisms.

Because of the nature of most difficulties, major emphasis is placed on multilayer-film interactions, the use of alloy rather than single-component films, and fabrication and preservation of shallow contacts to silicon. A novel approach encourages the formation of an intermetallic compound, but one which is self-limiting to further interaction. An example would be a reaction of Pb with AgAu alloy whereby some $PbAu_2$ may form but Pb and Ag do not form an intermetallic; as a result of free energy change arguments. The $PbAu_2$ formation ceases and the system reaches an equilibrium state. For shallow contacts to silicon, it is necessary to provide a means for minimizing loss of silicon by formation of a silicide. Three methods are described: (1) depositing a layer of silicon on the top surface of the metal or using a metal–silicon alloy prior to silicide formation, (2) using a metal system where M_xSi ($x = 5$) is stable, and (3) using an alloy AB where ASi forms and B separates to the top. The latter is multifunctional since the separation into layers produces a natural diffusion barrier to subsequent metal deposition and processing. For example, in the system $Pd_{80}W_{20}/Si$, Pd_2Si forms next to Si and W forms a surface layer. Not only is less Si used, but the W forms a barrier to Al diffusion and prevents Al degradation of the Pd_2Si. Extensive use of this reaction is made by the author to form controllable high-Schottky-barrier-height materials using near-noble metal–refractory metal alloys. Low Schottky barriers were made using rare-earth metals, e.g., Gd, in place of the near-noble metal.

In reading this chapter, it will be apparent how sophisticated the present research efforts to bring this technology into the future have become. Integration of some of these concepts into the manufacture of VLSI chips will be a formidable but necessary task.

Fabrication and Physical Properties of Ultrasmall Structures
(Chapter 8)

Thin-film and device structures are being patterned routinely in the laboratory with resolutions of 1 μm and in some cases 0.5 μm using electron-beam direct writing or x-ray lithography. It is only a matter of time before these technologies reach the product areas and provide the impetus for even higher integration levels and more stringent control over basic material properties. In fact, one of the more interesting possibilities in research at present is the use of even finer structures to alter properties or create new applications of thin films. Chapter 8 by Laibowitz and Broers is included as representative of this new area of thin-film research.

The authors developed a new fabrication method to produce their "nanostructures," which are of the order of 10–20 nm wide, inasmuch as other techniques are not workable down to this resolution level. They use surface oil contamination on their samples, which when exposed to a focused electron beam, builds up a carbonaceous deposit. This deposit is then used as an etch mask for subtractively removing unwanted material, leaving the exposed pattern behind. To illustrate the features of such fine lines, they studied Nb films and the superconducting behavior of one-dimensional conductors. They were able to illustrate theoretically predictable Josephson behavior, i.e., zero-voltage current and switching, which up to now has been observed only in superconducting tunnel junctions. Two of these "microbridges" in a loop arrangement also behaved as a SQUID (quantum interference device) with magnetic field detection of the order of Planck's constant. The microbridges have been used as high-frequency (>100 GHz) detectors, to study fluctuation effects, and to define a new term the authors call "average intergranular resistance," which applies when T_c across boundaries is lower than normal T_c within the grains.

Other metallic systems and physical phenomena are described in this chapter, and it is likely that the reader with some imagination can dream up many other possible applications of this technique to the study of fundamental material properties. Although not presently being pursued as a VLSI pattern generation method, ultimate technology extension may require such new procedures.

Part II

Variation of Microstructure of Thin Films

2

Molecular Beam Epitaxy of Superlattices in Thin Films

A. C. GOSSARD

Bell Laboratories
Murray Hill, New Jersey

I. Introduction

Superlattices are multilayered periodic structures having dimensions which approach the atomic spacings of the constituent materials comprising them. They are of interest because they are essentially new forms of matter with properties which often differ from those of their constituents. They may occur naturally as, for example, in layered intercalation compounds and in silicon carbide. They may also be synthesized artificially by alternate thin-film deposition. Artificial synthesis has the potential for great flexibility in the structures which can be achieved and has been used to make organic, metallic, semiconducting, and amorphous superlattices.

Early interest in semiconductor superlattices stemmed from proposals that novel transport phenomena would occur in such structures (*1*). The semiconductor superlattices have been extensively studied. The most useful growth technique for semiconductor superlattice deposition is molecular beam epitaxy (MBE), an ultra-high-vaccum evaporation technique for growth of epitaxial crystal films. MBE was developed by the work of Günther (*2*), Steinberg and Scruggs (*3*), Davey and Pankey (*4*), Arthur (*5*), and Cho (*6, 6a*).

With MBE it is possible to produce single-crystal semiconductor films possessing very smooth surfaces and having extremely finely defined film thicknesses—desirable features for superlattice formation. Reviews of the MBE technique may be found in References *7–10*. The smoothness and control can extend down to the scale of atomic sizes and allow the creation of multilayered structures of atomic dimensions (*11*).

Electrons in semiconductor superlattices are acted on by superlattice potential variations which can confine electrons in certain layers, producing new conductivity properties. The allowed energy levels of the electrons can be strongly altered by quantization effects when the confined regions are sufficiently thin. This in turn produces new optical properties. New lattice vibrational properties have also been observed in semiconductor superlattices.

Superlattices have been produced in other types of materials also. Multilayered organic films have been deposited by the Langmuir–Blodgett technique of repeated alternate dipping (*12*), and alternate-layer metal films have been produced by evaporation or sputtering (*13*). The superlattice structures of both of these classes of systems, as well as of the semiconductor superlattices, have been determined with x-ray diffraction measurements; they show ordered layered structures. The organic films and the alternate-metal films are both useful for artificial diffraction gratings for soft x-rays (*14, 15*). High x-ray scattering strengths are obtained in the organic films by incorporating heavy atoms in certain layers, and high scattering strengths are obtained in the metal superlattices by alternating layers of heavy and light atoms (e.g., tungsten and carbon). Magnetic properties of these superlattices are of interest also. Incorporation of manganese in Langmuir–Blodgett films has produced a realization of a two-dimensional magnetic system (*16*), and alternation of magnetic and nonmagnetic layers (e.g., copper and nickel) in metal superlattices affords an opportunity to observe the influence of the interface between layers of nominally magnetic atoms and nonmagnetic atoms in a transition metal (*17, 18*). Also of interest in the metal superlattices are enhancement of elastic moduli which occur in certain superlattices (*19*) and observation of interdiffusion constants which are especially strongly dependent on superlattice structure in cases where ordered phases of the constituents are possible (*20*). Metal superlattices in which constituents are superconducting have also been studied, and have shown critical fields which are strongly modified by the superlattice structure and superconducting properties which change between two- and three-dimensional behavior with layer thickness and temperature variations (*21*).

The organic and metallic superlattices tend to be highly oriented but not single-crystal films, unlike the semiconductor superlattices, which can be perfectly epitaxial (*22*). Crystallinity is not a prerequisite for superlattice formation though, and superlattices have been formed in amorphous materials with instructive results for the study of interdiffusion and magnetism in amorphous solids (*23*). Superlattices have also been formed between metals having different crystal structures, and have shown orientational texture and compositional coherence perpendicular to the layers, even though crystalline coherence lengths within the layer planes are short (*24*). Semiconductor superlattices have also been produced using techniques other than MBE. Superlattices of the elemental semiconductors silicon and germanium have been formed epitaxially on silicon by alternate evaporation of silicon and germanium in vacuum. These superlattices showed a layered structure, although they had heavy misfit dislocations because of the 4% difference in lattice spacing between the materials (*25*). Multitarget sputtering of GaSb and InSb onto glass substrates has produced superlattices with oriented polycrystalline structures (*26*). Alternate liquid-phase epitaxy of InP and $In_{1-x}Ga_xP_{1-x}As_z$ layers has produced epitaxial multiple layers $\lesssim 500$ Å thick (*27*). Metal-organic vapor deposition of multiple GaAs and $Al_xGa_{1-x}As$ layers has been successful in yielding epitaxial layers as thin as 50 Å by alternately introducing metal-organic gallium and aluminum reactants in the vapor stream of a reactor (*28*). Layers grown by metal-organic vapor deposition have high crystalline quality. However, MBE has been the most extensively used technique for multilayer synthesis. The superlattice systems which have been studied in the greatest detail and are the smoothest and most highly controlled are GaAs and $Al_xGa_{1-x}As$ multilayers (*11,29*) and InAs and GaSb multilayers (*30*).

II. Molecular Beam Epitaxy

The MBE technique of single-crystal film growth employs beams of atoms and molecules impinging in vacuum on a heated substrate crystal. Excellent reviews of the technique have been given recently by Cho and Arthur (*7*), Wood (*8*), and Ploog (*9*), and in a volume edited by Pamplin (*10*). The essential elements of a growth system are shown in Fig. 1 for a system capable of growing GaAs and AlAs with *n*- or *p*-type doping. Sources of the molecular beams are typically heated effusion ovens con-

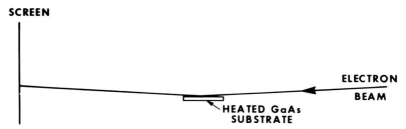

Fig. 1. Essential elements of a MBE system for GaAs and $Al_xGa_{1-x}As$ superlattice growth. Molecular beams effuse from heated evaporation sources onto a hot single-crystal GaAs substrate surface, where epitaxial growth occurs. Shutters in front of sources interrupt growth to allow layered structures to be formed. Electron diffraction may simultaneously be observed on the screen.

taining elemental charges of the crystal constituents. Electron-beam evaporation may also be used to provide beam sources. The effusion ovens may contain the compound semiconductors themselves rather than the elemental sources. Heating of the substrate crystal on which the beams are deposited is generally required to produce enough surface mobility of the atoms to grow single-crystal films in epitaxial register with the substrates, and special substrate preparation to provide a clean single crystal surface on which to start epitaxial growth is required. Preparation techniques for the growth substrate include mechanical polishing, chemical etching, solvent rinsing, ion sputter-cleaning, and heating in vacuum. Growth of pure crystals with few defects requires pure source materials, ovens which do not contaminate the sources or the vacuum, substrates with clean surfaces and few defects, and an ultra-high-vacuum environment. Chilled surfaces around the ovens and substrates are effective in trapping impurity gases and in preventing outgassing of impurities from surfaces which otherwise might be heated. Ion pumps, cryopumps, and sublimation pumps are all effective in producing the requisite ultrahigh vacuum for MBE. In addition to the common ultra-high-vacuum background gas constituents, the growth chamber will typically contain larger amounts of the more volatile growth components, which may partially be reflected from the growing film surface and from the chamber walls.

The MBE process consists of atoms or molecules impinging and adsorbing on the growth surface and migrating to locations where they can incorporate more or less permanently into the crystal structure. Group III–V compounds are most successfully grown with an excess of the Group V element fluxes relative to the Group III fluxes. The compounds have narrow stoichiometry ranges and the excess Group V flux, relative to that need to produce the stoichiometric composition ratio, desorbs from the surface under proper growth conditions (5, 31, 32). Dopant atoms vary in their probability of incorporation in the growing crystal (33). Some, such as the p-type dopant Zn for GaAs, largely reflect from the surface without incorporation, although they can be made to incorporate by being ionized in the vacuum and then implanted during GaAs growth by acceleration to kilovolt energies. More reactive atoms such as Si or Be stick with complete incorporation, whereas some, such as Sn in GaAs, adhere to the surface but tend to concentrate there, without being immediately incorporated in the growing film.

Because MBE takes place in an ultrahigh vacuum, it has the attractive feature that the films are available for surface analysis, even during the growth process itself. Electron diffraction from the growing surface is especially useful and can be observed from a glancing incidence electron beam of kilovolt or higher energies (6, 6a). Surface reconstructions and smoothness can be monitored. The chemical composition of the surface can be monitored by briefly interrupting growth to examine Auger spectra from the surface.

One of the remarkable features of MBE is the smoothness of the film surfaces which can be created. This can be observed, for example, from scanning electron microscopy (SEM) replicas of the grown surfaces or from the glancing incidence electron diffraction during deposition of the films (34) (Fig. 2). For smooth surfaces the electron diffraction patterns show streaks perpendicular to the crystal surface, which are characteristic of two-dimensional diffraction. The atoms producing the diffraction pattern lie predominantly in smooth surface planes, producing the streaked patterns. The pattern is direct evidence that the growing surface can be atomically smooth over the short distances probed by the incident electron beam wave packets. The physical mechanism underlying the smooth growth is surface migration of atoms to sites of larger binding energy at step edges. This occurs at the edges of low spots on the crystal surface and preferentially fills in the low-lying planes, producing a smooth crystal surface (35).

The smooth surface morphology is an important requisite for producing

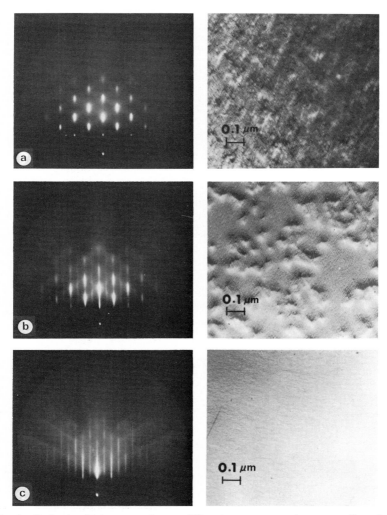

Fig. 2. Reflection high-energy electron-diffraction patterns and corresponding photomicrographs of Pt–C replicas of the same surface. (a) Polish-etched (001) GaAs substrate heated in vacuum to 855 K for 5 min. (b) Deposition of GaAs with an average thickness of 150 Å. (c) Deposition of 1 μm GaAs (7).

smoothly layered multiple-layer films, and a buffer layer for smoothing the substrate irregularities is preferably grown before superlattice deposition commences. The other principal requirement for creating ultrathin layers and multilayered structures is precise and abrupt control of the molecular beams. Rapid control can be obtained by shutters at the orifices of the effusion cell beam sources. When a shutter is closed between a source of atoms of high sticking coefficient and the remainder of the vacuum system, the effusing atoms stick to the shutter surface, and the flux of that species at the substrate crystal and in the rest of the system is abruptly reduced (*11*).

Shutter operating times for opening and closing by pneumatic or electromechanical means can readily be made much less than the deposition time for a monolayer, which is typically of order 1 s in MBE. For Group III–V compounds, the Group III elements which determine the growth rates stick nearly completely to the shutters. Thus, abruptly cutting off the group III species immediately stops growth of the crystal. Shuttering of the Group V element (e.g., As) is often not necessary, and in fact may purposely not be employed in order to maintain a flux at the surface of the crystal in order to replenish any Group V element which might preferentially evaporate while growth is stopped. Superlattices with different or mixed Group V elements (e.g., $GaSb_{1-y}As_y$ and $In_{1-x}Ga_xAs$) may also be grown. They present the complication that the different Group V element incorporation rates are not simply proportional to their relative arrival rates. In general, control of the flux rates is achieved by closely controlling the temperature of the effusion cells and monitoring the flux rates. This can be accomplished by closed-loop temperature control via thermocouple sensing of cell temperature (*7*) or by use of mass spectrometers (*7*), collimated ion gauge detectors (*9*), or optical fluorescence beam monitors adjacent to the crystal substrate (*11, 9*) to selectively measure beam fluxes and background constituents of the vacuum in order to determine appropriate cell temperatures. Absolute calibration of deposition rates results from physical or optical measurement of total deposited film thicknesses following growth. This is typically accomplished by step height measurements next to masked areas in which no growth occurs. For multiple, noncollinear molecular beams, as generally employed, separate shadows may be cast for different ovens, allowing separate measurement of deposition of different species (*36*).

In the same manner that the majority constituent beams can be controlled with shutters, dopant atom beams may also be switched on and off, allowing the growth of doping superlattices as well as composition superlattices (*37, 38*). Sharp doping profiles require the use of dopant atoms which not only can be interrupted by the shutter but which incorporate completely in the growing layer without surface segregation or concentration. The GaAs *n*-type dopants silicon and the *p*-dopant beryllium have this property, for example (*38, 39*).

III. Structure of Semiconductor Superlattices

Using the MBE techniques described above, a variety of multilayered semiconductor superlattices have been grown. Structural study of the superlattices, most of which have layer thickness dimensions in the submicron regime, requires high-resolution characterization techniques. Transmission electron microscopy (TEM) and x-ray diffraction are particularly useful probes, whereas sputter Auger profiling, SEM, and optical microscopy of angle-lapped structures are also helpful. Following early growth of relatively large-scale and imperfect multilayers by chemical vapor deposition (40) and liquid-phase epitaxy (41), MBE was used to produce alternate 1700-Å layers of GaAs and $Al_xGa_{1-x}As$ (42), which were observed by optical microscopy. Multilayer stacks of GaAs and AlAs films for optical interference filters with layer thicknesses of 1100 and 1300 Å were grown by MBE. These stacks showed the layering in SEM images of cleaved cross sections and also showed the predicted optical interference effects of resonant reflection and transmission (43, 44). Nuclear backscattering produced oscillatory backscattering spectra in MBE-grown multilayers with 1200-Å period (45, 46). The sharpness of the backscattered peaks suggested period variation of less than 200 Å over a 2-mm spot. Neither the optical technique, SEM, nor the backscattering method could resolve layers in the ≤100 Å thickness range, however. Auger electron compositional profiling during ion sputtering is capable of this level of resolution and was used to observe 50-Å-thick GaAs and $Al_xGa_{1-x}As$ MBE multilayers (47). Also showing that multilayers in this thickness range could be controllably grown by MBE were observations of separate Raman spectral lines from the different superlattice layers (48), observation of resonant tunneling to electrons bound in thin-layer quantum states (49), and optical observation of thin-layer quantum states of electrons (50). These effects will be discussed in greater detail in the next sections.

One of the most informative techniques for observation of superlattice structure and perfection is TEM of thin cross sections of superlattices. In this technique, a bar is initially cleaved from a crystal on which a superlattice has been grown and then thinned by mechanical polishing, followed by ion-mill thinning until parts of the cross section are thin enough to allow electron transmission (a few hundred angstroms) (51). As illustrated in Fig. 3, ordered layers of the superlattice present a regularly varying crystal potential to transmitted electrons, producing superlattice and fundamental-lattice diffraction spots as well as superlattice images in the transmitted electron beam. Use of an aperture in the diffraction plane allows the image to be enhanced by diffraction contrast. Regions of the superlattice which are disordered, random, or interdiffused, produce a random crystal poten-

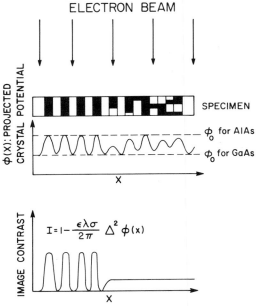

Fig. 3. Transmission electron microscope diffraction and imaging from cross section of a superlattice film containing ordered (left) and disordered (right) layers. Ordered layers provide a regular potential to the electron beam, resulting in coherent diffraction spots and a layered image of the ordered portion of the cross section.

tial, and do not contribute to the superlattice diffraction spots or show a superlattice image.

Using the transmission electron diffraction and imaging techniques, a number of MBE superlattices were studied. In the thickness range near 100 Å, multiple layers of GaAs and $Al_{0.4}Ga_{0.6}As$ grown for study of Ga and Al interdiffusion could be imaged with electrons from the (200) diffraction spot of GaAs (*51*) (Fig. 4). This diffraction spot is more intense for $Al_{0.4}Ga_{0.6}As$ than for GaAs (because of a near cancellation of the scattering intensities for gallium and arsenic), and consequently the aluminum-containing layers are imaged as bright regions. The brightness gives a measure of aluminum content, and densitometer traces of the interfaces allow determination of the interface sharpness, which is apparently of order 10 Å or less in the sample before interdiffusion annealing. The sample was grown at a substrate temperature of 600°C, but required 900°C annealing for 2 hr to produce the amount of interdiffusion seen in Fig. 4. The slight waviness of the interfaces seen in the figure is also well resolved in this kind of study, but is not present in all parts of the sample.

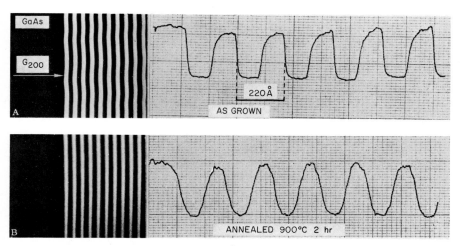

Fig. 4. TEM dark-field (200) images of 200-Å-period superlattice of GaAs and $Al_{0.4}Ga_{0.6}As$ before and after annealing at 900°C for 2 hr are shown on the left. Densitometer traces of plates are shown on the right. The (200) diffracted beam is more intense for $Al_xGa_{1-x}As$ than for GaAs, making $Al_xGa_{1-x}As$ layers bright.

Still thinner multilayers were grown by MBE and were found to be smooth and ordered in TEM cross-sectional studies. For example, sequences of 8.0 monolayers (22.6 Å) of GaAs and 1.3 monolayers (3.7 Å) of AlAs repeated ~400 times, followed by a 6.1 monolayer/3.4 monolayer sequence repeated ~400 times, gave an interface region image shown in Fig. 5 (*36*). The superlattice diffraction produced by the layers of the right-hand side of the image is shown at the bottom of the figure. The thinnest multilayers whose images could be clearly resolved in TEM have been alternate atomic bilayers of GaAs and AlAs on a (111) GaAs substrate, each of which has a thickness of 9.8 Å (*51*). Such an image is shown in Fig. 6, in which definite layering can be seen at the deposited alternate period, although with imperfections in the layer structure. The layering imperfections (marked by arrows) occur at spacings of several hundred angstroms, showing that the layers and interfaces are coherent to within two monolayers over lengths of hundreds of angstroms both parallel and perpendicular to the growth surfaces.

For still shorter, alternate single-monolayer deposition periods, TEM images could barely be resolved. But TEM electron diffraction could be observed from alternate single-monolayer depositions which produced alternate monolayer ordering (*22*). The superlattice diffraction spot intensities were sensitively dependent on substrate temperature during growth, as illustrated in Fig. 7. A growth temperature below a critical temperature

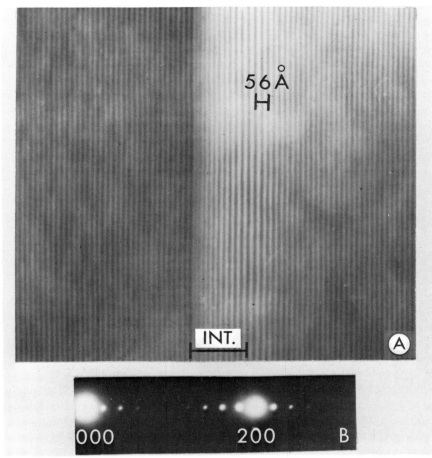

Fig. 5. Cross-sectional TEM image of $(GaAs)_n(AlAs)_m$ superlattices, where each period consists of n monolayers of GaAs and m monolayers of AlAs on a (100) GaAs substrate. For left-hand layers, $n = 8.0$ and $m = 1.3$. For layers at right, $n = 6.1$ and $m = 3.4$. Transmission electron diffraction pattern of the right-hand side is seen at the bottom. The (000) and (200) spots are fundamental diffraction lines of GaAs and remaining spots are superlattice diffraction spots.

of about 610°C was required to produce an ordered alternate-monolayer superlattice. At that temperature and above, no superlattice spots could be observed. Just below that temperature, random ordered and disordered alternate-monolayer domains were found. The superlattice periodicity $d = \lambda/(2 \sin \theta)$, where θ is the scattering angle between the fundamental GaAs spots at $(2n, 0, 0)$ and the superlattice spots, is in experimental

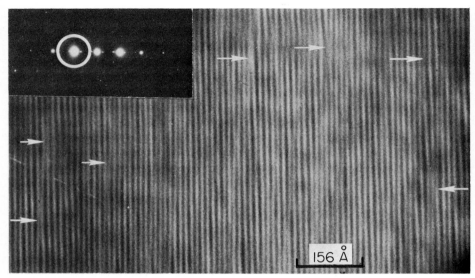

Fig. 6. Cross-sectional TEM bright-field lattice image of alternate bilayer superlattice $(GaAs)_2(AlAs)_2$ on a (111) substrate. Beams used to form image are shown within the circle. Arrows mark defects in the superlattice.

agreement with the deposition periodicity. Splitting of the superlattice diffraction spot is seen for nonintegral deposition periods, although an ambiguity exists as to which fundamental spot the superlattice scattering angle is to be measured from and consequently as to whether the period is slightly greater than or slightly less than two monolayers (*22*).

The observation of such evidence for ordered layered structures from alternate-monolayer MBE deposition gives direct information on the MBE crystal growth mechanism. One may conclude immediately that crystal growth in the ordered monolayer regime is occurring in a layer mode. The growth surfaces must be nearly atomically smooth, and interdiffusion between adjacent atom layers must not be extending more than a monolayer.

For the higher growth temperature where no monolayer ordering is observed, the growth surface could be atomically rough (*35, 52*), island growth could be occurring (*35*), or interdiffusion across layers could be occurring during growth. Interdiffusion across layers would have to be confined to growing surface layers, since interdiffusion studies (*53*) to be described below show that bulk interdiffusion far from the surface would be too slow to interdiffuse adjacent monolayers at any of the growth temperatures studied. The random nucleation of disordered domains on approach to the critical temperature makes it more likely that island growth

FILM GROWTH ON [100] SUBSTRATES

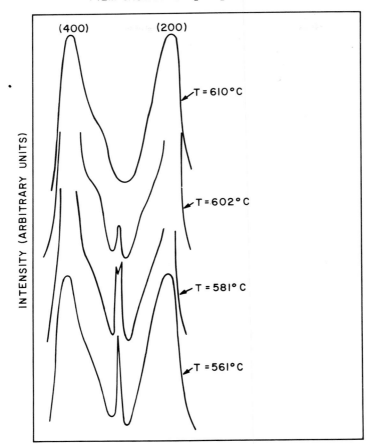

Fig. 7. TEM diffraction from alternate-monolayer superlattices deposited at various substrate temperatures. Alternate-monolayer superlattice diffraction spot at (300) is observed only at growth temperatures of 602°C and below.

and an atomically rough crystal surface are primarily responsible for the absence of monolayer ordering above the critical growth temperature for alternate-monolayer order (*22*).

The critical temperature for ordered layer growth is dependent on the layer periodicity and on the relative layer thicknesses (*22*). For example, growth temperatures of 630°C provided ordered layers of $(GaAs)_{2.9}(AlAs)_{0.9}$ but not of $(GaAs)_{0.9}(AlAs)_{2.7}$, where the subscripts refer to the number of (2.8 Å) monolayers deposited for each constituent in the alternate-growth sequence.

Nonintegral numbers of monolayers are deposited by shuttering off the molecular beams at a time other than the exact time needed to deposit integral numbers of monolayers. Because of variations in beam intensity across a substrate and because of uncertainties in measuring and controlling evaporation rates, essentially all depositions are of nonintegral numbers of monolayers. It should also be pointed out that because of inaccuracies in the orientation and cutting of substrate crystal slices and unevenness in their subsequent polishing and etching, substrates are essentially never aligned on exact principal crystal orientations. Consequently, surfaces from different atomic planes are simultaneously exposed and grown on. For all of these reasons, the lateral extent or coherence of a monolayer must be limited in length, and by similar considerations, the atomic layer sequence above any exact point in the crystal cannot be precisely the deposited sequence, although the average layer sequence may match the deposited layer sequence closely (*22*).

Although TEM showed coherent layered structures and the presence of alternate-atomic-monolayer composition modulation, it did not give a precise determination of the *amplitude* of the composition modulation in these regimes. This is because precise intensity measurements are difficult under the multiple-scattering conditions of transmission electron diffraction. A technique which is better suited to intensity measurement is x-ray diffraction, and this method has been applied to a number of superlattices. Sequences of GaAs and AlAs layers on GaAs substrates with a few $\sim$130-Å periods showed series of interference peaks in small-angle x-ray scattering, which agreed closely with theoretical calculations for smooth layers (*54*). More extended superlattices with shorter periods, down to alternate-monolayer structures also on GaAs substrates, produced superlattice diffraction spot satellites around the fundamental lattice Bragg peaks (200), (400), . . . , as shown in Fig. 8 (*53, 55*). Positions of the satellite peaks again yielded superlattice periods in agreement with the deposited periods of the epitaxial growth, with the splitting about $l = 3.00$ of the peak for the trace labeled (1.2, 1) coming from the deposition period of a nonintegral number of monolayers. Integration of the superlattice line intensities in directions parallel and perpendicular to the scattering vectors provided the input for Fourier transformation of the diffraction pattern in order to yield the real-space composition profiles of the superlattices (*53*). Absolute calibration of the superlattice intensities was obtained by comparing them with the fundamental-lattice diffraction spot intensities. Using this procedure, real-space profiles were obtained, such as that shown in Fig. 9 for a (7, 4) deposition sequence of GaAs and AlAs monolayers. These profiles showed an aluminum concentration of 100% in the center of the AlAs layers and a gallium concentration of 100% in the center of the GaAs

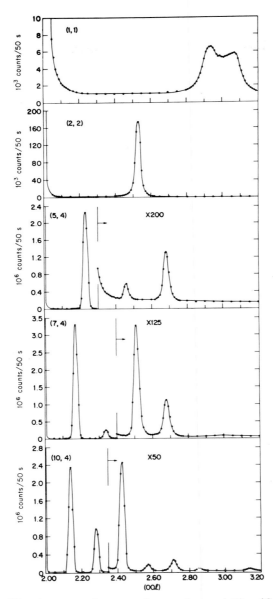

Fig. 8. X-ray diffraction spectra from monolayer scale superlattices $(GaAs)_n(AlAs)_m$ between (002) fundamental lattice peak and (3.2, 0, 0) for several superlattices.

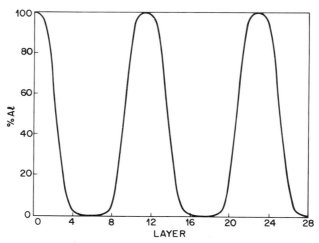

Fig. 9. Compositional profile of a $(GaAs)_7(AlAs)_4$ superlattice obtained from Fourier transformation of x-ray diffraction satellite spot intensities.

layers, to the precision of the measurement and calculation. The two layers at each interface showed a mixed average composition in the profile, and all other layers were within 10% of the nominal deposited concentration. Thus, the x-ray diffraction measurements provide a high-resolution means of determining quantitative composition profiles at the shortest distance scales and show sharp composition profiles in the GaAs/AlAs superlattice system. Mixed composition layers are confined predominantly to the atomic monolayers at the interfaces.

The x-ray diffraction technique can also be used to measure the average composition profiles in the still thinner alternate-single-monolayer range (53). For a sample with deposition sequence $(GaAs)_{1.2\ monolayers}$-$(AlAs)_{1.0\ monolayers}$, the amplitude of the superlattice satellites yielded a cosine-wave composition profile with maximum and minimum average aluminum content of 60% and 35%, respectively, in adjacent layers. The fact that 100 to 0% aluminum composition wave amplitude is not seen reflects partial compositional mixing between adjacent layers, as had been observed also at the interfaces in the longer-period superlattices above.

The same technique of obtaining composition profiles provides a sensitive probe for interatomic diffusion at the monolayer scale. Superlattice structures can be annealed after growth, and changes in the composition profile caused by interdiffusion can be monitored. An example of such profiles after annealing of a $(GaAs)_{12}(AlAs)_9$ superlattice for various amounts of time at 860°C can be seen in Fig. 10 (53). The annealing is done in an

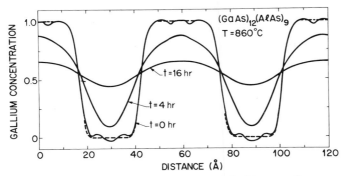

Fig. 10. Compositional profiles before and after 4- and 16-hr annealing treatments of a $(GaAs)_{12}(AlAs)_9$ superlattice. The annealing temperature is 860°C. Wiggles near Ga concentrations 0 and 1.0 are artifacts of the Fourier transformation technique.

arsenic atmosphere to prevent the creation of arsenic vacancies by loss of arsenic from the surface of the sample during annealing. Values of the diffusion constants obtained from this and other measurement techniques are shown in Fig. 11. It is notable that the diffusion constants for Ga in AlAs and Al in GaAs differ by an order of magnitude, with the rate in the GaAs layers being greater. Interdiffusion measurements have also been made by electron microscopy (*51*), by optical absorption spectrum measurements (*58*), and by Auger composition profiling during ion sputter etching (*56*). The basis for the optical absorption determination of interdiffusion is the change in the size-quantized electron energy levels in thin 200-Å layers from change in the potential well structure upon diffusion. This will be described in the following section (*57, 58*). The results from the various techniques are in qualitative, although not quantitative agreement. All measurements show that the superlattices are stable at the MBE growth temperature and at room temperature (Fig. 11). A probable mechanism for the interdiffusion is vacancy diffusion via the arsenic sublattice (*59*).

The homogeneity of the layering periods and the flatness of the layers may also be determined by diffraction measurements. Over large-area samples, the nonuniformity in layer periods was measured by variation in superlattice Bragg angles from point to point on the surface and was found to be governed by the geometry of the substrate and sources, which determine the distribution of arrival rates for the various species (*53*). Over shorter distances, of the sizes of the x-ray beam diameter and the total superlattice thickness, the superlattice diffraction spot longitudinal linewidth in the direction perpendicular to the layers gives an upper limit for the nonuniformity of the layering period and for the coherence length over

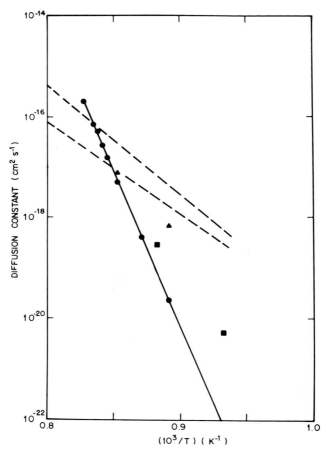

Fig. 11. Diffusion constants in $Al_xGa_{1-x}As$ superlattices as obtained by four different measurement techniques. Dashed lines represent composition-dependent measurements by Auger profiling. ■—The diffusion constant in GaAs by x-ray diffraction measurements; ▲, ●—the diffusion constants by electron microscopy and optical absorption spectrum measurements, respectively.

which the layering sequence continues before a major phase discontinuity. For (5, 4), (7, 4) and (10, 4) superlattices of $(GaAs)_n$ and $(AlAs)_m$ monolayers, this half-width is approximately 2% of the superlattice scattering angle, corresponding to a maximum period inhomogeneity of ±2% of the average period (*55*). For a (5, 4) superlattice, this is only ±0.5 Å, or less than the thickness of a single monolayer. The coherence length between faults in the stacking of the superlattice layers is more restrictively determined from TEM images, which, as mentioned above, exceed several hundred angstroms between faults (*51*). The half-widths of the superlattice spots of the (1.2, 1.0) superlattice of GaAs and AlAs were 5% of the scattering angle, corresponding to a ±0.3 Å inhomogeneity of the average period and a length of coherent atom stacking of ∼20 Ga atom planes or ∼60 Å.

The superlattice diffraction spot linewidth in the direction parallel to the growth surface provides a sensitive measure of flatness of the superlattice layers. Layers with a variation $\Delta\theta$ in their orientation from point to point within the x-ray beam will produce superlattice diffraction spots spreading over an angle $\Delta\theta$ from the fundamental spots, producing a superlattice linewidth parallel to the surface of $\Delta\theta$ times the superlattice scattering angle (*53*). The transverse widths shown in Fig. 12 are similar in magnitude to longitudinal widths, and correspond to flatness of ±15 mrad for the samples shown in the figure. In some but not all samples, the superlattice spot linewidths in the transverse directions were anisotropic, corresponding to greater flatness and longer coherence lengths in (110) directions than in ($\bar{1}$10) directions of the (100) growth plane (*53*). In those samples showing this anisotropy, ridgelike surface waviness could be resolved in Nomarski phase contrast optical microscopy of the epitaxial film surface. This demonstrates that the growth process is anisotropic, and that atom motion on the surface during epitaxial growth is inequivalent in the (110) and ($\bar{1}$10) directions. This is physically reasonable, since the growth surface reconstruction of 2 × 8 symmetry (*60*) is different in these two directions, as is the bonding of arsenic–gallium surface chains in the two directions. The magnitude of the effect is variable from sample to sample and its detailed etiology has not been determined.

A.   Other Superlattice Systems: GaAs/InAs, GaAs/Ge, GaAs/InSb, and Si/Ge

Gallium arsenide and aluminum arsenide make a favorable couple for superlattice growth because their lattice constants match to nearly 1 part in 10³, the Ga and Al constituents are isovalent, and the GaAs and AlAs crystal structures are identical. The 10^{-3} relative difference in lattice constants is enough that AlAs layers are compressed along the growth plane and the lattice parameter of the superlattice in the growth direction is expanded by the AlAs. However, misfit dislocations do not generally occur for these superlattices on GaAs substrates.

Effects of lattice mismatch are more pronounced in growth of Si/Ge superlattices (*25*) and in growth of GaAs/InAs superlattices (*11*). Silicon/germanium superlattice growth by ultra-high-vacuum evaporation on sub-

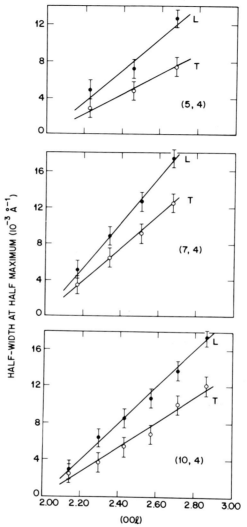

Fig. 12. Superlattice x-ray diffraction-spot linewidths in the longitudinal and transverse directions. Longitudinal linewidth shows that layers are uniform in thickness to ~2%. Transverse linewidth shows that layers are flat to ~15 mrad.

strates gave a heavily misfit-dislocated structure. The growth surface showed the crosshatched ridges characteristic of misfit dislocation networks (25). Alternate layers were deposited in the original studies and the resulting films were presumably layered, although structural studies were not reported.

A still greater difference in lattice constant exists for GaAs and InAs, with the InAs lattice spacing being ∼7% greater than that of GaAs. Alternate layer growth of this pair was studied with deposition by alternately shuttered gallium and indium ovens (*11*). Epitaxial films on GaAs were misfit-dislocated with characteristic crosshatched surface patterns. Transmission electron microscope cross-sectional images showed highly ordered layers in the regions between dislocations, however, illustrating that alternate layer growth in the monolayer regime of thicknesses can occur under conditions of appreciable lattice mismatch. X-ray diffraction superlattice patterns were also seen, with intensities containing contributions from both the difference in scattering strength of the superlattice constituents and the difference in interlayer spacing between the two constituents (*61*).

Superlattices constructed from pairs of mixed compound semiconductors containing a total of four or more atomic constituents offer added flexibility in matching lattice constants. For example, the compounds GaSb and InAs are lattice-matched to within 0.6%. An entire group of mixed compounds $In_{1-x}Ga_xAs$ and $GaSb_{1-y}As_y$ can be lattice-matched for the correct relative values of compositions x and y (*62, 63*). Exact control of the As/Sb composition ratio is difficult, however, because both As and Sb have nonunity incorporation coefficients. Nearly lattice-matched structures have been achieved, and interesting electronic properties have been observed in this class of superlattices, as will be discussed below.

Superlattice studies have also been pursued with the semiconductors germanium and gallium arsenide. This is a potentially interesting system because it consists of an elemental and a compound semiconductor, and because the two materials are based on the same crystal structure and have lattice constants which match within 0.1%. Smoothly layered multilayer crystal films were not obtained from this combination of semiconductors, however. The Ge layers nucleated smoothly on the GaAs surfaces, but GaAs atoms clustered in islands upon deposition on Ge surfaces, leading to columnar structures for alternate monolayer deposition on (100) surfaces (*64*). Alternate growth of Ga and AlAs, on the other hand, produced layered structures but with high dislocation densities (*64*). A tendency to avoid fractional occupancy of interface bonds and to avoid merging of islands with opposite phase of anion and cation sites (*65*) may be the source of this behavior.

A particularly interesting superlattice would be one composed of metal and semiconductor. Such a structure could provide the basis of contacting a many-layered electronic device, providing control, bias, and conductivity paths for electrons in a hot electron device, and providing proximity effect control for new superconductor geometries. Aluminum and GaAs would make an attractive combination for such a structure since the aluminum cubic lattice constant differs by nearly $\sqrt{2}$ from the GaAs constant and thus 45° rotation of crystal axes can produce a near lattice match and a basis for epitaxy (*66*). Epitaxial growth of Al on GaAs has been reported (*66*) and the growth of Al/GaAs superlattices has been described with layer thicknesses of ~1000 Å (*67*). Reactivity of the aluminum layers with the excess arsenic flux in the MBE chamber and from adjacent GaAs layers is unavoidable at growth temperatures for GaAs, however, so it is likely that much of the Al in the superlattices reacts to form AlAs.

For silicon, attractive metals for construction of a semiconductor/metal superlattice are metal silicides such as $NiSi_2$ and $CoSi_2$. The silicides may be formed either by annealing deposits of the metals on silicon (*68*) or by MBE by directly codepositing silicon and the metal on a heated silicon surface (*69*). In each case, epitaxial material is formed, as revealed in ion backscattering and channeling studies. Silicon has been grown epitaxially on the codeposited epitaxial silicides, although films grown over $NiSi_2$ were not smooth, and multilayered superlattices have not yet been reported. Layer thicknesses investigated were in the range 600–2000 Å (*69*).

In addition to the compositionally modulated form of superlattices described above, another form of superlattice is the doping superlattice. When the dopant concentration being grown in a molecular beam epitaxial films is varied or alternated, we may refer to the structure produced as a doping superlattice. A number of remarkable phenomena have been predicted to occur in doping superlattices (*37*). Analysis of the structure of such a superlattice is less direct than for a superlattice in which the major chemical constituents are the modulated species, however, because the interesting dopant concentrations are typically low compared to the host species concentrations. Fortunately, the charges of the dopants when ionized provide a means to detect them, and electrical capacitance–voltage measurements permit a profile of dopant concentration versus space to be obtained in the layers near a *p–n* junction or near a surface on which there is a metal Schottky barrier. An example of such profiles is shown in Fig. 13 for the *p*-type dopant beryllium in GaAs, deposited in 374-Å-thick layers (*39*). The dominant smearing in the calculated profile is produced by screening by the free carriers, and the calculated and measured profiles are in obvious agreement. The annealing results demonstrate that the superlattice is very stable thermally. Silicon and germanium in GaAs make good *n*-type dopants for superlattices since they can also be grown with sharp carrier profiles (*38, 70, 71*). Tin, which is a useful *n*-type dopant for relatively thick layers of GaAs, is less suitable for finely resolved dopant superlattice profiles because of the bottleneck in its incorporation into the crystal (*72*). This produces slow increases in carrier concentration, an accumulation of tin on the growing surface, and the inability to abruptly decrease the tin dopant concentration. As will be discussed later, the superposition of an

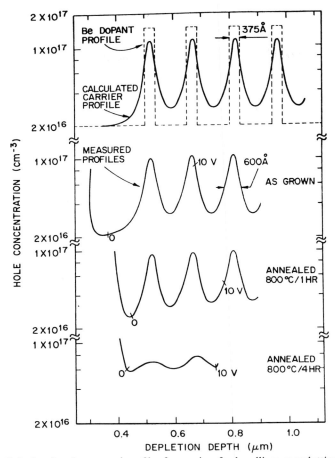

Fig. 13. Calculated and measured profiles for carriers for beryllium superlattice in GaAs.

n-type dopant superlattice on a heterostructure superlattice is also possible and can produce useful increases in carrier mobilities (38). Alternately, or in addition, a doping superlattice may be composed of two alternate opposite conductivity types, producing a possible band bending superlattice with carrier quantization, as well as a structure with widely variable band gap and carrier concentration (37). The most extensive study of this type of structure has been for GaAs and has been reviewed by Döhler and Ploog (37). Both the amphoteric dopant Ge for the two species and the n- and p-type dopants Si and Be for the two dopant types (73) were used.

IV. Properties of Superlattice Structures

A. Electronic and Optical Properties

The structure of a semiconductor superlattice affects the properties of electrons in the material. For superlattices with constituents having different electron affinities, electrons will tend to be confined in layers with greater electron affinity. Electron transport will occur more readily in directions parallel to the layers than in the direction perpendicular to the layers. When the confined-layer thicknesses are small, electrons are confined as size-quantized electron waves, and when barrier-layer thicknesses are small, electron tunneling between layers becomes important.

These effects have been extensively studied in $GaAs/Al_xGa_{1-x}As$ superlattices. A diagram of the conduction band and valence band edges for undoped layers is shown in Fig. 14. Bulk GaAs has a low-temperature fundamental direct band gap between conduction band and valence band states of about 1.5 eV. For $x < 0.45$, $Al_xGa_{1-x}As$ has a bulk band gap which is $1.25x$ eV greater than that of GaAs (75). Fits to data to be described below determine that most ($\sim 85\%$) of the band-gap difference is accommodated at the conduction band edge, producing a confining barrier of $\sim 1.1x$ eV for electrons in the conduction band. The remaining difference in band gap occurs at the valence band edge and confines holes

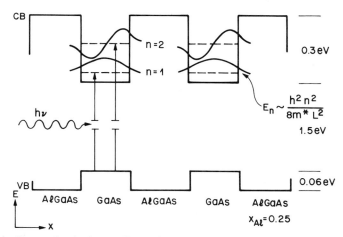

Fig. 14. Energy band-edge profiles and electron quantum-state energy levels in GaAs/$Al_{0.25}Ga_{0.75}As$ superlattice. CB and VB refer to conduction-band and valence-band edges. Photons of energy $h\nu$ excite electrons from valence-band to conduction-band quantum states. $E = h^2n^2/8m^*L^2$ is the energy of quantum state n for the case of infinitely high barriers.

to the GaAs layers with a barrier height of $\sim 0.2x$ eV, where x is the fractional aluminum content in the $Al_xGa_{1-x}As$ barriers.

The allowed energies of electrons in thin layers will be shifted appreciably by size quantization effects. For infinitely high confining barriers, the allowed minimum energies E_n for electrons are given by $E_n = h^2n^2/8m^*L^2$, where h is Planck's constant, m^* is the particle effective mass, L is the layer thickness, and n is an integer which is the number of half-wavelengths of the confined electron wave state. For finite barrier heights, the confining energies are smaller than for the infinite barrier. For electrons moving along the layers, their kinetic energy of motion parallel to the layers is added to the size-quantized energy (50, 74).

Effects of size quantization have been observed optically in MBE-grown GaAs superlattices by optical absorption (50, 76), photoluminescence (77), photoluminescence excitation spectra (78), Raman scattering (79), and photoconduction spectra (80). Figure 15 shows the absorption spectra of several GaAs superlattices and a single 4000-Å-thick film corresponding to the bulk case. The superlattices and film in each case were deposited by MBE on a GaAs substrate with (100) surface orientation, contained a total thickness of 4000 Å of GaAs, and were enclosed between 1-μm-thick $Al_{0.2}Ga_{0.8}As$ layers for support and isolation from air. The absorption measurements were made in transmission after removing the GaAs substrate by selective chemical etching. The absorption peaks correspond to exciting electrons from the valence band to the $n = 1, 2, 3, \ldots$ quantum states in the GaAs layers. The peaks are doublets because transitions originate from both the light and heavy hole bands of the valence band, which are quantized by the potential barriers of the valence band. The excited electrons are bound to the holes by Coulomb interactions, forming excitons. A detailed discussion of the processes and the selection rules is found in Reference 74. In general, the positions of the lines are well represented by energy levels calculated using bulk electron and hole masses and bulk band gaps, with 0.85 of the band-gap difference comprising the conduction band potential barrier and the remainder the valence band barrier. The shape of the optical absorption curves results from the steplike density of states for the two-dimensionally confined electrons and from the formation of excitons at the steps (Fig. 16). The spectra are remarkable in that they constitute one of the clearest demonstrations of size quantization of energy levels in an artificially synthesized structure.

The quantized energy levels have also been observed optically by Raman scattering in which electrons are excited from the lowest occupied quantum levels into higher levels. The measurements have been made both in cases in which the conduction band states are populated by optical excitation from the valence bands (81) and in cases in which the states are occupied

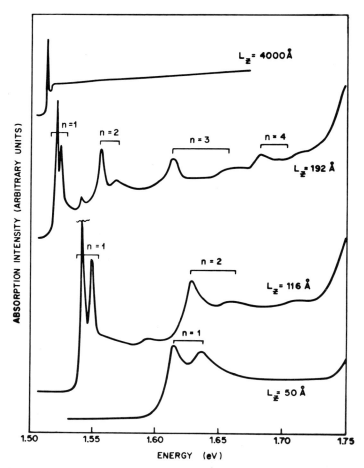

Fig. 15. Optical absorption spectra for a 4000-Å GaAs film and for superlattices with GaAs layers 192, 116, and 50 Å thick separated by ∼200-Å-thick $Al_{0.25}Ga_{0.75}As$ barriers. n is the quantum number referring to the number of half-wavelengths of electron wave in each quantum state.

by chemical doping (*79, 82*). The Raman scattering results agree closely with the energy levels and assignments from optical absorption and show further the effects of interactions between electrons and between electrons and phonons. The confirmation of the optical absorption results is especially interesting because the Raman scattering measures only the conduction electron energies, showing that the split-up of electron and hole potentials is essentially correct.

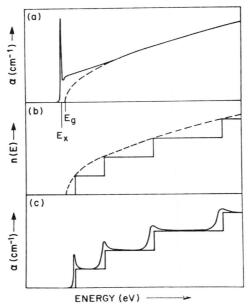

Fig. 16. (a) Absorption coefficient α (solid line) and density of states $n(E)$ (dashed line) for the three-dimensional electron system. (b) Density of states for three-dimensional (dashed line) and two-dimensional (solid line) electron systems. (c) Absorption coefficient with peaks from exciton formation for the two-dimensional electron system.

The luminescence properties of superlattices are also strongly affected by the superlattice structure. Whereas in bulk material and in thick (>1000 Å) films the photoluminescence is dominated by impurities and occurs at energies *below* the intrinsic band-edge free-exciton position, the strongest emission in high-quality MBE superlattices occurs at a position close to the lowest quantum-well absorption wavelength (*83*). Additionally, whereas low-temperature cathodoluminescence images of thick, *nonsuperlattice* films made in a scanning transmission electron microscope reveal discrete dark nonradiative centers at the main luminescence wavelengths, *no* nonradiative centers are observed in MBE-grown quantum-well superlattices (*84*). The superlattices show a spatially uniform cathodoluminescence emission. Furthermore, the superlattices show a higher luminescence efficiency than the thick-film double-heterostructure samples grown in the same MBE apparatus. These luminescence features are attractive for application to electroluminescent devices, and quantum-well superlattice lasers have been operated in a variety of configurations using both optical pumping (*77, 85, 86*) and electron injection (*87–89*). The sensitivity of the emission energy to quantum-well thickness makes possible programming of the operating wavelength of the laser by choice of the quantum-well layer thickness, and the high luminescence efficiencies allow low excitation thresholds for lasing in spite of the presence of the optically inactive barrier material and barrier interfaces (Fig. 17).

Since the size-quantization energies are determined by layer thickness L and are proportional to L^{-2}, the sharpness of superlattice absorption lines gives a sensitive measurement of the smoothness and uniformity of the layers (*90*). Linewidths of the optical spectra are found to be sensitive to growth conditions of the films, particularly the substrate temperature. Under conditions of arsenic-rich growth chosen to provide bright luminescence and smooth surfaces, a minimum of linewidths measured in the excitation spectra occurred near growth temperatures of 690°C (*91*). The magnitude of the minimum linewidth ΔE corresponds to a roughness $\Delta L = \frac{1}{2}(\Delta E / E)L$, which equals approximately one monolayer, and confirms the x-ray and electron diffraction and TEM imaging results that monolayer-scale

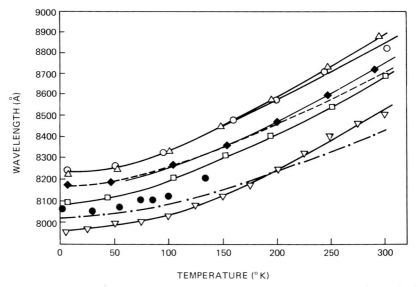

Fig. 17. Superlattice quantum-well lasing wavelengths for optically pumped superlattice lasers. The $n = 1$ optical absorption wavelength and photoluminescence wavelength are also shown for the 116-Å-well sample, together with the theoretical GaAs band-gap energy. ($\triangle$) LP 1141 (DH); ($\bigcirc$) 7-17-75 (DH); ($\blacklozenge$) 9-5-75 (ML)—188 Å; ($\square$) 10-1-75 (ML)—116 Å; ($\triangledown$) 4-10-74-I (ML)—92 Å; ($\bullet$) 10-1-75 (ML) PL; (– · –) 10-1-75 (ML) Abs.; (– – –) Thurmond E_g. Here DH refers to double heterostructures, ML refers to multilayers, LP refers to a liquid-phase epitaxy film, PL refers to photoluminescence peaks, and Abs. to absorption peaks.

smoothness is obtained under optimum growth conditions. Comparable smoothness is not obtained in all forms of epitaxial film growth, and alloy clustering of Al producing nonuniform quantum-well barriers has been reported for films grown by metal-organic chemical vapor deposition (*92*).

Another optical feature of the superlattice structures, as mentioned above, is the splitting of the light and heavy hole states, which produces the doublets in the absorption spectra (*50*). This occurs because the energy $E_n = n^2h^2/8m^*L^2$ of the confined particles is different for particles with different masses in a layer of thickness L. The layering imposed on the structure during growth has reduced the cubic symmetry of the parent materials to the uniaxial or tetragonal symmetry of the layered superlattice. Valence band wave functions which have different energy dispersion for motion parallel and perpendicular to the layers thus become nondegenerate, and the optical transition is split. This feature of the superlattice structure has special significance for the production of spin-polarized conduction electrons in GaAs, which is a prime source material for spin-polarized electrons (*78*). Although the maximum net electron spin polarization attainable by optical pumping is limited to 50% in bulk GaAs, no such limit exists in the superlattices. This is because the two hole states in bulk GaAs are pumped simultaneously and contribute electrons of opposing spin under circularly polarized pumping. In the superlattice, the splitting of the hole states in principle allows pumping of only one hole state and thus population of only one spin state. Spin polarizations in the conduction band as high as 0.70 have been obtained from GaAs superlattices (*78*).

When the film thickness of the barrier layers becomes thin enough, electrons can penetrate the barriers by tunneling. This process is sensitively measured in optical properties because the tunneling directly affects the electron energy levels in the layers (*76*). The optical absorption observed from a sample containing pairs of 50-Å GaAs layers separated by ~15-Å $Al_{0.2}Ga_{0.8}As$ barrier layers is contrasted in Fig. 18 with the absorption spectrum of single 50-Å GaAs layers separated from each other by much thicker 200-Å $Al_{0.2}Ga_{0.8}As$ layers (*76*). The thin barrier layers are penetrable by tunneling, so that electrons in the adjoining wells of the pairs are coupled. When the electron or hole wavefunctions in adjoining layers are coupled symmetrically, the lower energy symmetric states occur. With antisymmetric coupling of the wavefunctions, the higher-energy states are produced. The lower energy peaks in the spectra are transitions between the symmetric ("bonding") hole state and symmetric electron state, whereas the higher energy peaks arise from the antisymmetric ("antibonding") states. The positions of the peaks are in close quantitative agreement with the positions calculated quantum mechanically for square potential barriers (*76*). Resonant tunneling into quantum states has also been clearly observed in electron transport through MBE-grown layers (*49*).

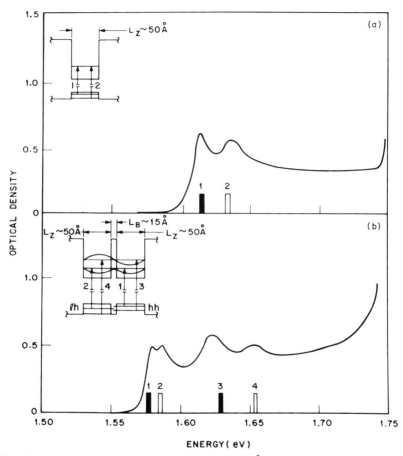

Fig. 18. Optical absorption spectra (a) for single 50-Å GaAs quantum wells and (b) for pairs of coupled 50-Å GaAs wells separated by thin ∼15-Å Al$_{0.2}$Ga$_{0.8}$As barriers. For the single wells, line 1 is a heavy hole to conduction band transition and line 2 is a light hole to conduction band transition. For the pairs of wells, symmetric coupling of the electron wave functions by tunneling through the narrow barrier creates the lower-lying "bonding" states and the higher "antibonding" states. Lines 1 and 2 are between symmetric electron and hole states and lines 3 and 4 are between antisymmetric electron and hole states.

These results demonstrate that barriers with accurately controllable tunneling can be attained by the MBE technique.

For longer series of coupled layers, the coupled states merge into bands described as superlattice minibands, with the widths of the bands determined by the degree of tunneling (*1*) (Fig. 19). As the layer widths ap-

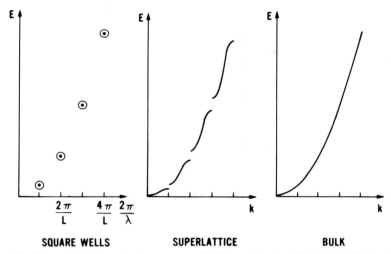

Fig. 19. Energy level dispersion for square wells (a), superlattices (b), and bulk GaAs (c).

proach monolayer thickness, the bands become very wide and the energy of the lowest states approaches the energy of a random alloy of equivalent average composition (*36*). However, the bands are anisotropic, reflecting the anisotropy of the layered structure. Edge luminescence from alternate-monolayer alloys is anisotropic, with σ-polarized emission markedly stronger than π-polarized emission (*36*). Alternate-monolayer films are also birefringent in the below-band-gap range of photon energy (*93*). Several authors have performed band structure calculations for the new band structures of the superlattices (*94–96*).

The GaAs/Al$_x$Ga$_{1-x}$As superlattices discussed up to this point are characterized by energy bands in which both electrons and holes tend to be confined in the same layers (the GaAs layers). A quite different situation occurs in GaSb/InAs superlattices, where *both* the conduction band edge and valence band edge in GaSb lie above the conduction band edge of InAs. This tends to confine *electrons* in the InAs layers and *holes* in the GaSb layers (*62*). The misalignment of band edges is so extreme in this case that in fact the electron states in the InAs can lie *below* the hole states in GaSb. The bottom of the conduction band of InAs lies below the top of the valence band of GaSb. This effect is a result of having different Group V atoms in the two superlattice components. For InAs layers with thickness greater than ~115 Å, overlap in the electron and hole states produces semimetallic behavior, with semimetal conductivity even in the absence of extrinsic doping (*97*). For thinner layers, the band structure of the superlattice is not simply the bulk band structures of the constituent films, and the superlattice is a semiconductor without overlap of hole and electron state energies (*62*). These effects have been directly observed experimentally in MBE-grown superlattices of these materials, as well as in mixed-alloy superlattices with composition $In_{1-x}Ga_xAs/GaSb_{1-y}As_y$ (which permits lattice matching) (*63*). Heterojunctions of the alloys show conductivity characteristics which shifted from rectifying behavior to ohmic behavior as values of x and y were reduced (*97*). The reduction in energy gap with increasing layer thicknesses was also observed directly by optical absorption measurements (*98*). Electrons confined in the InAs conduction band could also be probed by quantum transport studies. They exhibited cyclotron resonance at infrared frequencies (*99*) and Shubnikov–de Haas oscillations in the electrical resistance (*100*).

B. Electrical Transport

The optical properties discussed in the previous section showed that electrons can be accurately confined to selected layers of superlattices. When confined, their motion is two dimensional, leading to important ramifications in the electrical conductivity. Conduction electrons may be introduced into the layers by optical excitation from the valence bands, by injection from adjoining layers, or by chemical doping. Chemical doping

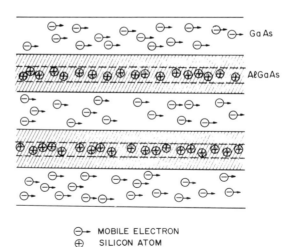

    ⊖→ MOBILE ELECTRON
    ⊕   SILICON ATOM

Fig. 20. Modulation-doped superlattice of GaAs and $Al_xGa_{1-x}As$ with doping restricted to central regions of $Al_xGa_{1-x}As$ layers. Mobile electrons are confined in GaAs layers, where they can move along the layers with reduced scattering from donor impurities, relative to the uniformly doped case.

is particularly important for electrical transport devices, and superlattices provide a special degree of flexibility in chemical doping in that dopant atoms can be concentrated in selected layers or portions of layers with interesting effects (Fig. 20).

Energy-band diagrams for undoped and doped superlattices are shown in Fig. 21. The energy levels in the undoped case are produced by the square-well potential barriers and were experimentally observed in the optical measurements described above (74).

The barriers in the doped cases are modified by band-edge curvature produced by space-charge effects. The donors in the barriers in the uniformly doped case contribute electrons to the quantum wells. Transfer of

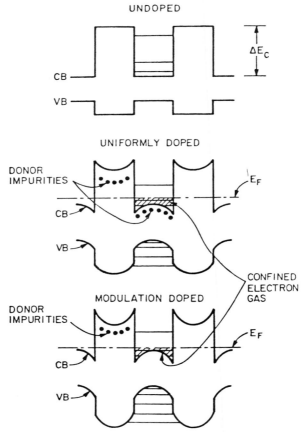

Fig. 21. Energy level diagram for undoped (a), uniformly doped (b), and modulation-doped superlattices (c).

electrons from the barrier donors to the well produces a space-charge separation which bends the band edges as shown, and electrons occupy the quantum-well states up to a Fermi level E_F. In the modulation-doped case only selected layers are doped (*38*). The band edges are similarly curved, but the conduction electrons may now be entirely separated from layers containing donor atoms. This requires that the electrons be confined in the wells and that the donor atoms be confined in the barrier layers. The desirable feature of this configuration is that the electrons can propagate within the layers with a reduced probability of being scattered by donor impurity atoms, which are confined to the barrier regions (as illustrated in Figs. 20 and 21). In another modulation doping configuration (not shown in Fig. 21), doping is confined to the wells, so that both donor atoms and conduction electrons occupy the same layer (*101*). This arrangement is desirable in cases where band-bending and associated lowering of the barrier height are to be avoided. Reversed band bending and barrier height enhancement would be produced by *p*-type doping of the barriers.

Modulated doping of these types has been produced in MBE of GaAs by use of silicon doping of barriers and/or wells (*38*). Silicon is a preferred *n*-type dopant for modulated doping because it is incorporated with near-unity sticking coefficient, does not concentrate on the surface during growth, and does not diffuse appreciably at MBE growth temperatures (*102*). Under arsenic-rich growth conditions, Si incorporates primarily on Ga sites, where it acts as a donor.

The first experiments to demonstrate the two-dimensionality of electron motion in layer structures were carried out in the uniform doping geometry (*103*). High-magnetic-field resistance measurements showed Shubnikov-de Haas oscillations in the resistance versus magnetic field. From the oscillation period, the number of carriers and the Fermi energy were determined. For barriers thicker than ∼50 Å only the components of magnetic field perpendicular to the superlattice layers were effective in determining the oscillation period, demonstrating that the electrons were being confined to two-dimensional orbits within the GaAs layers. A transition to three-dimensional conduction and isotropic oscillation periods occurred with thinner barriers, as the electrons penetrated the barriers by tunneling (*103*).

In attempts to improve the mobilities and scattering lifetimes of electrons in superlattices, a number of doping configurations have been examined (*38*). In uniformly doped layers, mobilities somewhat less than bulk mobilities were found. Efforts to enhance the electron mobilities by selectively doping only barrier layers proved successful, however. Structures of the type shown in Fig. 20 with doping levels in the barriers of 10^{17}–10^{18} cm^{-3}, layer thickness of 100–1000 Å, and no doping in the wells produced remarkably enhanced Hall mobilities (Figs. 22 and 23). Enhancement of the

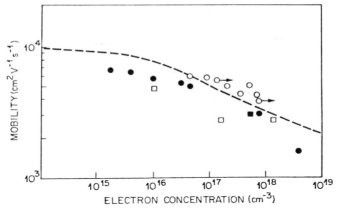

Fig. 22. Electron Hall mobilities versus electron concentration for modulation-doped 200-Å GaAs/Al$_x$Ga$_{1-x}$As layers at 300 K, relative to bulk values, uniformly doped superlattice values, and the Brooks–Herring theory for the maximum attainable mobilities for uniformly doped bulk GaAs. (●) Si-doped bulk MBE (Cho); (○) Si modulation-doped layered; (□) Si uniformly doped layered; (■) Si-doped bulk MBE (this work); (– – –) theory.

mobilities was greatest at low temperatures, where more than an order of magnitude increase in Hall mobility and a great increase in the sharpness and strength of magnetoresistance oscillation spectra could be produced with a carrier concentration of $\sim 10^{17}$ cm^{-3}. Peak mobilities near 10^5 cm^2 V^{-1} s^{-1} have been achieved (104) (Fig. 23). The dopant configuration producing the greatest enhancement was that in which doping was confined to barriers with a barrier region of ~ 50–100 Å near the GaAs interface left undoped (104–106). The reduction in Coulomb scattering from the charged donor atoms by spatial separation from the conduction electrons is the predominant mechanism of mobility enhancement. It is most marked at low temperature because the uniformly doped case suffers from increased Coulomb scattering at low temperatures, where low carrier thermal velocities allow strong carrier deflection and scattering. The modulation-doping mobility enhancement is also most marked at low temperature because the competing phonon scattering processes are weak at low temperature. The "setback" of the doping from the interface reduces Coulomb scattering from the impurities and reduces the probability of overlap between the mobile charge carriers and the donors. The wave function of the tail of electrons penetrating the barrier layer of potential E_B is of the form $\exp[-(2mE_B/\hbar^2)^{1/2}x]$ and so falls to $1/e$ in a distance $x \sim \hbar/(2mE_B)^{1/2}$ from the barrier boundary. For a 200-meV barrier, this distance is ~ 14 Å, which is readily achieved. Falloff of the Coulomb interaction with distance is less rapid, with the Bohr radius of an electron about a hydrogenic

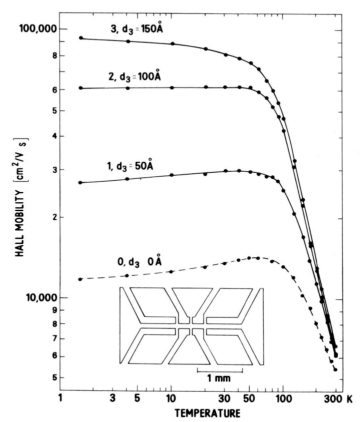

Fig. 23. Temperature dependence of electron Hall mobilities for modulation-doped 250-Å GaAs layers with doped Al$_{0.12}$Ga$_{0.88}$As layers having 0, 50, 100, and 150 Å of undoped "setback" at each interface.

impurity in GaAs being ~100 Å. Separations of this order or greater will be required to decouple the electrons from the donors. A limit on the degree to which it is possible to separate substantial numbers of electrons and donors is produced by the electrostatic energy of the space charge of the donors and electrons. For example, removal of an electron from the center of the edge of a uniformly positively charged layer of thickness L requires an energy $E = N_D e L^2 / 8\epsilon\epsilon_0$. This quantity is 70 meV for $L = 200$ Å and positive charge density $N_D = 10^{18}$ cm^{-3}. The energy difference between the electron bound to a donor in the barrier and the electron at the Fermi energy in the wells must be more than this electrostatic energy in order for the transfer of the electron from the barrier to the well to occur. Fermi energies are of the order of 60 meV at an electron concentration of 10^{18} cm^{-3}, and the lowest quantum confinement energies are approximately 10 meV in 200-Å wells. Taking into account the combined effect of these factors, it is possible to move charge densities of 10^{18} cm^{-3} by several hundred angstroms. Quantitative determination of these effects requires self-consistent treatments, as have been performed for several cases by Mori and Ando (*107*) and Hess (*108*), who have calculated theoretical mobilities in modulation-doped structures. For the case of no undoped spacer in the $Al_xGa_{1-x}As$ layers, Mori and Ando predict Hall mobilities near 10^5 cm^2 $V^{-1}s^{-1}$ for a carrier density of 10^{17}–10^{18} cm^{-3} in 200-Å wells with 200-Å barriers.

In the limit when the layer thicknesses in a modulation-doped structure become greater than the distance over which charge can be transferred, only those charges near the interface will be transferred. The transferred charge will be attracted to the positive donor charge in the barrier by the electrostatic field but will be prevented from returning to the donors by the heterojunction potential step. Electrons are thus confined at a single interface in a triangular potential well, where they occupy quantum states. However, they are free to move *along* the interface as in the case of modulation-doped narrow wells and barriers.

Modulation-doped single interfaces also have shown enhanced electron mobility (*105*, *106*, *109*, *110*). Mobility values of the same order as in multilayer structures have been reported for $GaAs/Al_xGa_{1-x}As$ interfaces for cases in which the GaAs layer is grown before the $Al_xGa_{1-x}As$ layer (*104–106*). Interfaces grown in the reverse order have not shown as great a mobility enhancement (*110*), suggesting that the interface formed in MBE has more scattering states for an $Al_xGa_{1-x}As$ surface than for a GaAs surface under the growth conditions employed in studies to date. Electrons bound at modulation-doped single interfaces have been proven to occupy two-dimensional states and to form two-dimensional orbits by means of observation of Shubnikov–de Haas magnetoresistance oscillations, which again are sensitive only to components of magnetic field perpendicular to the orbits and interfaces (*109*, *111*).

In the highest-mobility samples, the electrical resistance behavior in high magnetic fields and at low temperatures shows remarkable effects (*112*). The voltage drop along the interface in the direction of current flow does not merely undergo quantum oscillations, but reaches minima stretching over wide regions of field in which the voltage drop approaches zero (Fig. 24). This corresponds to a nearly dissipationless flow of current. In the same regions of field where the voltage drop approaches zero along the current flow, the Hall voltage across the current flow (parallel to the surface but perpendicular to the current flow and to the magnetic field) reaches

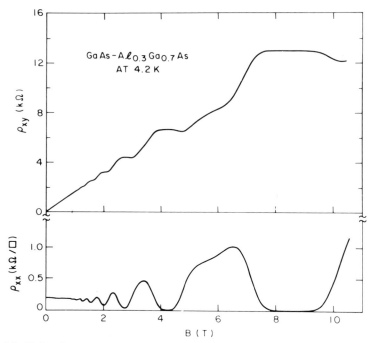

Fig. 24. Hall resistance ρ_{xy} and parallel resistance ρ_{xx} of a modulation-doped single interface of GaAs and Si-doped $Al_{0.3}Ga_{0.7}As$ at 4.2 K versus magnetic field B. The Hall resistance reaches flat plateaus at values of $12{,}907/i$ Ω, where $i = 1, 2, 3$. The parallel resistance drops to below 0.1 Ω in the plateau regions.

remarkably flat plateaus. The Hall resistance values here approach exact submultiples of the quantity h/e^2, where h is Planck's constant and e is the electronic charge. This new behavior is essentially similar to recent observations in inversion layers in silicon MOSFETs (*113*) and is a quantum phenomenon which is closely tied to the structure of the films. The interface binds electrons in quantum states as discussed above so that there is no degree of freedom for motion perpendicular to the interface. Motion of electrons along the interface is quantized into Landau (cyclotron-orbit) states by the magnetic field. The various Landau levels (cyclotron orbits) have energy levels $E_n = n\hbar eB/m^*$ in a magnetic field B. Broadening of these allowed energy levels by impurity scattering of the electrons is reduced by the modulation-doping technique. So few electrons remain at energies intermediate between the Landau energies that these remaining electrons are localized at residual irregularities remaining at the interface. Gaps in the density of states for electrons are produced, and whenever the Fermi level of the electrons lies in this gap, scattering is essentially suppressed (*114*). Remarkably this produces a nearly perfectly conducting state. The quantization of the number of electrons in the Landau levels apparently produces the field-independent Hall resistance plateaus. Much theorizing remains to be done before these mechanisms are understood in detail. An application of the effect would be the development of a quantum standard for electrical resistance (*112*), analogous in some ways to the Josephson junction standard for voltage. This standard would be based on the plateaus in the Hall resistance, whose magnitudes depend only on the fundamental constant ratio h/e^2.

The high mobilities which are obtained for both modulation-doped superlattices and modulation-doped single interfaces are also of interest for application in high-speed electronic devices. If the high mobilities can be used to obtain higher electron velocities and higher gains in devices, then speed of operation, power, and noise advantages may be anticipated. Modulation doping has been incorporated in experimental field-effect transistor structures (*115*).

In addition to confining electrons and providing enhanced electron mobilities, layered structures can also provide similar effects for holes. Although the valence band heterojunction discontinuities are smaller than the conduction-band discontinuities in the $GaAs/Al_xGa_{1-x}As$ system, holes have been introduced and confined by modulated acceptor doping of $Al_xGa_{1-x}As$ layers (*116*) and two-dimensional hole confinement has been observed. This confinement is produced by the $\sim 15\%$ portion of the band-gap discontinuity between GaAs and $Al_xGa_{1-x}As$ which occurs in the valence band at the interface between the two materials. The effects were observed with beryllium as the MBE acceptor dopant (*116*).

C. *Transport Perpendicular to Barrier Layers*

Heterostructure barrier layers provide a means for controlling carrier flow in directions perpendicular to superlattice layers. As mentioned in the discussions of superlattice electronic and optical properties, when these layers are thin ($\lesssim 50$ Å) particle tunneling occurs which is observable in the optical spectra and in resonant tunneling. When layers are thicker ($\gtrsim 250$ Å), the barrier layers should become essentially impenetrable to tunneling. A great deal of confusion has existed as to whether such barriers actually exist. The barrier at the heterojunction between *n*-type GaAs and *n*-type $Al_xGa_{1-x}As$ should be electrically rectifying according to the ideas presented up to this point and yet several studies showed an absence of rectification by such heterojunctions (*117*, *118*). It now seems likely that unintentional grading of the interfaces or trapping of charge in impurity or defect states at the interfaces has been responsible for this nonideal behavior and that the intrinsic potential steps were screened by trapped charge in cases where expected barriers were not observed. Work with carefully prepared interfaces shows the ideal predicted behavior and emphasizes the importance of the growth technique. Lightly doped barriers grown by liquid-phase epitaxy showed the predicted rectification (119) as have barriers grown by MBE (120, 121). The low-temperature conductivity of an eight-period modulation-doped superlattice with ~250-Å layers showed a conduction anisotropy of $>10^{12}$ for conductivity parallel and perpendicular to the layers, proving definitely the existence of the barriers. The effective height of the barriers can be determined from the thermal activation of conduction across the barriers. In the particularly simple case of an MBE-grown single undoped 500-Å rectangular barrier of $Al_{0.3}Ga_{0.7}As$ between layers of n-type GaAs ($n = 10^{18}$ cm^{-3}), a barrier height of 314 meV is determined from the low-voltage conduction temperature dependence. This agrees closely with a barrier height of 307 meV anticipated for 85% of the band-gap discontinuity occurring in the conduction band. By growing the layers with the barrier layer undoped, transfer of charge from dopants in the barrier is avoided and thus space charge which would distort the barrier shape is not set up in the barrier layer.

Application of a voltage across a rectangular barrier will have minimal effect on the potential discontinuity at the barrier interface if the potential step is truly abrupt. Since the structural studies on MBE GaAs/$Al_xGa_{1-x}As$ show the interface widths and associated potential steps to be only one or two monolayers wide, only about 1% of the voltage drop across the 500-Å rectangular barrier occurs over the interface region, and the potential step is preserved. The situation is radically changed, however, if the interface region can be *purposely graded* rather than abrupt. In this case, an appreciable portion of an applied voltage drop will occur across the graded region and the barrier potential height will be lowered or raised according to the sense of the voltage. This provides a voltage-controllable barrier height, and has been achieved by growing a film with a barrier layer having a triangular-shaped compositional profile of $Al_xGa_{1-x}As$, for example (120, 121) (Fig. 25). The $I–V$ characteristic for such a film is symmetric, in accord with the symmetric compositional profile of the triangular barrier layer. The growth of the compositionally graded layer was achieved by gradually opening and then gradually closing a shutter over the aluminum molecular beam source. The source aperture of ~1 cm is gradually exposed and then covered in this manner and the molecular beam intensity at the substrate is correspondingly changed. Comparison of the observed current to a simple diode equation with a voltage-controlled barrier height gives the correct form of the response, but suggests that the effective barrier is not lowered by the full amount of the applied voltage.

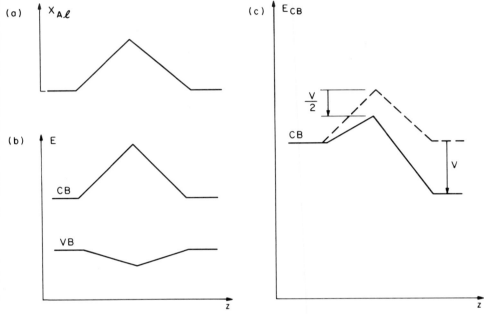

Fig. 25. Triangular potential barriers created by graded-interface barriers: (a) composition profile, (b) band-edge profiles, and (c) conduction band-edge profile under applied voltage V. GaAs layers are assumed to be doped n-type and barriers are undoped.

The graded and abrupt interfaces can be combined in a single barrier layer having a sawtooth composition and potential shape. This is produced in $Al_xGa_{1-x}As$ MBE by gradually opening and then abruptly closing an Al-source shutter. The asymmetric potential barrier for this case resembles somewhat the potential shape for metal–semiconductor Schottky barrier diodes. The asymmetry barrier shape is manifested in an asymmetric conduction characteristic, and electrical rectification is observed in this type of structure (Fig. 26). Since the layers on each side of the barrier are n-type semiconductors, and since the MBE technique can grow repeated superlattice structures, superlattices containing series of such rectifying barriers can be readily fabricated. A superlattice of five such barriers was made and operated at essentially five times the operating voltage of a single barrier (*120*).

Structures having graded potential barriers have also been grown with MBE by use of a doping technique referred to as "planar doping" (*122*). In this technique, the barrier consists of an undoped "*i*" layer containing a thin interior plane of dopant opposite in type to the adjoining contacting layers. The structures which were studied had an n–i–p–i–n doping structure in GaAs in which the n- and p-type dopants were Si and Be. The thin

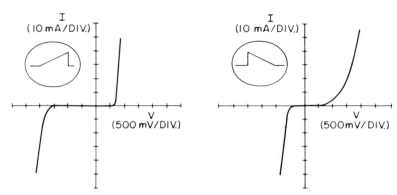

Fig. 26. Conduction characteristics for sawtooth-barrier diodes grown in two directions. Measurements are at 77 K, barrier widths are ~500 Å, and maximum Al concentration in the $Al_xGa_{1-x}As$ barriers is $x \sim 0.4$.

interior p-doped plane is doped lightly enough that the valence band merely bends upward but never approaches the Fermi level. All acceptors are charged with electrons from the conduction band, producing the desired band curvature, but no free holes occur in the structure. Symmetric or asymmetric barriers are produced according to whether the interior doping plane is at the center of the undoped layer or not. No $Al_xGa_{1-x}As$ is required for this technique, but it could be incorporated if desired to modify further the barrier shape. Ion implantation can also be used to produce asymmetric doping profiles and rectification, as was done in Si and the "camel diode" (*123*) and more recently for the "camel transistor" (*124*). MBE sawtooth diodes and planar doped barriers seem to offer advantages of flexibility and control in fabrication relative to the ion implantation technique, however, and provide access to multiple and superlattice barrier structures.

D. Lattice Vibrations of Superlattices

When superlattice layers contain atoms with different masses, new vibrational features are expected to occur. The layers with the different masses may be expected to vibrate against each other in new vibrational modes. Phonons propagating in the superlattice would be expected to propagate anisotropically because of the anisotropic structure of the medium. Additionally, phonons propagating with a wave vector equal to the wave vector of the superlattice would be expected to be reflected by the superlattice, and bands of energy in which phonons would not propagate would be expected. All of these effects have been observed in MBE-grown superlattices of GaAs and $Al_xGa_{1-x}As$.

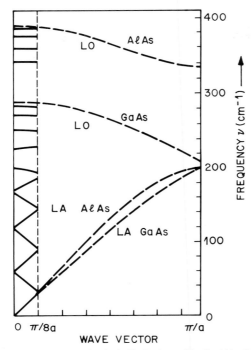

Fig. 27. Longitudinal phonon modes in bulk GaAs and bulk AlAs Brillouin zones and in $(GaAs)_4(AlAs)_4$ superlattice Brillouin zone. LO and LA refer to longitudinal optic and longitudinal acoustic modes, respectively.

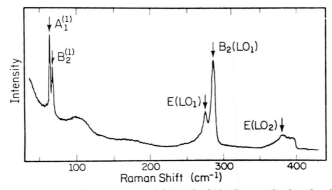

Fig. 28. Raman scattering spectrum of $(GaAs)_{4.8}(AlAs)_4$ superlattice showing new superlattice phonon modes $A_1^{(1)}$ and $B_2^{(1)}$. Broad line near 100 cm^{-1} is a superlattice zone-edge phonon mode. Higher-shift peaks are bulklike phonon modes. Temperature, 300 K; $\omega_L = 1.959$ eV; $Z(X,X)\bar{Z}$ scattering mode (back reflection, parallel polarization).

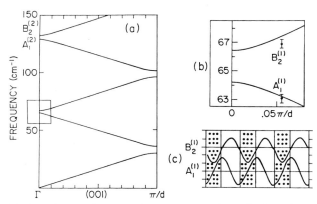

Fig. 29. (a) Superlattice phonon Brillouin zone for $(GaAs)_{4.8}(AlAs)_4$ superlattice. (b) Enlarged zone-center region of the Brillouin zone. (c) $B_2^{(1)}$ and $A_1^{(1)}$ mode geometries of the observed zone-center superlattice phonons.

The anisotropy of phonon propagation was observed by comparison of phonon frequencies observed in Raman scattering (*125*) and in far-infrared absorption (*126*) in a superlattice containing alternate "tetralayers" of GaAs and AlAs, having composition $(GaAs)_{4.8}(AlAs)_{4.0}$. Longitudinal optic (LO) phonons polarized along the layers lay lower than longitudinal optic phonons polarized perpendicular to the layers for both AlAs-like and GaAs-like modes (*126*). Confirming results were observed in the same structure by comparison of Raman scattering frequencies for the same LO phonon modes propagating in the two directions (*125*). This anisotropy is caused by the different dielectric constants of the AlAs and GaAs layers, and the boundary conditions in the superlattice which require that tangential components of **E** and normal components of **D** be continuous across the interfaces between the layers. Anisotropy was also observed by Raman scattering in superlattices consisting of alternate 50-Å layers of GaAs and AlAs (*125*).

Entirely new phonon modes were found in the $(GaAs)_{4.8}(AlAs)_{4.0}$ superlattice near the zone center (i.e., with low momentum and long wavelength relative to the fundamental lattice) (*127*). This occurred at energies far below the bulk optical phonon frequencies. These modes were observed by resonant Raman scattering, and correspond to acoustic phonons which are folded back to the zone center by the superlattice periodicity (Fig. 27). They consist of the vibrations of the superlattice layers against each other. The new peaks are sharp and occur at 63.1 and 66.9 cm^{-1} (Fig. 28). These energies correspond closely to the energies calculated for elastic waves in a layered continuum having the elastic constants and dimensions of the

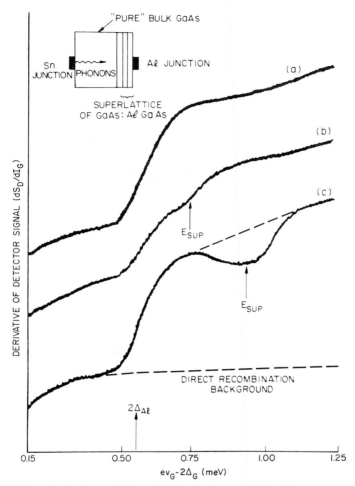

Fig. 30. Superlattice phonon filter and transmission curves. Inset shows superconducting junction phonon source and detector and GaAs/Al$_x$Ga$_{1-x}$As superlattice and GaAs substrate. Detected signal versus generator voltage is shown for (a) substrate, (b) (100) superlattice, and (c) (111) superlattice.

GaAs and AlAs layers. Scattering at ~ 100 cm^{-1} from the longitudinal modes at the *border* of the superlattice Brillouin zone was also seen (*127*). The phonon dispersion curves in the superlattice Brillouin zone are shown in Fig. 29 along with a diagram of the new zone-center modes at 63.1 and 66.9 cm^{-1}. The sharpness of the phonon lines suggests that the layers in the superlattice are equivalent in thickness to within approximately 2% and

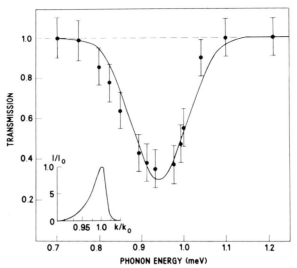

Fig. 31. Phonon transmission versus phonon energy for $GaAs/Al_{0.5}Ga_{0.5}As$ superlattice with 122-Å period. Dip in transmission occurs at the phonon energy where the superlattice period is half the wavelength of the phonons. $Z_1/Z_2 = 0.88$; $\gamma = 0.1$ meV.

that the phonon scattering lifetime must be longer than the reciprocal of the 3-cm^{-1} linewidth, i.e., longer than $\sim 10^{-11}$ s.

Phonons propagating near the lowest superlattice Brillouin zone boundary have half-wavelengths approaching the superlattice period. Phonons having energies in the forbidden gap at this boundary would be expected to be reflected by the superlattices (*128*). The selective transmission of phonons by a superlattice has been used to probe these effects by use of superconducting phonon generators and detectors affixed to the substrate and surface of $GaAs/Al_{0.5}Ga_{0.5}As$ superlattices. A schematic diagram of the measuring geometry is shown in Fig. 30, along with the detected phonon signal versus detector voltage (which is proportional to phonon energy) for a substrate and for two superlattices with $\sim$100-Å periods. In each case an increase in signal level occurs above the energy at which quantum generation of phonons from the aluminum phonon source occurs. The superlattice samples then show dips in the received phonon signal at energies corresponding to zone-boundary phonons. The superlattice acts as a filter for these zone-boundary phonons, and a minimum in the transmission of phonons at this zone boundary energy occurs (Fig. 31). Effects of this type hold promise for use in coherent phonon optics. The superlattice represents an improvement relative to previous bulk structures, since earlier structures were severely limited by degradation of the phonons by the interfaces of the media. In the present case, the phonons pass through ∼100 interfaces without noticeable degradation, which implies that fewer than 1% of the phonons are scattered at any interface.

V. Concluding Remarks

In conclusion, it is interesting to survey the limitations and the potentialities for superlattice materals in light of the results which have been described in the preceding sections.

The level of perfection of artificial superlattices which has been attained in the best structures is encouragingly high, with interfacial sharpness near the monolayer level. Additional progress toward perfect monolayer sharpness will probably be difficult, however, because of the statistical and kinetic factors involved in nucleation, and because of the limiting factors in the preparation of substrates for deposition. The short-period superlattices will continue as an instructive medium for study of crystal growth at the finest scale. Superlattice interfaces can freeze the images of the atomic surface at particular points in growth time, and subsequent probing by diffraction and cross-sectional imaging techniques can provide a wealth of detailed information on crystal growth processes. Much progress remains to be made in the study of interaction between different species on surfaces by this technique, and the possibility of creation of new metastable chemical compounds by superlattice deposition is intriguing.

The quality of semiconductor superlattices in terms of purity and carrier lifetimes and mobilities is high. In spite of this quality, an unresolved frustration has been the inability to achieve a superlattice oscillator of the type envisaged by Esaki and Tsu (*1*) or to observe Bloch oscillation (*129*) in which electrons oscillate upon being Umklapp-reflected between superlattice minizone boundaries. Both of these effects require long electron scattering times for electrons moving or tunneling perpendicular to the superlattice layers. Whereas mobilities have been greatly enhanced for electrons moving *along* superlattice layers, no comparable enhancement in mobility or scattering time has been achieved for motion in the perpendicular direction. It appears that further materials development, use of other materials, or new conceptual approaches will be required for experimental realization of superlattice oscillators. The high mobility for motion within the planes does bode well for improvement of more conventional electronic devices by use of superlattices, though. As mentioned above, active development of field-effect transistors with modulation doping of layers is under way. Quantum-well superlattice lasers have attractive features based on the superlattice structures also and will probably undergo further development.

Superlattice structures with multiple barriers offer a means for the study or control of electron motion between barrier layers. The work described in this article showed that barrier shapes and sizes can be accurately controlled. This should provide a means of electron injection and a means of analysis of electron motion across barriers. Structures of this type might be adaptable for ballistic electron devices such as the hot electron transistor (*130*), but should also be useful for study of electron dynamics under injection or nonequilibrium conditions.

The use of superlattices for phonon manipulation will likely be further developed. Selective mirrors or filters for phonons which might be built with superlattices would be an important part of a coherent phonon-optics system and might be used in various components of a system, such as phonon deflectors and phonon lasers.

When electrons are constrained to two-dimensional motion, entirely new effects are encountered, e.g., in the high-magnetic-field effects with quantized Hall resistances and vanishingly small current dissipations. Further developments in this area are very probable. If electrons could be confined to one-dimensional motion, many additional interesting features would undoubtedly be developed. Proposals have been made for localizing electrons to one-dimensional motion at the edges of quantum layers (*131*). Superlattices of one-dimensional conducting channels can be conceived using similar lines of development, and would be expected to show sharply modified properties related to restricted scattering processes and to singularities in the densities of electronic states occurring at edges of energy bands in one-dimensional structures.

Further development is also to be expected in the field of metal superlattices as many more configurations are explored. Metal superlattices have generally been grown in lower-performance vacuum systems and with less source and substrate control and preparation than has been the case for semiconductor superlattices. The semiconductor MBE has been performed against a backdrop of device application requirements. Emphasis has been placed in semiconductor MBE on smooth, high-quality surfaces suitable for device applications. Increased sophistication for metal superlattice deposition will continue and should lead to more reproducibility of metal superlattices. Only a relatively small number of material combinations have been explored in either metal or semiconductor superlattices, and extension to new materials and combinations will also be developing. The construction of GaSb/InAs superlattices demonstrates the extension of compound semiconductor superlattices to quaternary systems requiring a fourth major beam constituent, and provides interesting new features in the electronic energy bands and associated transport. Construction of ordered superlattices of GaAs and InAs with highly (7%) mismatched lattice constants portends well for extension to systems with lattice match less ideal than that of GaAs and AlAs. However, observation of island nucleation and filamentary growth in alternate-monolayer deposition of a Group IV and a Group III–V semiconductor (Ge–GaAs) suggest limitations on the materials systems and growth conditions under which nearly perfect superlattices may be attained. The enormous range of structures and properties with which thin-film superlattice structures have been built and can be made, however, suggest wide if not universal applicability of the superlattice technique.

Acknowledgments

I wish to acknowledge collaboration and helpful discussions with my colleagues C. L. Allyn, A. S. Barker, Jr., A. Y. Cho, C. Colvard, P. D. Dernier, R. Dingle, R. M. Fleming, M. V. Klein, D. A. Kleinman, D. V. Lang, D. B. McWhan, R. Merlin, J. L. Merz, R. C. Miller, D. Moncton, V. Narayanamurti, M. B. Panish, P. M. Petroff, A. Pinczuk, H. L. Störmer, W. T. Tsang, D. C. Tsui, J. P. van der Ziel, C. Weisbuch, W. Wiegmann, and J. M. Worlock.

References

1. Esaki, L., and Tsu, R. (1970). *IBM J. Res. Dev.* **14,** 61.

2. Günther, K. G. (1958). *Z. Naturforsch.* **13a,** 1081.

3. Steinberg, R. F., and Scruggs, D. M. (1966). *J. Appl. Phys.* **37,** 4586.

4. Davey, J. E., and Pankey, T. (1968). *J. Appl. Phys.* **39,** 1941.

5. Arthur, J. R. (1968). *J. Appl. Phys.* **39,** 4032.

6. Cho, A. Y. (1970). *J. Appl. Phys.* **41,** 2780.

6a. Cho, A. Y. (1979) *J. Vac. Sci. Tech.* **16,** 275.

7. Cho, A. Y., and Arthur, J. R. (1975). *Prog. Solid State Chem.* **10,** 157.

8. Wood, C. E. C. (1980). *In* "Physics of Thin Films, Vol. 2" (C. Haff and M. Francombe, eds.). Academic Press, New York.

9. Ploog, K. (1980). *Cryst. Growth Prop. Appl.* **3,** 75.

10. Pamplin, Brian R., ed. (1980). "Molecular Beam Epitaxy" Pergamon, Oxford.

11. Gossard, A. C. (1979). *Thin Solid Films* **57,** 3.

12. Gaines, G. L. (1966). "Insoluble Monolayers at Liquid-Gas Interfaces." Wiley (Interscience), New York.

13. Cook, H. E., and Hilliard, J. E. (1969). *J. Appl. Phys.* **40,** 2191.

14. Stephens, J. F., and Tuck-Lee, C. (1969). *J. Appl. Crystallogr.* **2,** 1.

15. Spiller, E., Segmüller, A., Rife, J., and Haelbich, R. (1980). *Appl. Phys. Lett.* **37,** 1048.

16. Pomerantz, M., and Segmüller, A. (1980). *Thin Solid Films* **68,** 33.

17. Thaler, B. J., Ketterson, J. B., and Hilliard, J. E. (1978). *Phys. Rev. Lett.* **41**, 336.
18. Gyorgy, E. M., Dillon, J. F., Jr., McWhan, D. B., Rupp, L. W., Jr., Testardi, L. R., and Flanders, P. J. (1980). *Phys. Rev. Lett.* **45**, 57.
19. Yang, W. M. C., Tsakalakos, T., and Hilliard, J. E. (1977). *J. Appl. Phys.* **48**, 876.
20. Paulsen, W. M., and Hilliard, J. E. (1977). *J. Appl. Phys.* **48**, 2117.
21. Ruggiero, S. T., Barbee, T. W., Jr., and Beasley, M. R. (1980). *Phys. Rev. Lett.* **45**, 1299.
22. Petroff, P. M., Gossard, A. C., Wiegmann, W., and Savage, A. (1978). *J. Cryst. Growth* **44**, 5.
23. Dublon, G., Rosenblum, M. P., and Vetterling, W. T. (1980). *Proc. Intermag. 80, IEEE Trans. Mag.* **mag-16**, 1126.
24. Schüller, I. K. (1980). *Phys. Rev. Lett.* **44**, 1597.
25. Kasper, E., Herzog, H. J., Kibbel, H. (1975). *Appl. Phys.* **8**, 199.
26. Eltoukhy, A. H., Zilko, J. L., Wickersham, C. E., and Greene, J. E. (1977). *Appl. Phys. Lett.* **31**, 156.
27. Rezek, E. A., Holonyak, N., Jr., Vojak, B. A., Stillman, G. E., Rossi, J. A., Keune, D. L., and Fairing, J. D. (1977). *Appl. Phys. Lett.* **31**, 288.
28. Dupuis, R. D., Dapkus, P. D., Kolbas, R. M., and Holonyak, N., Jr. (1979). *IEEE J. Quantum Electron.* **15**, 756.
29. Chang, L. L., Esaki, L., Howard, W. E., Ludeke, R., and Schul, G. (1973). *J. Vac. Sci. Technol.* **10**, 655.
30. Chang, L. L., and Esaki, L. (1979). *Prog. Cryst. Growth Charact.* **2**, 3.
31. Joyce, B. A., and Foxon, C. T. (1975). *J. Cryst. Growth* **31**, 122.
32. Foxon, C. T., and Joyce, B. A. (1975). *Surf. Sci.* **50**, 434.
33. See, for example, ref. 9 and references cited therein.
34. Cho, A. Y. (1970). *J. Appl. Phys.* **41**, 2780.
35. Burton, W. K., Cabrera, N., and Frank, F. C. (1951). *Philos. Trans. R. Soc. London* **243A**, 299.
36. Gossard, A. C., Petroff, P. M., Wiegmann, W., Dingle, R., and Savage, A. (1976). *Appl. Phys. Lett.* **29**, 323.
37. Döhler, G. H., and Ploog, K. (1979). *Prog Cryst. Growth Charact.* **2**, 145.
38. Dingle, R., Störmer, H., Gossard, A. C., and Wiegmann, W. (1978). *Appl. Phys. Lett.* **33**, 665.
39. Ilegems, M. (1977). *J. Appl. Phys.* **48**, 1278.
40. Blakeslee, A. E., and Alliotta, C. F. (1970). *IBM J. Res. Dev.* **14**, 686.
41. Woodall, J. W. (1972). *J. Cryst. Growth* **12**, 32.
42. Cho, A. Y. (1971). *Appl. Phys. Lett.* **19**, 467.
43. van der Ziel, J. P., and Ilegems, M. (1975). *Appl. Opt.* **14**, 2627.
44. van der Ziel, J. P., and Ilegems, M. (1976). *Appl. Opt.* **15**, 1256.
45. Mayer, J. W., Ziegler, J. F., Chang, L. L., Tsu, R., and Esaki, L. (1973). *Appl. Phys. Lett.* **44**, 2322.
46. Chang, L. L., Esaki, L., Howard, W. E., Ludeke, R., and Schul, G. (1973). *J. Vac. Sci. Technol.* **10**, 655.
47. Ludeke, R., Esaki, L., and Chang, L. L. (1974). *Appl. Phys. Lett.* **24**, 417.
48. Tsu, R., Kawamura, H., and Esaki, L. (1972). *Proc. Conf. Phys. Semicond., 11th Warsaw* p. 1135.
49. Chang, L. L., Esaki, L., and Tsu, R. (1974). *Appl. Phys. Lett.* **24**, 593.
50. Dingle, R., Wiegmann, W., and Henry, C. H. (1974). *Phys. Rev. Lett.* **33**, 827.
51. Petroff, P. M. (1977). *J. Vac. Sci. Technol.* **14**, 973.
52. Gilmer, G. H. (1977). *J. Cryst. Growth* **42**, 3.
53. Fleming, R. M., McWhan, D. B., Gossard, A. C., Wiegmann, W., and Logan, R. A. (1980). *J. Appl. Phys.* **51**, 357.

54. Chang, L. L., Segmüller, A., and Esaki, L. (1976). *Appl. Phys. Lett.* **28,** 39.
55. Dernier, P. D., Moncton, D. E., McWhan, D. B., Gossard, A. C., and Wiegmann, W. (1977). *Bull. Am. Phys. Soc.* **22,** 293.
56. Chang, L. L., and Koma, A. (1976). *Appl. Phys. Lett.* **29,** 138.
57. Dingle, R. (1977). *J. Vac. Sci. Technol.* **14,** 1006.
58. Dingle, R., Gossard, A. C., and Wiegmann, W. (1976). *Bull. Am. Phys. Soc.* **21,** 367.
59. van Vechten, J. A. (1980). *In* "North Holland Semiconductor Handbook" (S. P. Keller, ed.). North-Holland Publ., Amsterdam.
60. Cho, A. Y. (1976). *J. Appl. Phys.* **47,** 2841.
61. McWhan, D. B., Gossard, A. C., and Wiegmann, W. (1982). Unpublished observations.
62. Sai-Halasz, G. A., Tsu, R., and Esaki, L. (1977). *Appl. Phys. Lett.* **30,** 651.
63. Chin-an Chang, Ludeke, R., Chang, L. L., and Eskai, L. (1977). *Appl. Phys. Lett.* **31,** 759.
64. Petroff, P. M., Gossard, A. C., Savage, A., and Wiegmann, W. (1979). *J. Cryst. Growth* **46,** 172.
65. Phillips, J. C. (1981). *J. Vac. Sci. Technol.* **19,** 545.
66. Cho, A. Y., and Dernier, P. D. (1978). *J. Appl. Phys.* **49,** 3328.
67. Ludeke, R., Chang, L. L., and Esaki, L. (1973). *Appl. Phys. Lett.* **23,** 201.
68. Chiu, K. C. R., Poate, J. M., Feldman, L. C., and Doherty, C. J. (1980). *Appl. Phys. Lett.* **36,** 544.
69. Bean, J. C., and Poate, J. M. (1980). *Appl. Phys. Lett.* **37,** 643.
70. Cho, A. Y. (1975). *J. Appl. Phys.* **46,** 1733.
71. Wood, C. E. C., Metze, G., Berry, J., and Eastman, L. F. (1980). *J. Appl. Phys.* **51,** 383.
72. Ploog, K., and Fischer, A. (1978). *J. Vac. Sci. Technol.* **15,** 255.
73. Döhler, G. H., Künzel, H., and Ploog, K. (1982). *Phys. Rev.* **B25,** 2616.
74. Dingle, R. (1975). *In* "Festkörperprobleme (Advances in Solid State Physics)" (H. J. Queisser, ed.), Vol. XV, p. 21. Pergamon, Oxford.
75. Casey, H. C., and Panish, M. B. (1978)."Heterostructure Lasers, Part A: Fundamental Principles," p. 192. Academic Press, New York.
76. Dingle, R., Gossard, A. C., and Wiegmann, W. (1975). *Phys. Rev. Lett.* **34,** 1327.
77. Miller, R. C., Dingle, R., Gossard, A. C., Logan, R. A., Nordland, W. A., Jr., and Wiegmann, W. (1976). *J. Appl. Phys.* **47,** 4509.
78. Miller, R. C., Kleinman, D. A., and Gossard, A. C. (1979). *Inst. Phys. Conf. Ser. No.* 43, Ch. 27, p. 1043.
79. Esaki, L. (1977). *Proc. Int. Vac. Congr., 7th, Int. Conf. Solid Surf., 3rd, Vienna* p. 1907.
80. Tsu, R., Chang, L. L., Sai-Halasz, G. A., and Esaki, L. (1975). *Phys. Rev. Lett.* **34,** 1509.
81. Pinczuk A., Shah, J., Gossard, A. C., and Wiegmann, W. (1981). *Phys. Rev. Lett.* **46,** 1307.
82. Pinczuk, A., Störmer, H. L., Dingle, R., Worlock, J. M., Wiegmann, W., and Gossard, A. C. (1979). *Solid State Commun.* **32,** 1001.
83. Weisbuch, C., Miller, R. C., Dingle, R., Gossard, A. C., and Wiegmann, W. (1981). *Solid State Commun.* **37,** 219.
84. Petroff, P. M., Weisbuch, C., Dingle, R., Gossard, A. C., and Wiegmann, W. (1981). *Appl. Phys. Lett.* **38,** 965.
85. van der Ziel, J. P., Dingle, R., Miller, R. C., Wiegmann, W., and Nordland, W. A., Jr. (1975). *Appl. Phys. Lett.* **26,** 463.
86. Kolbas, R. M., Holonyak, N., Jr., Dupuis, R. D., and Dapkus, P. D. (1978). *Pis'ma Zh. Tekh. Fiz.* **4,** 69 (*Sov. Tech. Phys. Lett.* **4,** 28).
87. Rezek, E. A., Holonyak, N., Jr., Vojak, B. A., and Shichijo, H. (1978). *J. Appl. Phys.* **49,** 69.

88. Dupuis, R. D., Dapkus, P. D., Holonyak, N., Jr., Rezek, E. A., and Chin, R. (1978). *Appl. Phys. Lett.* **32**, 295.

89. Holonyak, N., Jr., Kolbas, R. M., Rezek, E. A., Chin, R., Dupuis, R. D., and Dapkus, P. D. (1978). *J. Appl. Phys.* **49**, 5392.

90. Weisbuch, C., Dingle, R., Gossard, A. C., and Wiegmann, W. (1980). *J. Vac. Sci. Technol.* **17**, 1128.

91. Weisbuch, C., Dingle, R., Petroff, P. M., Gossard, A. C., and Wiegmann, W. (1981). *Appl. Phys. Lett.* **38**, 840.

92. Holonyak, N., Jr., Laidig, W. D., Vojak, B. A., Hess, K., Coleman, J. J., Dapkus, P. D., and Bardeen, J. (1980). *Phys. Rev. Lett.* **45**, 1703.

93. van der Ziel, J. P., and Gossard, A. C. (1977). *J. Appl. Phys.* **48**, 3018.

94. Caruthers, E., and Lin-Chung, P. J. (1978). *Phys. Rev.* **B17**, 2705.

95. Andreoni, W., and Car, A. (1980). *Phys. Rev.* **B21**, 3334.

96. Schulman, J. N., and McGill, T. C. (1979). *Phys. Rev.* **B19**, 6341.

97. Sakaki, H., Chang, L. L., Ludeke, R., Chang, C.-A., Sai-Halasz, G. A., and Esaki, L. (1977). *Appl. Phys. Lett.* **31**, 211.

98. Sai-Halasz, G. A., Chang, L. L., Welter, J. W., Chang, C.-A., and Esaki, L. (1978). *Solid State Commun.* **26**, 935.

99. Guldner, Y., Vieren, J. P., Voisin, P., Voos, M., Chang, L. L., and Esaki, L. (1980). *Phys. Rev. Lett.* **45**, 1719.

100. Sakaki, H., Chang, L. L., Sai-Halasz, G. A., Chang, C.-A., and Esaki, L. (1978). *Solid State Commun.* **26**, 589.

101. Allyn, C. L., Gossard, A. C., and Wiegmann, W. (1980). *Appl. Phys. Lett.* **36**, 373.

102. Cho, A. Y., and Hayashi, I. (1971). *Met. Trans.* **2**, 777.

103. Chang, L. L., Sakaki, H., Chang, C.-A., and Esaki, L. (1977). *Phys. Rev. Lett.* **38**, 1489.

104. Störmer, H. L., Pinczuk, A., Gossard, A. C., and Wiegmann, W. (1981). *Appl. Phys. Lett.* **38**, 691.

105. Witkowski, L. C., Drummond, T. J., Stanchak, C. M., and Morkoc, H. (1980). *Appl. Phys. Lett.* **37**, 1033.

106. Witkowski, L. C., Drummond, T. J., Barnett, S. A., Morkoc, H., Cho, A. Y., and Greene, J. E. (1982). Submitted.

107. Mori, S., and Ando, T. (1980). *J. Phys. Soc. Jpn.* **48**, 865.

108. Hess, K. (1979). *Appl. Phys. Lett.* **35**, 484.

109. Störmer, H. L., Dingle, R., Gossard, A. C., Wiegmann, W., and Sturge, M. D. (1979). *Solid State Commun.* **29**, 705.

110. Drummond, T. J., Morkoc, H., Su, S. L., Fischer, R., and Cho, A. Y. (1981). *Electron. Lett.* **17**, 870.

111. Störmer, H. L., Dingle, R., Gossard, A. C., and Wiegmann, W. (1978). *Conf. Ser. Inst. Phys. London* **43**, 557.

112. Tsui, D. C., and Gossard, A. C. (1981). *Appl. Phys. Lett.* **38**.

113. von Klitzing, K., Dorda, G., and Pepper, M. (1980). *Phys. Rev. Lett.* **45**, 494.

114. Prange, R. E. (1981). *Phys. Rev.* **B23**, 4802.

115. Mimura, T., Hiyamizu, S., Fujii, T., and Nanbu, K. (1980). *Jpn. J. Appl. Phys.* **19**, L225.

116. Störmer, H. L., and Tsang, W. T. (1980). *Appl. Phys. Lett.* **36**, 685.

117. Garner, C. M., Su, C. Y., Shen, Y. D., Lee, C. S., Pearson, G. L., Spicer, W. E., Edwall, D. D., Miller, D., and Harris, J. S., Jr. (1979). *J. Appl. Phys.* **50**, 3383.

118. Sahai, R., Harris, J. S., Eden, R. C., Bubulae, L. O., and Chu, J. C. (1975). *Crit. Rev. Solid State Sci.* **5**, 565.

119. Chandra, A., and Eastman, L. F. (1970). *Electron. Lett.* **15**, 91.

120. Allyn, C. L., Gossard, A. C., and Wiegmann, W. (1980). *Appl. Phys. Lett.* **36**, 373.
121. Gossard, A. C., Brown, W., Allyn, C. L., and Wiegmann, W. (1982). *J. Vac. Sci. Technol.* **20**, 694.
122. Malik, R. J., AuCoin, T. R., Ross, R. L., Board, K., Wood, C. E. C., and Eastman, L. F. (1980). *Electron. Lett.* **16**, 836.
123. Shannon, J. M. (1979). *Appl. Phys. Lett.* **35**, 63.
124. Shannon, J. M. (1979). *Solid State Electron Devices* **3**, 142.
125. Merlin, R., Colvard, C., Klein, M. V., Morkoc, H., Cho, A. Y., and Gossard, A. C. (1980). *Appl. Phys. Lett.* **36**, 43.
126. Barker, A. S., Jr., Merz, J. L., and Gossard, A. C. (1978). *Phys. Rev.* **B17**, 3181.
127. Colvard, C., Merlin, R., Klein, M. V., and Gossard, A. C. (1980). *Phys. Rev. Lett.* **45**, 298.
128. Narayanamurti, V., Störmer, H. L., Chin, M. A., Gossard, A. C., and Wiegmann, W. (1980). *Phys. Rev. Lett.* **43**, 1536.
129. Pavlovich, V. V., and Epshtein, E. M. (1976). *Sov. Phys. Semicond.* **10**, 1196.
130. Sze, S. M. (1969). "Physics of Semiconductor Devices," p. 587. Wiley (Interscience), New York.
131. Sakaki, H. (1980). *Jpn. J. Appl. Phys. Lett.* **19**, L735.

3

Epitaxial Growth of Silicon Structures—Thermal, Laser-, and Electron-Beam-Induced

S. S. LAU

University of California at San Diego
La Jolla, California

and

J. W. MAYER

Cornell University
Ithaca, New York

I. Introduction

Epitaxial growth of silicon is a well-established technology whether the growth technique is chemical vapor deposition (CVD) or molecular beam epitaxy (MBE). In the spirit of this volume, we concentrate on epitaxial growth of Si structures from deposited thin films. We begin the discussion with a review of the growth mechanism of implanted-amorphous Si layers. These studies of regrowth provided many of the insights into thermal and laser-induced epitaxial growth of deposited films. The implanted layers have two striking advantages: high-purity amorphous layers can be formed, and the interface between the amorphous layer and single-crystal substrate is free of contamination. As we will see in our discussion of deposited films, epitaxial growth depends critically upon the nature of the interface and the purity and structure of the deposited layers.

The precursors of studies of epitaxial growth were investigations of crystallization in amorphous deposited films (see, for example, Barna *et al.*, 1972; Germain *et al.*, 1977a,b). It was also found that crystallization could be enhanced if amorphous Ge or Si were in contact with metal films (Herd *et al.*, 1972; Ottaviani *et al.*, 1974; Koster, 1972). These studies provided much of the background for the early work on epitaxial growth of Si through metal films. The study of crystallization of deposited layers is still under investigation (Germain *et al.*, 1979; Zellama *et al.*, 1979a,b). In this work we are concerned with epitaxial growth rather than crystallization alone.

The first studies of epitaxial growth of Si in the solid phase were based on the deposition of amorphous Si on metal layers covering single-crystal substrates. The crystallization occurs by an initial dissolution of the amorphous Si into the metal film solvent followed by the epitaxial growth of the Si out of the solid solvent and onto the single-crystal substrate (Ottaviani *et al.*, 1974). Here the metal film, whether it be elemental or a silicide phase, was employed not only as a transport medium, but also to provide a clean interface. Later studies showed clearly that the properties of contamination in the interface played a vital role in crystal growth (see, for example, Ottaviani and Majni, 1979). Figure 1 shows a SEM picture and a schematic view of an epitaxial island grown from deposited Si transported across a solid palladium silicide layer (Canali *et al.*, 1976). This result demonstrates that single crystal layers could be grown at temperatures around 500°C.

It was found that such epitaxial layers could be intentionally doped by incorporating the dopant species within the metal layer. Figure 2 shows a SEM picture [obtained in the electron-beam-induced-current (EBIC) mode] of a mesa-etched epitaxial layer of Si grown through a palladium silicide layer containing a very thin Sb layer (~ 5 Å) (Lau *et al.*, 1976). The EBIC results show that the epitaxial layer is n-type and that the response of the junction is uniform across the mesa area. The epitaxial Si layer was heavily doped with Sb, and hence the p–n junction characteristics

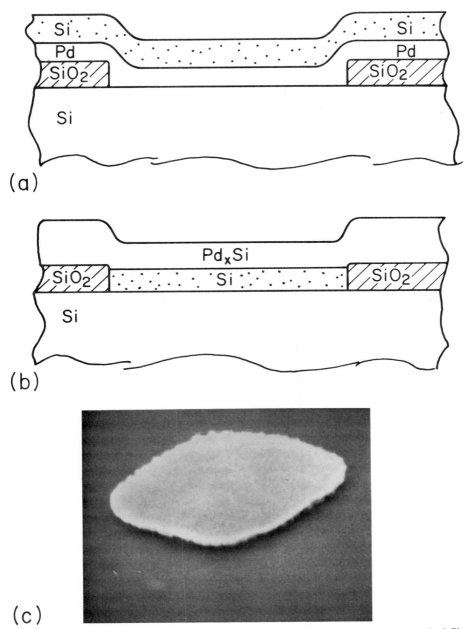

Fig. 1. SEM picture and schematic view of an epitaxial island grown from deposited Si transported across a solid Pd-silicide layer. (From Canali *et al.*, 1974.)

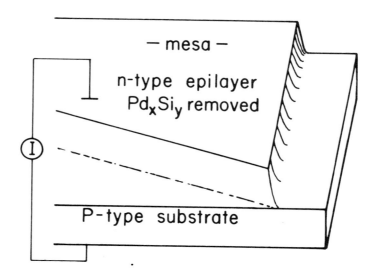

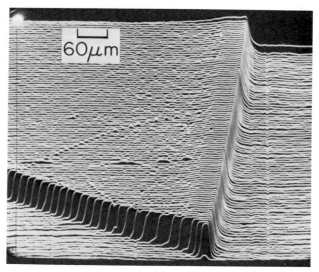

Fig. 2. SEM picture obtained in the EBIC mode with y axis modulation of a mesa-etched epitaxial layer of Si grown through a palladium silicide layer containing a very thin Sb layer ($\sim$5 Å). E_b = 15 keV, electron beam energy. A schematic view of the mesa structure is also shown. (From Lau et al., 1976.)

reflect more the quality of the underlying Si than the epitaxial layer itself. Subsequent investigation of epitaxial growth through metal films showed that trapping of metal within the growing layer occurred over a wide range of growth conditions. Although the amount of metal inclusions could be reduced by appropriate growth techniques, they were not entirely eliminated. These epitaxial layers (reverse-biased), then, were satisfactory for use as blocking contacts in nuclear particle detectors or as injecting contacts in studies of electron–hole luminescence studies. They were not satisfactory for active devices based on carrier transport within the epitaxial layer itself. Epitaxial growth through metal films provided the metallurgical insight into factors influencing crystal growth, but violated the concept of high purity required for electronic structures.

Rapid strides have been made in epitaxial growth based on minimizing the impurity content of the epitaxial films. As an example of high-purity epitaxial growth, Fig. 3 shows an optical micrograph of an enhanced mode n-channel MOSFET (J. A. Roth and J. G. Nash, personal communication). These n-channel MOSFETs were fabricated on 7500-Å-thick Si films deposited and grown in a ultra-high-vacuum (UHV) system. The MOSFET

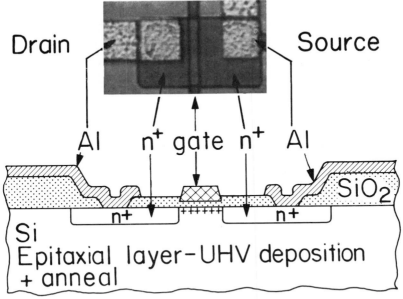

Fig. 3. Optical micrograph and schematic view of an enhanced mode n-channel MOSFET. These n-channel MOSFETs were fabricated on 7500-Å-thick Si films deposited and grown in a UHV system. (From J. A. Roth and J. G. Nash, Hughes Research Lab., Malibu, personal communication).

structure was then fabricated using masks and processes employed routinely for short-channel MOS integrated circuit production on bulk Si wafers. In all respects (transconductance, channel mobility, threshold voltage, and leakage rates) the solid-phase epitaxial FETs performed identically to their counterparts formed on bulk Si wafers. These results show dramatically that high-quality epitaxial layers can be formed from deposited Si layers. The possibility of device-quality epitaxy at low process temperatures adds a new dimension in the fabrication of integrated circuits. One can conceive of three-dimensional device architecture.

II. Thermal and Laser-Induced Epitaxy: Implanted-Amorphous Silicon

Ion implantation provides a simple and reproducible method of producing amorphous Si and Ge. By implanting Si ions at 250 keV, amorphous layers nearly 5000 Å thick can be formed on a single-crystal substrate, as shown schematically in Fig. 4. Channeling effect measurements with mega-electron-volt He ions are used to measure the thickness of the amorphous layer and the lateral uniformity of the interface region where the transition from amorphous to crystalline material occurs. Thermal annealing of these layers at temperatures around 550°C ($\sim\frac{1}{2}T_m$ of Si in degrees Kelvin) resulted in epitaxial growth as shown schematically on the right side of Fig. 4 (Lau et al., 1980). Although epitaxial growth of implanted-amorphous Si was

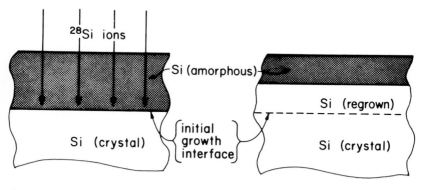

(a) formation of amorphous   (b) partial regrowth of
     layer by implementation   epitaxial Si by thermal
                                            annealing.

Fig. 4. Formation of an amorphous Si layer by self-ion-implantation (a) and the subsequent interface movement by partial regrowth of epitaxial Si (b) during thermal annealing at temperatures $\sim\frac{1}{2}T_m$.

recognized as early as 1967 (Mayer *et al.*, 1968), it was not until a decade later that systemic studies were made of the growth kinetics. In effect, the interest in this subject changed from the investigation of annealing of disorder in implanted crystals to the study of crystal growth using implantation as a sample preparation technique.

The growth kinetics of $\langle 100 \rangle$-oriented Si are particularly simple. The amorphous–crystal interface moves with a uniform velocity toward the surface, maintaining a laterally uniform front with a well-defined activation energy of 2.4 eV. The velocity of the interface of self-ion-implanted Si is 1.5 Å/s at 550°C, resulting in a relatively defect-free epitaxial layer (Csepregi *et al.*, 1975, 1976). The regrowth of implanted-amorphous Si requires no long-range transport of Si as in the case of epitaxial growth through metal films. The growth process only requires a rearrangement of the bonds at the amorphous–crystal interface. Based on this concept, the growth rate v is given by

$$v = av_0 \exp(-\Delta E_a/kT) \tag{1}$$

where a is the atomic spacing along the $\langle 100 \rangle$, v_0 the jump frequency, and ΔE_a the activation energy for the bond-breaking process. The calculated growth rates are lower than the experimental rates by a factor of 2 to 3 and hence one visualizes a single broken bond propagating along the interface and causing reconstruction of the lattice in its wake (Spaepen, 1978; Spaepen and Turbull, 1979).

The growth of epitaxial layers on a $\langle 100 \rangle$ surface is uniform and characterized by layer-by-layer growth. In contrast, the growth behavior on $\langle 111 \rangle$-oriented Si is more complex: The growth is not linear with time, twins are formed, and the growth interface is laterally nonuniform. Figure 5 shows a SEM review of $\langle 111 \rangle$-oriented samples that were partially reground (Csepregi *et al.*, 1976) (the amorphous layer was removed in the picture). The nonuniform nature of the growth interface is clear. The lower portion of the figure shows the presence of twins in the grown structure. In the $\langle 111 \rangle$ direction, one would anticipate such irregular growth because of the structure of the covalent lattice in which atoms in (111) planes have one bond connecting them to an atom in the adjacent (111) plane. This connecting bond provides no rotational orientation information for the next set of covalent bonds. Consequently, growth occurs along the ledges rather than normal to the (111) plane (Spaepen, 1978). The growing (111) planes are inclined to the amorphous–crystalline interface, and hence one anticipates an irregular growth front and planar defect formation (i.e., twins and faults).

The presence of impurities (implanted in the amorphous layer) also has a strong influence on the growth rate (Csepregi *et al.*, 1977; Kennedy *et*

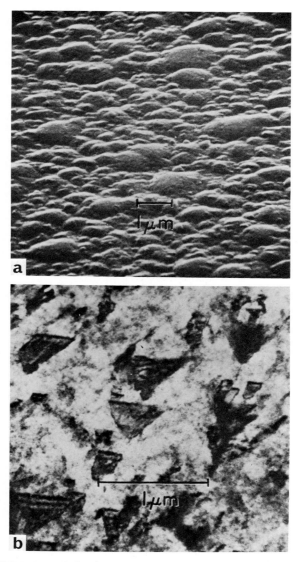

Fig. 5.   (a) SEM view of a ⟨111⟩-oriented sample, partially regrown and with amorphous layer removed. (b) TEM picture of the same sample showing the presence of twins. (From Csepregi *et al.*, 1975.)

al., 1976). Figure 6 shows that the presence of P(AsB) causes an increase in growth rates and the presence of O(CN) causes a decrease in growth rates. It was found that the local impurity concentration at the amorphous–crystal interface determines the growth rate rather than average impurity concentration within either the amorphous or crystal layer. One, then, pictures the interfacial impurities as either enhancing or suppressing bond reconstruction. The presence of high concentrations of oxygen reduces the growth rate by four orders of magnitude at 550°C (Kennedy *et al.*, 1976).

Whereas the presence of either *n*-type or *p*-type impurities alone enhances the regrowth rate at moderate concentrations (0.25–0.5 at. %), the mingled presence of both types of impurity (*n*- and *p*-type) has a compensating effect on the regrowth rate. It has been shown recently (Suni *et al.*, 1981a,b) that single implants of ^{11}B, ^{31}P, or ^{75}As are found to increase regrowth rates, whereas compensated layers with equal concentrations of ^{11}B and ^{31}P or ^{11}B and ^{75}As are found to decrease the regrowth rates to a level obtained for amorphous layers implanted with Si only. In cases

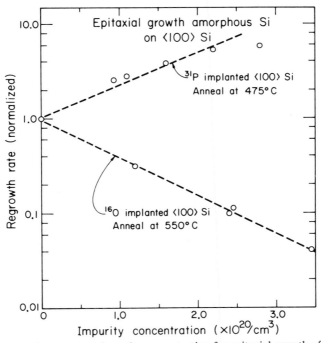

Fig. 6. Regrowth rate versus impurity concentration for epitaxial growth of amorphous Si on ⟨100⟩ Si. The presence of phosphorus increases the regrowth rate, whereas the presence of oxygen reduces the rate. (From Kennedy *et al.*, 1977.)

where the amorphous layers have overlapping ^{75}As and ^{31}P (only n-type impurities) profiles, no compensation has been found.

In a simple bond rearrangement model for solid-phase epitaxial regrowth, the rate is controlled by the formation of point defects at the amorphous–crystalline interface. Csepregi et al. (1977a) have pointed out the close similarity between the activation energies for the epitaxial regrowth and the energies for vacancy formation in both Si and Ge. This suggests that the defects controlling the regrowth rate are vacancies. The density of neutral vacancies N^x available for the bond breaking process can be described by a simple equation:

$$N^x = N^\circ \exp(-\Delta E/kT) \tag{2}$$

where ΔE is the formation energy of neutral vacancies and N° is the density of lattice sites. This neutral vacancy concentration (equilibrium concentration) is fixed at a given temperature. According to the vacancy model of Van Vechten (1976), the density of charged vacancies is given by the position of the Fermi level, E_F, with respect to the energy levels of the acceptor (E^-) or donor (E^+) type vacancies:

$$N^- = N^x \exp[(E_F - E^-)/kT] \tag{3}$$

$$N^+ = N^x \exp[(E^+ - E_F)/kT] \tag{4}$$

This means that for each neutral vacancy, the number of charged vacancies is enhanced by an exponential factor according to Eqs. (3) and (4). The effective activation energy ΔE_{eff} for the formation of charged vacancies is therefore equal to

$$\Delta E_{eff} = \Delta E - (E_F - E^-) \quad \text{for} \quad N^- \tag{5}$$

$$\Delta E_{eff} = \Delta E - (E^+ - E_F) \quad \text{for} \quad N^+ \tag{6}$$

which is less than the formation energy ΔE for neutral vacancies. According to existing data, the E^- level is located about 0.55 eV below the conduction band edge, and E^+ is about 0.35 eV above the valence band edge of Si (Van Vechten, 1976).

For sufficiently high doping concentrations, the Fermi level will shift away from midgap, leading to a rapid increase of charged vacancies according to Eqs. (3) and (4). Since the regrowth rate is controlled by the concentration of vacancies, the rate will be enhanced by doping. This model thus correctly predicts a rise of the growth rates and a lowering of the activation energy for regrowth with increasing doping, as was indeed observed in the experiments. The model also explains why doping compensation reduces the enhancement and increases the activation energy to the intrinsic value.

To quantify the effect of doping on the activation energy for regrowth, Suni *et al.* (1981b) assumed that the Fermi level for ^{11}B-doped (≤ 0.5 at. %) Si is at the valence band edge (E_v) and that the Fermi level for ^{31}P- and ^{75}As-doped (≤ 0.5 at. %) Si is at the conduction band edge (E_c). With $E_c - E^- = 0.55$ eV and $E^+ - E_v = 0.35$ eV, they obtained $\Delta E_{eff} = \Delta E - (E_F - E^-) = 1.95$ eV for *n*-type Si and $\Delta E_{eff} = \Delta E - (E^+ - E_F) = 1.75$ eV for *p*-type Si, if ΔE is taken to be 2.3 eV for the undoped Si. This trend of smaller regrowth activation energy for heavily doped Si has been observed by Lietoila *et al.* (1982) (2.85 eV for intrinsic Si, 2.5 eV for ^{31}P-doped Si); Csepregi *et al.* (1977) (2.3 eV for intrinsic Si, 1.9 eV for ^{11}B-doped Si); and Suni *et al.* (1981a) (2.3 eV for intrinsic Si, 2.0 eV for ^{31}P-doped Si, 1.9 eV for ^{11}B-doped Si). Although the absolute values of activation energies differed from one investigation to the other, the tendency of lowering the activation energy by doping has been consistently observed by all investigators.

Williams *et al.* (1975, 1982) have studied the influence of high implant concentrations on the epitaxial regrowth in Si. They have suggested that for concentrations below a few atomic percent, recrystallization of amorphous silicon is predominantly via solid-phase epitaxial regrowth. At higher concentrations, the regrowth rate may be slowed down sufficiently such that spontaneous nucleation of polycrystallites within the amorphous layer competes with the epitaxial regrowth. They speculated further that high local stress levels due to accommodation of high implant concentration in the near-surface layer may both retard the rate of epitaxial regrowth and promote nucleation of polycrystallites. Although supersaturation during the solid-phase epitaxial regrowth has been observed for slowly diffusing impurities with low solid solubility (Campisano *et al.*, 1980), the solubility of the implanted species ultimately will limit the regrowth at high concentrations. The solubility limit for arsenic in Ge is about 0.5 at. % (Trumbore, 1960). This agrees with the value at which Suni *et al.* (1981b) have observed retardation in the regrowth rate of Ge doped with As.

A dependence of the regrowth rate of amorphized Si has also been reported by Campisano *et al.* (1981) for Te-implanted Si. They find that the regrowth rate is enhanced below about 7×10^{19} Te/cm^3 and depressed above that value. They also attribute this effect to Te concentrations rising above the solubility limit.

Laser and electron beam annealing have been applied to study the regrowth of implanted-amorphous semiconductors (see, for example, Ferris *et al.*, 1979; Anderson *et al.*, 1980). With lasers (or electron beams), localized surface regions of the sample can be heated without major disturbance to the adjacent regions. Thermal annealing, on the other hand, requires heating of the entire substrate. Consequently, the concept of localized energy deposition, local in both lateral extent and depth, was considered to be in line with the concept of integrated circuit fabrication. Perhaps an even more compelling reason for interest in these annealing techniques was that the initial results showed a strong reduction in the amount of disorder in implanted samples.

The initial investigations on Q-switched-laser or pulsed-electron-beam anneal of implanted amorphous layers revealed that good epitaxial growth could be achieved. The following features were puzzling because they did not agree with the results obtained from thermal annealing in the solid phase:

(1) There was a threshold in laser energy below which the amorphous region was converted into polycrystalline material and above which good epitaxy was obtained (Fig. 7) (see, for example, Lau *et al.*, 1979; Foti *et al.*, 1978).

(2) Good epitaxial growth was obtained in both ⟨100⟩- and ⟨111⟩-ori-

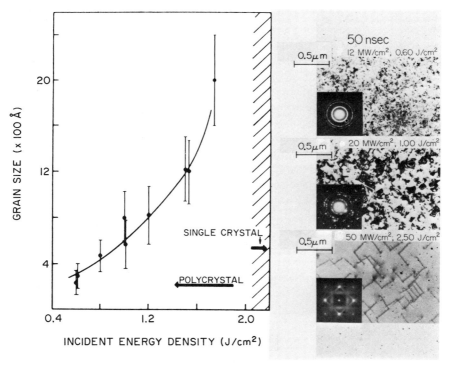

Fig. 7. Grain size versus incident laser energy density (J/cm²). Transmission electron microscopy pictures show the microstructure of samples processed by laser at various energy densities. A threshold energy for epitaxy can be clearly seen. (From Foti *et al.*, 1978.)

ented Si substrates, in marked contrast to thermal annealing where the grown layer for $\langle 111 \rangle$ Si was heavily twinned.

(3) In laser-annealed samples containing impurities, there is a marked redistribution of the impurities to depths as great as 3000–4000 Å (White et al., 1979a,b). In solid-phase epitaxial growth at temperatures around 500–600°C, the impurities did not redistribute in depth. This preservation of impurity profile during regrowth was expected because the activation energy for diffusion is roughly twice that for epitaxial growth (Lau et al., 1979).

(4) In pulsed-laser or pulsed-electron-beam annealing the regrowth velocity estimated from the pulsed duration was about 1 m/s (Auston et al., 1979). An extrapolation of the solid-phase thermal-anneal growth rate gave an upper limit of about 10^{-3} m/s as a maximum rate around 1400°C (Lau et al., 1979).

These differences were recognized early as indications of a difference in growth mechanisms between thermal and pulsed-laser annealings. It became rather obvious that the mechanism for epitaxial growth induced by a Q-switched laser was a liquid-phase phenomenon in which the incident laser power was sufficient to melt through the amorphous layer into the underlying single-crystal substrate. Upon termination of the pulse, typically 10^{-7} s in duration, the crystal–liquid interface would grow back to the surface as shown in Fig. 8. Indeed, measurements of infrared (IR) reflectivity indicated the presence of a liquid region (Auston et al., 1979), calculations of energy absorption and heat flow showed that such a melt–regrowth regime was indeed possible (Baeri et al., 1979), and measurements of conductance established the liquid/crystal kinetics (Galvin et al., 1982). The differences between solid-phase thermal anneal and liquid-phase transient anneal could be explained simply:

(1) The existence of a threshold occurs because epitaxial growth will not be found unless the laser power is sufficient to melt the amorphous layer.

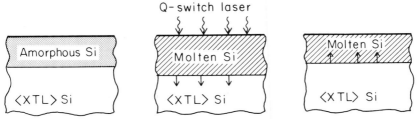

Fig. 8. Liquid-phase epitaxy of amorphous Si as a result of laser irradiation.

(2) In liquid-phase epitaxy, crystal orientation does not have a strong influence, and one would expect that the crystal quality of $\langle 100 \rangle$- and $\langle 111 \rangle$-oriented layers would be similar to first order.

(3) The redistribution of impurities is a consequence of the high diffusivity, $D \simeq 10^{-4}$ cm^2/s, of impurities in liquids.

(4) A growth rate of ~ 1 m/s is quite consistent with measurements of the undercooled metallic liquid (Spaepen, 1978) (liquid Si is metallic in nature).

There is another regime in laser and electron-beam annealing that was also investigated: scanned cw beams where the incident energy resides in a local region for times $\sim 10^{-2}$–10^{-3} s. The results of these investigations, both theoretical and experimental, showed that epitaxial regrowth occurred in the solid phase at temperatures around 900°C and above. In the cw annealing regime, one finds the same orientation effects and absence of dopant redistribution as is found in the lower temperature thermal annealing (Williams *et al.*, 1978). The scanned cw laser can be viewed as a short-duration heat gun.

Kokorowski *et al.* (1982) have investigated solid-phase regrowth of ion-implanted Si over the temperature range from 450 to about 1400°C. Furnace annealing is used for relatively low temperature regrowth experiments (~ 450 to ~ 600°C) and a cw Ar laser is used to induce regrowth in the high-temperature regime. The regrowth velocity is measured by the reflectivity of the sample using a He–Ne laser. It is found that the activation energy for regrowth is 2.62 eV for layers with $\sim 2 \times 10^{19}$ cm^{-3} As concentration and 2.52 eV for layers with $\sim 4 \times 10^{19}$ cm^{-3} As concentration. In the temperature range of 450 to 1000°C, the activation energy is independent of the temperature; and the regrowth rate follows a simple Arrhenius expression. At higher temperatures, the regrowth rates and the activation energy appear to deviate (they are slightly reduced) from those determined by the simple Arrhenius expression valid between 450°C and 1000°C. Using their data and recognizing the transient temperature effects near 1400°C, the solid-phase regrowth rate is estimated to be about 0.1– 1 cm/s.

Epitaxial growth of implanted-amorphous layers has been investigated in three time regimes: thermal annealing characterized by a time of 1000 s, cw-beam annealing characterized by solid-phase growth in 10^{-2} s, and Q-switched or pulsed beams in which epitaxy occurs in the liquid phase within 10^{-7} s. As a rough rule, each time domain differs from the others by about a factor of 10^5 s. Naturally, there are wide variations in these times, but the general features of recrystallization seem to hold in each time domain.

The same division into solid and liquid phases can also be seen in the application of ion beams to achieve epitaxial regrowth of implanted-amorphous Si. The analogy to the solid phase is provided by bombardment of Si ions through the amorphous–crystal interface. The samples are held at an elevated temperature of 200–400°C to minimize formation of further amorphous regions during ion bombardment (Golecki *et al.*, 1979; Nakata and Kajiyama, 1982). The annealing beam, however, does introduce additional damage in the crystal (Golecki *et al.*, 1979). In the other extreme, intense pulsed ion beams (200-keV H^+ ions at $\sim$100 A/cm^2) were used to produce good crystallinity in implanted-amorphous Si (Hodgson *et al.*, 1980). In this case, the beam energy is sufficient for melting, and growth is initiated from the single-crystal substrate. Channeling measurements on As-implanted Si showed results comparable to those achieved in pulsed-laser annealing: high substitutional As concentration and good minimum yield in the Si.

III. Deposited Layers of Silicon on Silicon

A. *Clean Interface and Low-Impurity-Content Films*

One of the objectives in studies of deposited layers of Si on Si was to determine if the good epitaxial growth seen in implanted-amorphous films can be duplicated in deposited amorphous films. With this objective in mind, experiments were done in UHV systems in which the interface could be cleaned by Ar-ion bombardment and subsequent heat treatment. Silicon films, 1000–7500 Å thick, were deposited at a pressure below 10^{-6} Pa (below 10^{-8} Torr). Epitaxial growth of the deposited films was induced by heating the sample in the UHV chamber to 500–600°C (Roth and Anderson, 1977). Selective-area electron diffraction, TEM, and Rutherford backscattering channeling effect analyses all indicated that the epitaxial layer was of high quality. For example, Fig. 9 shows 2-MeV ^{4}He$^+$ channeling spectra of such films. The large reduction in backscattering yield between the random (solid circles) and channeled (open circles) spectra is strong evidence for the epitaxial orientation of the grown film. The ratio of the random to aligned spectrum heights in the near-surface region is $\simeq 1/25$ (minimum yield, $\chi_{min} = 4\%$). The aligned yield in the interface region shows no evidence of excessive dechanneling, which is again indicative of a clean interface. There are some defects in this region, since TEM analysis indicates the presence of a few dislocations that originate near the

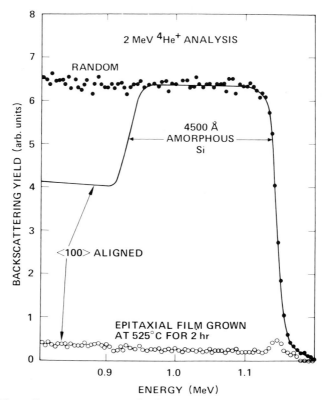

Fig. 9. Channeling spectra of 2-MeV ^{4}He$^+$ ions showing solid-phase epitaxy of an initially amorphous 4500-Å Si film (——) into an epitaxial single-crystal layer (○). (From Roth and Anderson, 1977.)

substrate–film interface and extend through the epitaxial layer. The number of dislocations is sufficiently small so that they have a negligible influence on the electron transport properties of the epitaxial layer. In fact, this growth procedure was used for the samples shown in Fig. 3.

Thus, it has been demonstrated that high-quality epitaxial layers of Si on Si can be grown by taking stringent precautions to obtain a clean interface to deposit a film under good vacuum conditions and annealing the film *in situ*. The questions we now address are concerned with how "forgiving" the epitaxial growth requirements can be. We also review the application of laser annealing techniques to satisfy some of the interface and deposition requirements.

B. Interface Requirements

The results of epitaxial growth depend upon the deposition conditions as well as interface cleanliness. Consequently, in this section we will refer to samples in which the deposition parameters were kept nearly the same and only the crystal surface preparation was altered. The samples were prepared by electron-beam evaporation of Si at a deposition rate of 30–50 Å/s at a pressure during deposition below 7×10^{-5} Pa (5×10^{-7} Torr). The film thicknesses range between 1000 and 5000 Å. The procedures used to clean the Si crystal surface are important in deciding the outcome of epitaxial quality. Since slight variations in procedure from laboratory to laboratory can lead to large changes in the quality of the epitaxial layer, we discuss the influence of the interface only in general terms.

When a Si film is deposited on a native oxide (a well-cleaned surface allowed to stand in room air for some days), heat treatment results in the formation of a polycrystalline layer (Fig. 10). In this case, the oxide layer is sufficiently thick that the deposited layer is unable to communicate with the crystal arrangement in the substrate. Channeling measurements have shown that these native oxide layers on $\langle 100 \rangle$ Si attain 6×10^{15} oxygen atoms/cm², corresponding to a thickness of about 10–15 Å of SiO_2 (Cheung *et al.*, 1979).

When the surface is cleaned using organic solvents, a polycrystalline layer is also formed after deposition and heat treatment. In this case, it was found that the amount of oxygen at the surface was similar to that on samples with a thin native oxide layer. Nuclear reaction measurements [$^{16}O(d, \alpha)^{14}N$] were used to determine the areal density of oxygen at the interface.

The amount of oxygen at the interface can be reduced by a factor of 10–20 by dipping the sample in dilute HF followed by a final H_2O rinse prior to insertion in the vacuum system (von Allman *et al.*, 1979, 1980; L. S. Hung, personal communication, 1980). We refer to such samples as

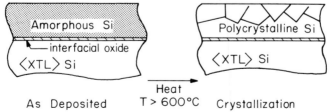

Fig. 10. Polycrystallite formation when the amorphous–crystal interface has a native oxide layer.

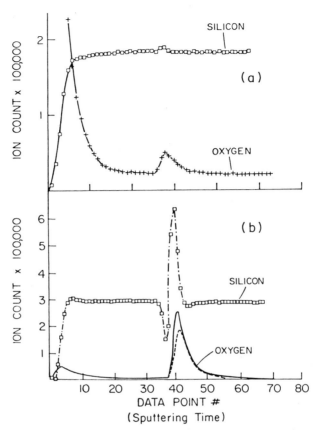

Fig. 11. SIMS data showing the oxygen at the interface for two samples prepared in the identical fashion except for surface cleaning procedures. (a) The sample was HF cleaned followed by a final H₂O rinse; (b) the sample was cleaned only by organic solvents. The oscillations in the Si ion yield are due to the presence of a relatively thick impurity layer near the amorphous–substrate interface. After normalization of the Si ion yield, the oxygen concentration is depicted by the dashed line. (From Williams and Baker, 1980.)

"HF cleaned and H₂O rinsed." The SIMS data shown in Fig. 11 compare the oxygen at the interface of two samples prepared in the identical fashion except for the surface cleaning procedure (Williams and Baker, 1980). In one case the sample was cleaned with HF followed by a final H₂O rinse, and in the other the sample was cleaned only with organic solvents. There is a significant difference in the amount of oxygen in the two samples. A further reduction in amount of oxygen at the interface can be achieved by using a dilute HF solution as a final rinse (the samples are referred to as

TABLE I

	Interfacial oxygen ($\times 10^{14}$ cm^{-2})	
Substrate cleaning procedure	SIMS[a]	Nuclear[b]
Organic solvents only	~40	60
HF cleaned and H$_2$O rinsed	~2	2–3
HF rinsed	0.5–1	Not performed

[a] Data from P. Williams, University of Illinois.
[b] Data from D. Scott, California Institute of Technology.

"HF rinsed"). Table I compares the amount of oxygen at the interface as determined by SIMS and nuclear reactions for the three surface preparation techniques.

Epitaxial growth can be achieved in samples in which the Si surface has been HF cleaned and H$_2$O rinsed as shown schematically in Fig. 12. The epitaxial growth has a different character than that of the epitaxy of implanted-amorphous Si where layer-by-layer growth occurs. In these deposited layers, epitaxy initiates at local spots and spreads laterally (von Allmen *et al.*, 1979). This growth behavior is illustrated in Fig. 13 by the decrease of the aligned yield in the portion of the spectrum corresponding to the deposited layer. The decrease in the spectrum height for the 150-min anneal time corresponds to the formation of localized epitaxial regions that cover ~30% of the deposited layer. The region outside of the epitaxial column remains amorphous. After a longer period of anneal there is an increase in the amount of epitaxial Si due to lateral growth of the epitaxial columns, as evidenced by the further decrease of the aligned yield.

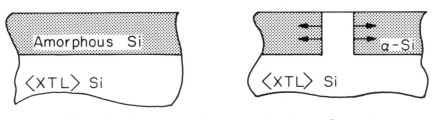

Fig. 12. Lateral growth of epitaxial columns in a deposited Si layer where the surface has been "HF cleaned and H$_2$O rinsed." The columns were initiated locally.

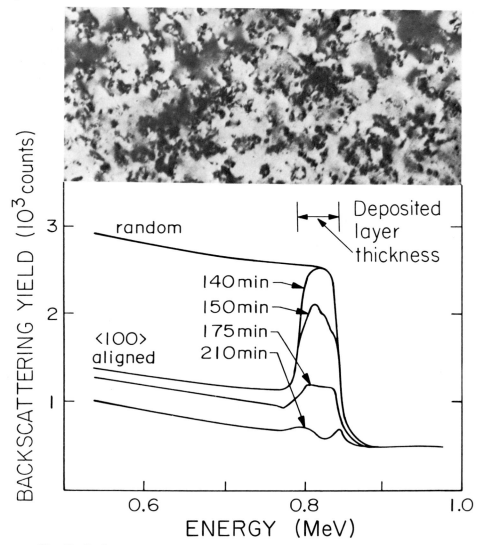

Fig. 13. Backscattering spectra for a Si (deposited) on a $\langle 100 \rangle$ Si sample in which the surface has been "HF cleaned and H_2O rinsed." There is a "delay" period of 140 min before the onset of epitaxial growth. The TEM micrograph (inset) shows the presence of microtwins of an average size of $\sim$200 Å. (From von Allmen *et al.*, 1979.)

In the example shown in Fig. 13, the deposited film has grown into a single crystal of reasonably good quality after annealing for 210 min. After the sample is annealed for longer times, channeling measurements (Fig. 13) show a near-surface minimum yield (χ_{min}) of 4.6% (only slightly higher than that obtained from Si crystal substrate). The "bump" in the aligned yield near 0.8 MeV reflects the presence of residual disorder near the original amorphous–crystal interface. The TEM picture (inset of Fig. 13) shows the presence of microtwins of average size 200 Å in the grown layer.

The residual disorder observed in these deposited layers is usually not found in epitaxial layers grown from implanted-amorphous layers on $\langle 100 \rangle$ Si, and is an indication of the effect of interfacial impurities on the growth process. The data in Fig. 13 indicate that there is a delay period of 140 min before the onset of epitaxial growth. Following this long delay, there is a shorter period in the transition from the amorphous to the crystalline structure. The delay period is attributed to the presence of oxygen and/or carbon at the interface. For example, in this delay period the estimated growth rate of 10^{-2}–10^{-1} Å/min is consistent with an oxygen content of $\sim 10^{21}$ oxygen atoms/cm^3 ($\sim 2 \times 10^{14}$ oxygen atoms in an ~ 10-Å region).

Measurements of the time necessary to crystallize 80% of the sample area as a function of anneal time showed that the growth behavior has an activation energy of 2.4 eV. The same activation energy was found in implanted-amorphous layers, but the growth time for the deposited layer is roughly an order of magnitude longer, due to the delay period (von Allmen *et al.*, 1979).

When the surface preparation technique before deposition is changed to HF cleaned only, the amount of oxygen at the interface is decreased (Table I) and the nature of the growth process changes from columnar to layer-by-layer behavior. If an impurity-free layer is deposited on such a clean Si surface, the epitaxial growth rate is close to that found in self-ion-implanted-amorphous Si. To demonstrate the similarities in the growth rate, we have implanted Si ions through the deposited layer below the interface. Layer-by-layer growth occurs in both amorphous layers as indicated by the decrease in the energy width of the aligned yields shown in Fig. 14. There is a time delay of 120 min when the growth front reaches the interface. The delay is appreciably shorter than that for the HF cleaned and H_2O rinsed samples. The annealing times required to grow the same thickness are nearly the same before and after the delay time at the original interface. The sloping rear edge of the channeling spectrum taken after 152 min of anneal time indicates there is some nonuniformity in the growth front. However, after a longer anneal, good crystal quality is obtained. There is no evidence in channeling measurements for residual disorder at

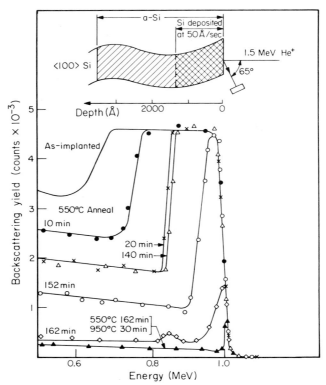

Fig. 14. Backscattering spectra for a sample in which the surface has been "HF cleaned only." An amorphous layer was formed below the deposited-layer–crystal interface by implanting Si ions at LN$_2$ temperatures to a dose of 1×10^{15} cm^{-2} (150 keV). (From L. Hung, Calif. Inst. of Technology, personal communication.)

the interface between the original crystal and the epitaxial layer in well-annealed (550 + 950°C) samples.

The results presented in this section showed that the surface preparation technique and hence the interfacial impurities have a controlling influence on the growth process and the quality of the epitaxial layer. With sufficiently clean interfaces, layer-by-layer growth occurs similar to that found with implanted-amorphous samples.

C. Impurities and Structure of Deposited Films

In this section the emphasis is upon the impurities and structure of the deposited layer. Therefore, we refer only to samples in which the crystal substrate has been carefully cleaned so that the interface is not the major concern.

It is also known from studies of implanted-amorphous layers that concentrations of oxygen and carbon greater than 0.1 at. % can have a pronounced influence on the growth rate (see, for example, Csepregi *et al.*, 1977; Kennedy *et al.*, 1977; Lau *et al.*, 1978b). Consequently, we focus our attention on films deposited under high-vacuum conditions so that the as-deposited film has a low concentration of impurities (oxygen ≤ 0.1 at. %).

For samples prepared with a clean interface and a Si deposition rate of 1–5 Å/s (slow), it was found with annealing in high vacuum that epitaxial growth occurred in layer-by-layer fashion similar to that found in implanted-amorphous layers. Exposure to room air had a pronounced effect on growth kinetics. Oxygen penetrates into the film to a depth of 1000–4000 Å, and the growth rate slows dramatically in the region of high oxygen content (Fig. 15) (Bean and Poate, 1980).

Measurements of the growth kinetics of different deposited layer thicknesses showed that the retardation of the growth rate occurred near the surface region where the oxygen concentration was high. Based on a series of such experiments, it was deduced that the deposited films (at slow de-

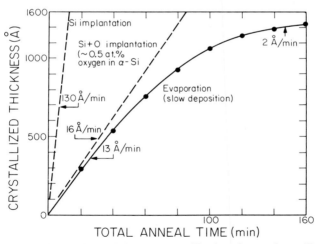

Fig. 15. Effect of fabrication technique on crystallization of amorphous silicon at 562°C. Crystallized thickness versus annealing time for samples prepared with a clean interface and a Si deposition rate of 1–5 Å/s (slow). Upon exposure to air, oxygen penetrates into the film to a depth of 1000–4000 Å. The growth rate slows dramatically in the region of high oxygen content near the surface region of the deposited layer as shown by the decreasing slope for deposited samples. As a comparison, the growth rates for Si implanted-amorphous layers and for "Si + O" implanted-amorphous layers are also shown. (From Beam and Poate, 1980.)

position rates) have a porous structure which permits penetration of oxygen into the film (Bean and Poate, 1980).

The extent of oxygen penetration depends on the method used to prepare the amorphous layer. Figure 16 shows pronounced differences in the oxygen depth profiles between implanted-amorphous and deposited-amorphous films. We note that the oxygen penetration in implanted-amorphous films is similar to that in single crystals (only surface oxide layers). The absence of oxygen penetration in implanted-amorphous layers can also be deduced from the fact that sample storage in room air for longer than 2 years did not result in appreciable change in the growth kinetics. The stability of these implanted-amorphous layers, in fact, is a key feature in our ability to transport samples to different laboratories for different processing steps and different methods of analysis. The major feature shown in Fig. 16 is that the penetration of oxygen depends on the deposition rate. Samples prepared by deposition at a rate of ~ 1 Å/s (slow) have a deeper oxygen penetration than samples deposited at ~ 35 Å/s (fast). We believe that the structure and hence the porosity of the deposited layers are influenced by the rate at which the Si is deposited.

We have concentrated on oxygen as the major impurity that causes a reduction in the growth rate. Carbon can also reduce growth rates, but the reduction in rate is not as great (less by a factor of 4 or 5) than that of oxygen at the same concentration. Consequently, carbon, unless present

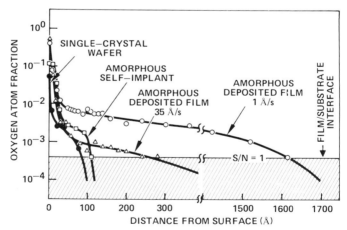

Fig. 16. Auger spectroscopy depth profiles of oxygen for samples with different deposition rates of Si. Samples prepared by deposition at rate of ~ 1 Å/s (slow) have a deeper oxygen penetration than samples deposited at ~ 35 Å/s (fast). Oxygen penetration in implanted-amorphous film is similar to that of simple crystal (only surface oxide layer). (From Hess *et al.*, 1980.)

in large concentration, is not a major concern. Nitrogen, although it has the same influence on growth rate as oxygen, does not appear to be incorporated within the deposited layer to the same extent as oxygen. Consequently, we believe that nitrogen is not a major concern either. It is possible to incorporate rather a large amount of hydrogen within the deposited layer. Until now, experiments on the influence of hydrogen on growth rates have not led to conclusive results.

Experiments have also been done with sputter-deposited films (Wittmer et al., 1979). In all cases, the amount of sputtering gases (inert gases) retained in the sputtered films exceeds 1 at. %. These values are much higher than the maximum concentration that can be tolerated in epitaxial growth of implanted-amorphous Si. Consequently, epitaxial growth was blocked by the excessive concentration of gas atoms.

Epitaxy can be achieved not only in the case of deposited Si layers on Si, but also in the case of Ge on Si (Mäenpää et al., 1981; Tsaur et al., 1981a). Recently epitaxial growth of Ge on Si has been investigated by two techniques: vacuum deposition and chemical vapor deposition (Kuech et al., 1981; Mäenpää et al., 1982). Vacuum-deposited Ge layers (physical vapor deposition) on a heated Si substrate ($\leq 500°C$) have smooth surface morphologies with a surface crystalline quality which improves with Ge thickness. Layers prepared by the chemical vapor deposition technique at 500–600°C are comparable to the vacuum-deposited layers. The main defects occurring in both layers prepared by these techniques are dislocations initiating at the Ge/Si interface. Chemical vapor-deposited Ge layers grown at a substrate temperature of 700–800°C exhibit poor crystalline quality; however, when the substrate temperature is raised to 900°C, the crystalline quality improves again. In this case, in addition to dislocations, stacking faults are present. The best crystalline quality can be obtained by growing Ge by the CVD method on a vacuum-deposited Ge layer on Si. Layers of Ge on Si prepared by these methods are better in crystalline quality than those obtained by pulsed laser (or electron beam) processed Ge layers on Si (Lau et al., 1978a; Leamy et al., 1980).

D. Laser and Electron-Beam Annealing

Use of laser or electron-beam annealing, whether pulsed or scanned cw, allows one to overcome some of the constraints imposed by interface preparation and deposition procedures. Of course, the laser is no panacea; for example, if the interfacial oxide layer is too great, epitaxial growth can be blocked.

Since cw scanned annealing is carried out essentially in the solid phase, but at high temperature, there is no dramatic improvement over the epitaxial growth that can be achieved by conventional thermal anneal. One must still be concerned about the interface, impurity, and the structure of the film. For example, cw scanned-laser annealing of slowly deposited films on clean interfaces resulted in partial epitaxial growth of the film (Hess *et al.*, 1980) similar to that discussed in the preceding section.

Q-switched-laser or pulsed-electron-beam annealing has resulted in good epitaxial growth using sample preparation conditions where poor epitaxy would be found in conventional thermal annealing. In this case, epitaxial growth can be achieved if the molten zone penetrates into the substrate crystal. For example, epitaxial regrowth was found in samples where the substrates were prepared with either atomically clean surfaces, residual Ar^+-sputtered damaged surfaces, or some monolayers of residual oxide (Williams *et al.*, 1978). An increase in energy density is required for high-quality epitaxy for substrates containing residual impurities. In other studies of deposited Si on Si, high-quality epitaxial growth was also achieved with pulsed laser radiation. TEM measurements showed a few isolated dislocations in the grown layer (Lau *et al.*, 1978a).

We have shown that good epitaxial layers can be grown by conventional thermal annealing if adequate care is taken during substrate preparation and deposition steps. Consequently, the advantage of laser annealing lies in its application as a "localized region" processing step rather than as a technique to overcome inadequacies in sample preparations.

IV. Epitaxial Silicides

A. *Introduction*

Epitaxial silicides with resistivities of 20–100 $\mu\Omega$ cm have been grown on single-crystal Si. Aside from the interest in such epitaxial silicides from the standpoint of crystal growth, such structures may provide metallic templates for epitaxial growth of deposited Si layers as was shown in Section II. It is possible to grow Si on Si by paying attention to the interface and deposition conditions. Here, we envisage the growth of Si on an epitaxial silicide as a complementary structure. Such a buried silicide can lead to the revival of the metal-base transistor and the solid-state triode.

However, our reason for including the epitaxial silicide in this article is that the formation of these silicides introduces two new concepts in epitaxial growth: (1) the self-cleaning interface and (2) a polycrystal-to-epitaxial transformation rather than an amorphous-to-epitaxial transformation. We

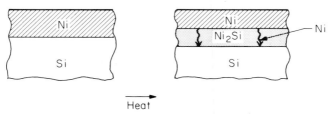

Heat

Fig. 17. Ni_2Si formation: As the Si sample with a layer of deposited Ni is thermally annealed, the first compound to form is the Ni_2Si phase. The dominant moving species in the formation of Ni_2Si is the Ni atoms, as indicated by arrows. Some of the Si substrate has been consumed, thus providing a clean interface between the Si and the silicide.

illustrate the concept of the self-cleaning interface in Fig. 17. In formation of the silicide, the first step is to deposit the metal, in this case, Ni. The sample is heat-treated to form the first phase of the silicide, in this case, Ni_2Si. In the formation of Ni_2Si, some of the Si substrate is consumed. This provides a clean interface between Si and the silicide. With nickel silicide, polycrystalline NiSi is the precursor to the formation of epitaxial $NiSi_2$. Not only is Si consumed, but there is a transformation of a polycrystalline film to an epitaxial layer. It has also been possible to form epitaxial $NiSi_2$ by pulsed ion beam annealing (Chen *et al.*, 1982)

B. Structure

The results obtained in the formation of epitaxial $CoSi_2$, $NiSi_2$, Pd_2Si, and PtSi are summarized in Table II. The structures of both $CoSi_2$ and $NiSi_2$ are cubic (CaF_2) with a lattice constant close to that of Si; the greatest mismatch is for $CoSi_2$ which has a mismatch of 1.1%. The hexagonal structure of Pd_2Si and the orthorhombic structure of PtSi necessitate the use of $\langle 111 \rangle$-oriented Si. For example, Fig. 18 shows the atomic arrangement of Pd_2Si on the (111) plane of Si (Buckley and Moss, 1972).

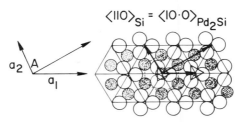

Fig. 18. Schematics showing the atomic arrangement of Pd_2Si on the (111) plane of Si. (After Buckley and Moss, 1972.)

TABLE II

CHARACTERISTICS OF EPITAXIAL SILICIDE FILMS[a]

Characteristic	Silicide[b]			
	PtSi	Pd$_2$Si	NiSi$_2$	CoSi$_2$
Structure	Orthorhombic MnP	Hexagonal	Cubic (CaF$_2$) $a = 5.406$ Å	Cubic (CaF$_2$) $a = 5.367$ Å
Resistivity ($\mu\Omega$ cm)	35–50[c]	25–35[c]	50–60[e] 35[h]	18–25[e] 15[h] 10[i]
Barrier height (ϕ_B^n/eV)	0.86[d]	0.74[d]	0.66[e]	0.64[f]
Bulk density (g/cm^3)	12.40	9.46	4.84	4.92
Bulk density (10^{22} mol/cm^3)	3.35	2.37	2.53	2.57
Substrate for epitaxial growth	111	111	111, 100, 110	111, 100
Process temp. (°C)	750	720	800	700
χ_{min} (1.5 MeV)	30%	10%	5%	6%[g]
σ, crystal deviation	>0.5°	~0	~0	≤0.5°

[a] Table adapted from H. Ishiwara (1980).
[b] Si, $a = 5.428$, bulk density 2.33 g/cm^3, 5×10^{22} atoms/cm^3.
[c] Wittmer (1980).
[d] Ottaviani et al. (1980).
[e] Murakawa (1979).
[f] Van Gump (1975).
[g] Saitoh et al. (1980).
[h] Saitoh et al. (1981).
[i] Tung et al. (1981).

It is clear from the figure that the hexagonal structure of the Pd$_2$Si can be matched with the arrangement of the Si atoms.

A cross-sectional view (Fig. 19, TEM, dark field) of Pd$_2$Si on $\langle 111 \rangle$-oriented Si shows that rather uniform and smooth silicide–Si interfaces can be formed (Cheung et al., 1980). As will be seen in Section IV, C, the uniformity of the interface is not universal.

The epitaxial nature of the silicide layer has been investigated by electron diffraction techniques and more commonly by channeling and Rutherford

Fig. 19. Cross-sectional view (TEM, dark field) of a 2500-Å-thick layer of Pd$_2$Si on $\langle 111 \rangle$ Si showing rather uniform and smooth silicide–Si interfaces. (From Cheung *et al.*, 1980.)

backscattering measurements. Channeling measurements (see, for example, Sigurd *et al.*, 1973; Tu *et al.*, 1974; Ishiwara and Furukawa, 1976; Ishiwara *et al.*, 1979, 1980; Chiu *et al.*, 1980; Lau and Cheung, 1980) have the advantage that they are sensitive to the angular distribution of the mosaic structure of the epitaxial layer. The angular distribution θ (sketched schematically in Fig. 20) is characterized by a Gaussian distribution with a standard deviation σ. In channeling measurements, the collimated beam of incident He ions can be steered (channeled) by a slightly tilted crystal as long as the misorientation with the direction of the beam is less than the critical angle ($\psi_{1/2}$) for channeling. For 1-MeV ^{4}He$^+$ ions, $\psi_{1/2} = 0.5$–$0.7°$ and varies as $E_b^{-1/2}$, where E_b is beam energy. Consequently, values of σ ranging from 0.1 to 1° can be easily determined from channeling measurements. Such small values of σ are difficult to measure with con-

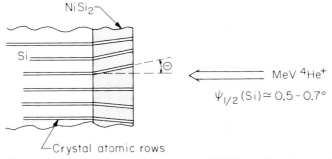

Fig. 20. Schematics showing a mosaic structure of NiSi$_2$ on Si substrate. The mosaic nature of the NiSi$_2$ layer is represented by the angular distribution θ of the crystallites, characterized by a Gaussian distribution with a standard deviation σ. The collimated beam incident ions can be steered (channeled) by a slightly tilted crystal as long as the misorientation with the direction of the beam is less than the critical angle $\psi_{1/2}$ for channeling. The critical angle for MeV ^{4}He$^+$ ions in Si varies between 0.5 and 0.7°.

ventional x-ray diffraction techniques and, hence, channeling measurements provide a convenient method of evaluating epitaxial films.

Figure 21 shows a channeling and backscattering measurement of an epitaxial $NiSi_2$ layer on Si (Chiu *et al.*, 1980). The random spectrum indicates that the silicide layer is 720 Å thick (assuming bulk density), and the low-energy edge of the Si indicates that the silicide layer is uniform in thickness over a lateral extent of at least several millimeters. In this sample, the minimum yield is ~5%. This value of χ_{min} is close to that obtained from bulk Si and, hence, the epitaxial silicide layer is of high quality. Analysis of the aligned spectra in the region of the rear interface shows that interfacial disorder is minimal (at values less than 2.5×10^{15} displaced atoms/cm^2). The values of χ_{min} depend upon the thickness of the

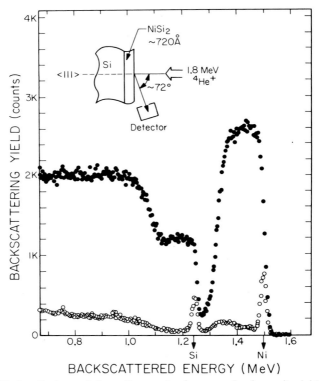

Fig. 21. Backscattering and channeling spectra for a sample of an epitaxial $NiSi_2$ (~720 Å) on $\langle 111 \rangle$ Si. The low-energy edge of the Si signal indicates that the silicide layer is uniform in thickness over a lateral extent of at least several millimeters. The near-surface minimum yield χ_{min} is ~5%—a value close to that obtained from single-crystal Si substrate. (From Chiu *et al.*, 1980.)

silicide layer; for example, the value of χ_{min} for PtSi increases when the film thickness exceeds 300 Å. The values listed in Table II are for film thicknesses of about 500 Å.

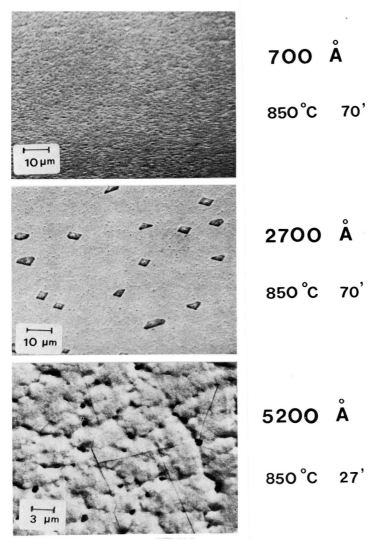

700 Å

850°C   70'

2700 Å

850°C   70'

5200 Å

850°C   27'

Fig. 22. SEM views of the top surface of $NiSi_2$ of three different thicknesses processed at ~850°C: (a) 700 Å, 70'; (b) 2700 Å, 70'; (c) 5200 Å, 27'. For the two thick films (b, c), flake-offs and fracture lines are clearly visible. (From Lau and Cheung, 1980.)

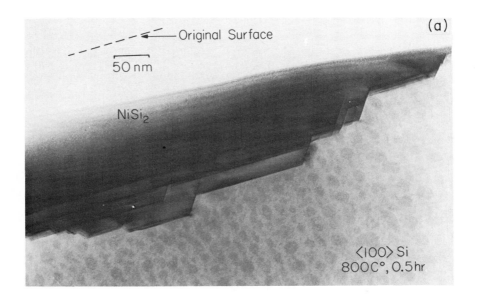

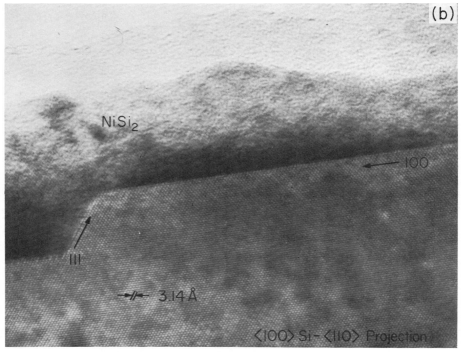

Fig. 23. Cross-sectional TEM views of a steplike and terraced NiSi₂–Si interface. (a) A sample annealed at 800°C for 0.5 hr; (b) at higher magnification. (From Föll *et al.*, 1981.)

C. Growth and Interfacial Morphology of NiSi$_2$

The four epitaxial silicides form uniform layers for film thicknesses less than a few hundred angstroms. For larger thicknesses, fracture, flaking, and other features associated with stresses manifested themselves. Figure 22 shows SEM views of the top surface of three different thicknesses of NiSi$_2$ processed at 850°C. For the two thicker films, flake-offs and fracture lines are clearly visible.

Cross-sectional TEM views indicate the presence of a steplike and terraced NiSi$_2$–Si interface (Fig. 23). The morphology of the interface depends upon the orientation of the underlying Si substrate because the orientation of the steps depends upon the substrate orientation. We believe that the origin of the corrugated interface arises from the formation process (Lau and Cheung, 1980). Nucleation of NiSi$_2$ originates at localized positions along the NiSi–Si interface; a localized crystallite of NiSi$_2$ grows to the surface and then grows laterally. If the lateral growth rate is much faster than the nucleation rate of the remaining unreacted NiSi–Si interface, the grains will grow until impingement, thus leading to a relatively flat NiSi$_2$–Si interface between the initial nucleation sites where the grains protrude into the Si substrate.

Recently emphasis has been placed on UHV processing of epitaxial silicides. It has been shown that UHV preparation of $\langle 111 \rangle$ Si surface leads to highly perfect CoSi$_2$ layers for both reacted and codeposited (MBE) films (Gibson et al., 1981; Tung et al., 1981, 1982). A unique interfacial defect structure is associated with this epitaxy, in which the silicide layers are rotated 180° with respect to the Si substrates. Resistivities of nearly perfect epitaxial films are lower than those prepared under less stringent conditions. High-quality Si films can be grown on the silicides to form semiconductor–metal silicide–semiconductor heterostructure.

V. Crystallization of Deposited Films

In previous sections we have concentrated on epitaxial growth where interface and bulk impurities play a dominant role. In this section we consider the more general aspect of crystallization in deposited films where a clean crystal substrate is not available for epitaxial growth. In these deposited films, crystallization takes place by nucleation and growth. The process is envisaged as the formation of crystallites of a critical size; these crystallites then grow and transform the amorphous film into a polycrystalline layer. Since polycrystallite formation is always a competing mechanism to epitaxial growth, one can gain insights into the film and temperature constraints permissible in epitaxial growth by considering the kinetics of crystallization. The crucial factor in crystallization studies was the realization that sample preparation, impurities, and annealing ambient could play a critical role in the recrystallization of deposited layers. The recent studies (Thomas *et al.*, 1978) on samples processed under high-vacuum and high-purity conditions have demonstrated that one can obtain crystallite growth velocities similar to those obtained in epitaxial growth of implanted-amorphous layers. This is a critical feature if one wishes to compare crystallization and epitaxial growth.

In this section we also treat graphoepitaxy, in which a macroscopic rather than a microscopic template is provided for epitaxial growth. We also review studies of laser-induced crystal growth in polycrystalline films.

A. High-Vacuum Processing

In early studies of crystallization of deposited layers, a wide variation in behavior was noted. Impurities incorporated during deposition or introduced during annealing may well have been responsible for the variation in crystallization behavior. Recently, ultra-high-vacuum deposition and *in situ* measurements have been employed in the study of crystallization (Thomas *et al.*, 1978). Electron spin resonance was used to measure dangling-bond paramagnetic defects in the amorphous films. The density of spin centers in carefully prepared samples was equivalent to about 1 center/ 1000 Si atoms ($\eta_s = 7 \times 10^{19}$ cm^{-3}). The results indicated that the centers were not due to impurities or the presence of a free surface. A model of isolated dangling bonds is in agreement with the experimental observation. Since the concentration of spins is low, a well-prepared amorphous layer can be treated as a continuous random network in which the covalent bonds are satisfied by allowing some distortion of the elementary tetrahedrons. This model is consistent with the picture (Spaepen, 1978) used to explain epitaxial growth of implanted-amorphous Si (Lau *et al.*, 1980). The deposited films of Thomas *et al.* (1978) were of high quality, as evidenced by the fact that they observed a sharp decrease in the number of spins at a temperature of ~580°C. The decrease in spins was associated with the crystallization of the layer. This crystallization temperature is consistent with results found in epitaxial regrowth of implanted-amorphous Si.

The annealing ambient was found to influence the spin density and the linewidth of the EPR signals. The time-dependent number of spins after the samples are exposed to air and the dependence on gas pressure were attributed to diffusion of gases into the film. Thomas *et al.* (1978) concluded that films deposited at room temperature are porous. This result is in agreement with results reported in Section III,C, where oxygen penetration influenced the epitaxial growth rate in samples exposed to air. Although Thomas and co-workers did not correlate film porosity with deposition rate directly, as was discussed in Section III,C, they did show that films deposited at a high substrate temperature ($T_s < 430°C$) were insensitive to gas contamination.

The kinetics of crystallization were determined from the measurement of the conductance $\Sigma(t)$ versus time during isothermal runs at various temperatures at a vacuum of 10^{-6} Torr. The ratio $\Sigma(t)/\Sigma_\infty$ of the conductivities of polycrystalline and amorphous layers is sufficiently large so that measurements are made *in situ*. An example of the variation in conductance for a 1.16-μm-thick sample annealed at 560°C is shown in Fig. 24. It had been shown earlier (Germain *et al.*, 1977b) that when the crystallization is induced at the surface of the amorphous layer and when the crystallites are large compared to the thickness of the layer, then the crystalline fraction varies linearly with time. From data such as that shown in Fig. 24, a characteristic time $\tau(t)$ is found from the point at which the linear portion breaks off. The value of τ must be corrected for the induction time, which is larger for Si than Ge deposited films (Zellama *et al.*, 1979a). The growth velocity V_g is found by dividing the film thickness by the value τ; for the sample shown in Fig. 24, $\tau = 8.3$ hr, so that $V_g = 0.38$ Å/s. In the tem-

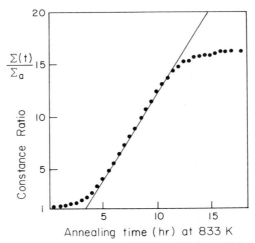

Fig. 24. Conductance versus annealing at 560°C for a 1.16-μm-thick amorphous Si sample. A characteristic time τ is found from the point at which the linear portion breaks off. The value of τ must be corrected for the induction time in which nucleation occurs. (From Zellama *et al.*, 1979a.)

perature range of 550–600°C, they found (Zellama *et al.*, 1979a) that the growth is thermally activated with an activation energy of 2.4 × 0.1 eV— a value which coincides with that found for the regrowth of implanted-amorphous Si.

In Fig. 25, we plot the growth rate versus the reciprocal of temperature for implanted-amorphous Si on ⟨100⟩ and ⟨111⟩ substrate orientations (Kennedy *et al.*, 1977). We believe that the agreement between the crystallite and epitaxial growth rates measured in implanted-amorphous layers on ⟨111⟩ Si simply reflects the fact that crystallite growth is determined by the slowest-growing facets. It was also found (Germain *et al.*, 1977b)

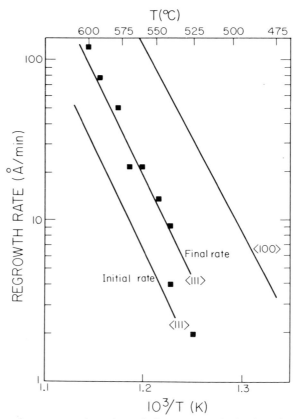

Fig. 25. Growth rate versus the reciprocal of temperature for implanted-amorphous Si for ⟨100⟩ and ⟨111⟩ substrates. There are two lines for the ⟨111⟩ orientation: the lower line is for the slow rate observed in the initial 1000 Å of growth, and the upper line represents the break to a faster growth rate. (From Kennedy *et al.*, 1977.) (■) The results obtained from measurements of the crystallite growth rates in deposited films. (From Zellama *et al.*, 1979a.)

that the crystallization of deposited Ge had a growth rate close to that of implanted-amorphous $\langle 111 \rangle$ Ge samples.

It is obvious, then, from the growth kinetics that epitaxial growth and crystallization of the amorphous layer are strongly competitive processes. At first glance, it would appear that one would always find polycrystalline regions in regrown layers. The fact that a high-quality epitaxial layer can be grown without polycrystallite inclusions reflects the fact that there is a finite time required for the nucleation of crystallites. The data of Fig. 24 show that the induction time (Germain *et al.*, 1979; Zellama *et al.*, 1979a) before the pronounced rise in conductivity can be comparable to the crystallization time. The induction time is also temperature dependent. We show in Fig. 26 the induction time (extracted from the data of Zellman *et al.*, 1979a) versus the reciprocal of temperature. From our viewpoint, one must complete epitaxial growth at times less than the induction time

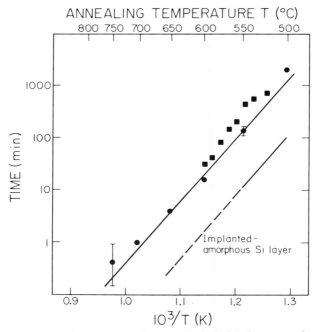

Fig. 26. Induction time (taken from Zellama *et al.*, 1979a) before onset of crystallization versus the reciprocal of temperature (■). To avoid polycrystalline formation, epitaxial growth time must be less than the induction time. Also shown are the times for epitaxial growth of 1000 Å Si deposited on $\langle 100 \rangle$ Si (HF + H$_2$O rinse) where the surface was marginally cleaned (●). It is clear from the comparison of the induction time and the growth time that there is only a limited leeway allowed in surface preparation. The lowest line is for self-ion-implanted-amorphous layers on $\langle 100 \rangle$ Si. This represents the best case that can be achieved.

if one wants to avoid the formation of polycrystalline regions. We also show, for comparison, the time required to grow a 1000-Å-thick epitaxial layer. The system with the slowest time for successful formation of an epitaxial layer (von Allman *et al.*, 1979) is Si deposited on a $\langle 100 \rangle$ substrate where the surface was marginally cleared with "HF cleaned and H_2O rinsed" (see Section III,B, Table I). The time for epitaxial growth of such a sample is also shown in Fig. 26. It is clear from comparison of the induction and growth times that there is only a limited leeway allowed in surface preparation if epitaxial growth is to be achieved. Formation of epitaxial layers at a faster rate than that shown in Fig. 26 can be achieved by using an HF rinse only, as shown by the data in Fig. 14. The lowest curve is for implanted-amorphous layers on $\langle 100 \rangle$ Si. This represents the best case that could be achieved.

The results shown in Fig. 26 also suggest that high-temperature processing (such as afforded by scanned cw lasers) will not allow one to overcome improper surface preparation. Use of pulsed annealing in the melting regime, of course, will lead to epitaxial growth if the melt front extends below the interface.

B. Graphoepitaxy

Large-area, oriented Si crystal layers can be grown by providing a macroscopic surface template structure for crystallite orientation. The term "graphoepitaxy" was introduced by Geis *et al.* (1979b) to denote the use of surface-relief gratings etched into amorphous substrates to achieve uniform crystallographic orientation of deposited layers.

The concept (Geis *et al.*, 1979a,b) is that deposited films with one particular plane parallel to the substrate surface should yield uniformly oriented films if a crystallographically appropriate surface relief structure is provided. For $\langle 100 \rangle$-oriented films, the relief structures are oriented at right angles as shown in Fig. 27. The relief grating with a spatial period of 3.8 μm was etched into fused silica substrates to a depth of 1000 Å. About 5000 Å of amorphous Si was deposited and then later crystallized using a scanned cw Ar laser.

We believe that laser annealing provides the high temperature required for crystallite orientation. In experiments with deposited layers on $\langle 100 \rangle$ Si (Geis *et al.*, 1979b), it was found that initially polycrystalline film could be reoriented into an epitaxial layer at thermal annealing temperatures of $0.8 T_m$ (T_m is the melting point of Si in degrees Kelvin). This reorientation was achieved in films in which some of the crystallites were aligned with the substrate. In graphoepitaxy the initial alignment is provided by the

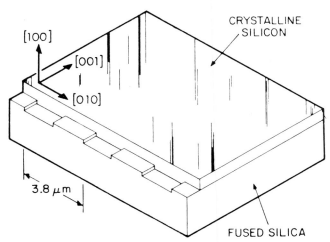

Fig. 27.   Schematic showing the composite structure of graphoepitaxy. The relief quality of 3.8-μm spatial period was etched into fused-silica substrates to a depth of ~1000 Å. About 5000 Å of amorphous Si was deposited and then laser-crystallized using a scanning cw Ar laser. (From Geis *et al.*, 1979b.)

corners of the relief structure. We believe that reorientation occurs during high-temperature processing.

C.   Laser Annealing

Laser annealing has been used to increase the grain size of polycrystalline films deposited on amorphous Si_3N_4 or SiO_2 films (Gat *et al.*, 1978; Gibbons *et al.*, 1979; Kamins *et al.*, 1980). In the initial study (Gibbons *et al.*, 1979), 0.4-μm-thick polycrystalline films (average grain size ~500 Å) were annealed with a scanned Ar laser beam with a 40-μm beam diameter. Large columnar crystallites with a typical surface geometry of ~2 × 10 μm (maximum length ≃ 32 μm) were found to develop at an angle to the direction of the scan. In order to transform the fine-grain polycrystalline Si film to large-grain material, the laser annealing is carried out in the melting regime (Gibbons *et al.*, 1979). Silicon gate MOS transistors fabricated on the large-grain polycrystalline Si material were well behaved. The channel electron mobilities (~300 cm² V⁻¹ s⁻¹) were about an order of magnitude larger than the value observed for transistors fabricated in similarly doped, fine-grain polycrystalline Si (Kamins *et al.*, 1980).

Scanned laser annealing of isolated polycrystallite islands 2 × 20 μm in dimension was found to produce essentially single-crystal ⟨100⟩-oriented material (Gibbons *et al.*, 1979). With larger isolated polycrystalline islands, laser annealing resulted in the formation of a polycrystalline rather than single-crystal structure, indicating that the formation of single-crystal islands may be size-restructured.

In another approach, Fan *et al.* (1980) used a cw Nd–YAG laser beam focused to a slit image of about 50 μm $\times$ 1.5 mm to induce crystallization in amorphous Ge films on fused-silica substrates. It was found that large crystallites of dimensions of $\sim$(2–3) $\times$ 100 μm can be formed by scanning the laser across the sample surface. In this case the solid-phase crystallization is greatly accelerated by the liberation of the latent heat of transformations. It is speculated that large-grained or even single-crystal sheets of Ge can be prepared on amorphous substrates by a proper choice of energetic beam, substrate temperature, and other processing parameters.

An alternate approach is to use large-diameter ($\sim$10 mm) Q-switched laser beams to anneal polycrystalline Si films (Tamura *et al.*, 1980). In this case only a moderate increase in grain size to a maximum size of 1500 Å was found. Melting occurred as evidenced by the single-crystal growth over the oxide layer in the region adjacent to oxide windows in which the polycrystalline Si is in direct contact with single-crystal Si. In this "bridging epitaxy," the lateral growth distance of the single-crystal layer is about 1.2 μm from the edge of the oxide window.

Scanning-laser annealing produces a large change in grain size—single-crystal isolated islands—whereas pulsed annealing results in only minor changes in grain size. We believe that the scanning action, in which the trailing edge of the scan beam cools first, is responsible for the formation of the crystallites.

D. Lateral Growth of Silicon

Important advances have been made recently in the growth techniques of large-area single Si sheets over amorphous (SiO_2) substrates. There are two approaches to this lateral growth technique: (1) lateral epitaxy by seeded solidification (LESS) (Fan *et al.*, 1981) and (2) unseeded lateral growth. In the case of LESS, continuous single-crystal Si sheets over SiO_2 with areas of several cm² have been produced from poly-Si films by using two graphite strip heaters. One of the heaters is movable and is used for zone melting the Si film. Seeding is achieved either with a narrow strip opening in a recessed SiO_2 layer on a single-crystal Si substrate or with an external single crystal seed. N-channel MOSFETs have been fabricated with these layers with electron surface mobility as high as 700 cm² V^{-1} s^{-1}. For unseeded lateral growth, strip heaters were again used to recrystallize poly-Si layers interposed between composite Si_3N_4/SiO_2 layers (Tsaur *et al.*, 1981b, 1982). In this case, the recrystallized layer is polycrystalline in nature, with grain sizes up to several mm $\times$ 2 cm. All crystallites exhibit a (100) texture, and are separated by low-angle boundaries. For both seeded and unseeded growth the presence of dual dielectric (Si_3N_4/SiO_2) layers is essential in producing good-quality recrystallized layers. The exact function of the dual dielectric layer is not clear and is the subject of active research at present.

VI. Summary

In this article we have shown that deposited amorphous layers of Si can be grown epitaxially on an underlying single-crystal substrate. Impurities incorporated in the film can produce major changes in the growth rate. However, sufficiently pure Si films can be deposited with conventional high-vacuum deposition systems so that epitaxial growth rates comparable to those in high-purity implanted-amorphous Si can be achieved.

The cleanliness of the surface before deposition presents a major problem in achieving epitaxial growth. Again, with an appropriate chemical cleaning procedure the surface oxide and other contaminants can be reduced to a level low enough for the growth of good epitaxial layers.

In studies of the crystallization of deposited-amorphous films, it was found that the growth rate of the crystallites (during the amorphous-to-polycrystalline film transition) was comparable to the epitaxial growth rate of implanted-amorphous Si on $\langle 111 \rangle$ substrate. Therefore, in deposited-amorphous films on crystal substrates, epitaxial growth and polycrystallite growth are competing processes. Due to the finite induction time before the crystallites can grow to a critical size, epitaxial growth can be the dominant feature. If the interface between single crystal and deposited-amorphous film is contaminated so that the delay in the epitaxial growth exceeds the induction time, polycrystalline formation can dominate. Therefore, in order to form single-crystal epitaxial film from deposited-amorphous films, one must complete the epitaxial growth process in a time shorter than the crystallization induction time. The requirement of a clean interface between the amorphous and crystal region cannot be overcome by laser annealing unless it is carried out in the melting regime.

Acknowledgments

We gratefully acknowledge the cooperation of our colleagues in other laboratories who sent preprints and additional information concerning their work. We appreciate the discussions with them and our colleagues at the California Institute of Technology. Financial support was provided in part by the Office of Naval Research (L. Cooper) and by the Defense Advanced Research Projects Agency (S. Roosild).

References

Anderson, C. A., Celler, G. K., and Rozgonyi, G. A., eds. (1980). *Proc. Electrochem. Soc. Symp. Laser Electron Beam Process. Electron. Mat., Los Angeles, 1979* **80–1**.

Auston, D. H., Golovchenko, J. A., Simons, A. L., Slusher, R. E., Smith, P. R., Surko, C. M., and Venkatesan, T. N. C. (1979). *In* "Laser–Solid Interactions and Laser Processing, 1978 (MRS, Boston)" (S. D. Ferris, H. J. Leamy, and J. M. Poate, eds.), p. 11. American Inst. of Physics, New York.

Baeri, P., Campisano, S. U., Foti, G., and Rimini, E. (1979). *J. Appl. Phys.* **50**, 788.

Barna, A., Barna, P. B., and Polza, J. F. (1972). *J. Non-Cryst. Solids* **8–10**, 36.

Bean, J. C., and Poate, J. M. (1980). *Appl. Phys. Lett.* **36**, 59.

Buckley, W. D., and Moss, S. C. (1972). *Solid State Electron.* **15**, 1331.

Campisano, S. U., Rimini, E., Baeri, P., Foti, G. (1980). *Appl. Phys. Lett.* **37**, 170.

Campisano, S. U., and Barbarino, A. E. (1981). *Appl. Phys. Lett.* **25**, 153.

Canali, C., Mayer, J. W., Ottoviani, G., Sigurd, D., and van der Weg, W. (1974). *Appl. Phys. Lett.* **25**, 3.

Chen, L. J., Hung, L. S., Mayer, J. W., Baglin, J. E. E., Neri, J. M. and Hammer, D. A. (1982). *Appl. Phys. Lett.* **40**, 595.

Cheung, N. W., Feldman, L. C., Silverman, P. J., and Stensgarrd, I. (1979). *Appl. Phys. Lett.* **35**, 859.

Cheung, N., Lau, S. S., Nicolet, M.-A., Mayer, J. W., and Sheng, T. T. (1980). *Proc. Electrochem. Symp. Thin Film Interf. Interact., Los Angeles, 1979* **80–2**, 494.

Chiu, K. C. R., Poate, J. M., Feldman, L. C., and Doherty, C. J. (1980). *Appl. Phys. Lett.* **36**, 544.

Csepregi, L., Mayer, J. W., and Sigmon, T. W. (1975). *Phys. Lett.* **54A**, 157.

Csepregi, L., Mayer, J. W., and Sigmon, T. W. (1976). *Appl. Phys. Lett.* **29**, 92.

Csepregi, L., Küllen, Mayer, J. W., and Sigmon, T. W. (1977a). *Solid State Commun.* **21**, 1019.

Csepregi, L., Kennedy, E. F., Gallagher, T. J., Mayer, J. W., and Sigmon, T. W. (1977b). *J. Appl. Phys.* **48**, 4234.

Fan, J. C. C., Zieger, H. J., Gale, R. P., and Chapman, R. L. (1980). *Appl. Phys. Lett.* **36**, 158.

Fan, J. C. C., Geis, M. W., and Tsaur, B.-Y. (1981). *Appl. Phys. Lett.* **38**, 365.

Ferris, S. D., Leamy, H. J., and Poate, J. M., eds. (1979). "Laser–Solid Interactions and Laser Processing—1978, (MRS Boston)." Am. Inst. of Physics.

Föll, H., Ho, P. S., and Tu, K. N. (1980). *J. Appl. Phys.* **52**, 250 (1981).

Foti, G., Rimini, E., Tseng, W. F., and Mayer, J. W. (1978). *Appl. Phys.* **15**, 365.

Galvin, G. J., Thompson, M. O., Mayer, J. W., Hammond, R. B., Paulter, N., and Peercy, P. S. (1982). *Phys. Rev. Lett.* **48**, 33.

Gat, A., Gerzberg, L., Gibbons, J. F., Magee, T. J., Peng, J., and Hong, J. D. (1978). *Appl. Phys. Lett.* **33**, 775.

Geis, M. W., Flanders, D. C., and Smith, H. I. (1979a). *Appl. Phys. Lett.* **35**, 71.

Geis, M. W., Flanders, D. C., Smith, H. I., and Antoniadis, D. A. (1979b). *J. Vac. Sci. Technol.* **16**(6), 1640.

Germain, P., Squelard, S., Bourgoin, J. C., and Georghiu, A. C. (1977a). *J. Non-Cryst. Solids* **23**, 93.

Germain, P., Squelard, S., Bourgoin, J. C., and Gheorgiu, A. (1977b). *J. Appl. Phys.* **48**, 1909.

Germain, P., Zellama, K., Squelard, S., Bourgoin, J. C., and Georghiu, A. (1979). *J. Appl. Phys.* **50**, 6986.

Gibbons, J. F., Lee, K. F., Magee, T. J., Peng, J., and Omond, R. (1979). *Appl. Phys. Lett.* **34**, 831.

Gibson, J. M., Bean, J. C., Poate, J. M., and Tung, R. T. (1981). Presented at the MRS Conference. To be published in *Thin Solid Films*.

Golecki, I., Chapman, G. E., Lau, S. S., Tsaur, B. Y., and Mayer, J. W. (1979). *Phys. Lett.* **71A**, 267.

Herd, S. R., Chaudhari, P., and Brodsky, M. H. (1972). *J. Non-Cryst. Solids* **7**, 309.

Hess, L. D., Roth, J. A., Olson, G. L., Dunlap, H. L., von Allmen, M., and Peng, J. (1980). *Proc. Symp. Laser Electron Beam Process. Mat., 1979 (MRS, Cambridge).*

Hodgson, R. T., Baglin, J. E. E., Pal, R., Neri, J. M., and Hammer, D. Å. (1980). *Appl. Phys. Lett.* **37**, 187.

Hung, L. S., Lau, S. S., von Allmen, M., Mayer, J. W., Baker, J., Williams, P., and Tseng, W. F. (1980). *Appl. Phys. Lett.* **37**, 909.

Ishiwara, H. (1980). *Proc. Electrochem. Soc. Symp. Thin Film Interf. Interact., Los Angeles, 1979,* **80–2**, 159.

Ishiwara, H., and Furukawa, S. (1976). *Appl. Phys. Lett.* **47**, 1686.

Ishiwara, H., Hirosaka, K., Nagatomo, M., and Furukawa, S. (1979). *Surf. Sci.* **86**, 711.

Kamins, T. I., Lee, K. F., Gibbons, J. R., and Saraswat, K. C. (1980). *IEEE Trans. Electron Devices* **ED-27**, 290.

Kennedy, E. F., Csepregi, L., Mayer, J. W., and Sigmon, T. W. (1976). *In* "Ion Implantation in Semiconductors" (F. Chernow, J. A. Border, and D. K. Brice, eds.), p. 511. Plenum, New York.

Kennedy, E. F., Csepregi, L., Mayer, J. W., and Sigmon, T. W. (1977). *J. Appl. Phys.* **48**, 4241.

Kokorowski, S. A., Olson, G. L., and Hess, L. D. (1982). *Appl. Phys. Lett.* **53**(2), 921.

Koster, U. (1972). *Acta Metall.* **20**, 1361.

Kuech, T. F., Mäenpää, M., and Lau, S. S. (1981). *Appl. Phys. Lett.* **39**(3), 245.

Lau, S. S., and Cheung, N. (1980). *Thin Solid Films*

Lau, S. S., Canali, C., Liau, Z. L., Nakamura, K., Nicolet, M.-A., Mayer, J. W., Blattner, R. J., and Evans, C. A., Jr. (1976). *Appl. Phys. Lett.* **28**, 148.

Lau, S. S., Tseng, W. F., Nicolet, M.-A., Mayer, J. W., Eckard, R. C., and Wagner, R. J. (1978a). *Appl. Phys. Lett.* **33**, 130.

Lau, S. S., Tseng, W. F., Nicolet, M.-A., Mayer, J. W., Minnucci, J., and Kirkpatrick, A. R. (1978b). *Appl. Phys. Lett.* **33**, 235.

Lau, S. S., and van der Weg, W. F., (1978c). *In* "Thin Films—Interdiffusion and Reaction" (J. M. Poate, K. N. Tu, and J. W. Mayer, eds.), p. 433. Wiley, New York.

Lau, S. S., Mayer, J. W., and Tseng, W. F. (1979). *In* "Laser–Solid Interactions and Laser Processing—1978 (MRS, Boston)" (S. D. Ferris, H. J. Leamy, and J. M. Poate, eds.), p. 84. American Inst. of Physics, New York.

Lau, S. S., Mayer, J. W., and Tseng, W. F. (1980). *In* "Handbook on Semiconductors" (S. P. Keller, ed.), Vol. 3, Ch. 7.

Leamy, H. J., Doherty, C. J., Chiu, K. C. R., Poate, J. M., Sheng, T. T., and Celler, G. K. (1980). *In* "Laser and Electron Beam Processing of Materials" (C. W. White and P. S. Peercy, eds.), p. 581. Academic Press, New York.

Lietoila, A., Wakita, A., Sigmon, T. W., and Gibbons, J. F. (1982). *J. Appl. Phys.* **53**, 4399.
Mäenpää, M., Hung, L. S., Grimaldi, M. G., Suni, I., Mayer, J. W., Nicolet, M.-A., and Lau, S. S. (1981). *Thin Solid Films* **82**, 347.
Mäenpää, M., Kuech, T. F., Nicolet, M.-A., Lau, S. S., and Sadana, D. K. (1982). *J. Appl. Phys.* **53**(2), 1076.
Mayer, J. W., Eriksson, L., Picraux, S. T., and Davies, J. A. (1968). *Can. J. Phys.* **45**, 663.
Murakawa, S. P. (1979). *Proc. Int. Electron Device Meet., Washington, D. C.* p. 454.
Nakata, J., and Kajiyama, K. (1982). *Appl. Phys. Lett.* **40**, 686.
Ottaviani, G., and Majni, G. (1979). *J. Appl. Phys.* **50**, 6865.
Ottaviani, G., Sigurd, D., Marrello, V., Mayer, J. W., and McCaldin, J. O. (1974). *J. Appl. Phys.* **45**, 1730.
Ottaviani, G., Tu, K. N., and Mayer, J. W. (1980). *Phys. Rev. Lett.* **44**, 284.
Roth, J. A., and Anderson, C. L. (1977). *Appl. Phys. Lett.* **31**, 689.
Saitoh, S., Ishiwara, H., and Furukawa, S. (1980). *Electrochem. Soc. Meet., 157th, St. Louis.*
Saitoh, S., Ishiwara, H., Assano, T., and Furukawa, S. (1981). *Jpn. J. Appl. Phys.* **22**, 1118.
Sigurd, D., Bower, R. W., van der Weg, W. F., and Mayer, J. W. (1973). *Thin Solid Films* **19**, 319.
Spaepen, F. (1978). *Acta Metall.* **26**, 1167.
Spaepen, F., and Turbull, D. (1979). *In* "Laser–Solid Interactions and Laser Processing— 1978 (MRS, Boston)." Am. Inst. of Physics.
Suni, I., Göltz, G., Grimaldi, M. G., Nicolet, M.-A., and Lau, S. S. (1981a). *Appl. Phys. Lett.* **40**(3), 269.
Suni, I., Göltz, G., Nicolet, M.-A., and Lau, S. S. (1981b). Presented at the MRS Conference, Boston. To be published in *Thin Solid Films.*
Tamura, M., Tamura, H., and Tokyama, T. (1980). *Jpn. J. Appl. Phys.* **19**, L23.
Thomas, P. A., Brodsky, M. H., Kaplan, D., and Lepine, D. (1978). *Phys. Review Ser. B* **18**, 3059.
Trumbore, F. A. (1960). *Bell Syst. Tech. J.* **39**, 205.
Tsaur, B. Y., Fan, J. C. C., and Gale, R. P. (1981a). *Appl. Phys. Lett.* **38**, 176.
Tsaur, B.-Y., Geis, M. W., Fan, J. C. C., Silversmith, D. J., and Mountain, R. W., (1981b). *Appl. Phys. Lett.* **39**, 909.
Tsaur, B.-Y., Fan, J. C. C., and Geis, M. W. (1982). *Appl. Phys. Lett.* **40**, 322.
Tu, K. N., Alessandrini, E. I., Chu, W. K., Krautle, H., and Mayer, J. W. (1974). *Jpn. J. Appl. Phys. Suppl.* **2**, Pt. 1, 669.
Tung, R. T., Bean, J. C., Gibson, J. M., Poate, J. M., and Jacobson, D. C. (1982). *Appl. Phys. Lett.*, in press.
Tung, R. T., Poate, J. M., Bean, J. C., Gibson, J. M., and Jacobson, D. C. (1981). Presented at the MRS Conference, to be published in *Thin Solid Films.*
van Gump, G. (1975). *J. Appl. Phys.* **46**, 4308.
Van Vechten, J. A., and Thurmond, L. D. (1976). *Phys. Rev.* **B14**, 3539.
von Allmen, M., Lau, S. S., Mayer, J. W., and Tseng, W. F. (1979). *Appl. Phys. Lett.* **35**, 280.
von Allmen, M., Lau, S. S., Scott, D. M., Mayer, J. W., Tseng, W. F., Sheng, T. T., Williams, P., and Baker, J. E. (1980). *Proc. Electrochem. Soc. Symp. Thin Film Interf. Interact., Los Angeles, 1979* **80–2**, p. 195.
White, C. W., Pronko, P. P., Wilson, S. R., Appleton, B. R., Naragan, J., and Young, R. T. (1979a). *J. Appl. Phys.* **50**, 3261.
White, C. W., Narayan, J., Appleton, B. R., and Wilson, S. R. (1979b). *J. Appl. Phys.* **50**, 2967.
Williams, J. S., and Elliman, R. G. (1982). *Appl. Phys. Lett.* **40**(3), 266.

Williams, J. S., Christodoulides, and Grant, W. A. (1975). *Rad. Eff.* **48,** 157.

Williams, J. S., Brown, W. L., Leamy, H. J., Poate, J. M., Rodgers, J. W., Roussean, D. G. A., Rozgonyi, G. A., Shelnutt, J. A., and Sheng, T. T. (1978). *Appl. Phys. Lett.* **33,** 544.

Williams, J. S., Brown, W. L., and Poate, J. M. (1979). *In* "Laser–Solid Interaction and Laser Processing—1978 (MRS, Boston)" (S. D. Ferris, H. J. Leamy, and J. M. Poate, eds.), p. 399. Am. Inst. of Physics.

Williams, P., and Baker, J. E. (1980). *Appl. Phys. Lett.* **36,** 842.

Wittmer, M. (1980). *Proc. Symp. Laser Electron Beam Process. Electron. Mat.* **804,** 484.

Wittmer, M., Roth, J., and Mayer, J. W. (1979). *J. Electrochem. Soc.* **136,** 1247.

Zellama, K., Germain, P., Squelard, S., Bourgoin, J. C., and Thomas, P. A. (1979a). *J. Appl. Phys.* **50,** 6995.

Zellama, K., Morhange, J. F., Germain, P., and Bourgoin, J. C. (1979b). *Phys. Status Solidi A* **56,** 717.

4

Characterization of Grain Boundaries in Bicrystalline Thin Films

F. COSANDEY

Department of Mechanics and Materials Science
Rutgers University
Piscataway, New Jersey

and

C. L. BAUER

Department of Metallurgy and Materials Science
Carnegie-Mellon University
Pittsburgh, Pennsylvania

I. Introduction

Crystalline solids generally contain a variety of point, line, and plane defects, such as vacancies, dislocations, and interfaces. One of the most ubiquitous types of (internal) interface is the grain boundary, which demarcates two adjacent grains of dissimilar crystallographic orientation. Such boundaries are especially important because they impart unique chemical, kinetic, and mechanical properties to solids, and it is well appreciated that such properties depend intimately on concomitant grain boundary structure (McLean, 1957; Chaudhari and Mathews, 1972; Watler, *et al.*, 1975; Chadwick and Smith, 1976). Therefore, the ultimate goal of research in this field is to characterize the structure of grain boundaries at the highest possible level of resolution and to relate results to important engineering properties. Macroscopic characterization, such as determination of grain size and preferred orientation, has certainly been helpful, but now it is generally realized that characterization at the microscopic (submicron) level is necessary in order to fully appreciate effects of grain boundary structure on concomitant properties (Baïlon *et al.*, 1974; Biscondi and Goux, 1975).

Grain boundaries play an even greater role in thin films because these films generally contain a relatively larger porportion of grain boundary area, thus facilitating certain kinetic reactions by short-circuit diffusion under conditions which could not possibly promote such reactions in bulk materials. Therefore, thin-film technology is even more severely affected by defect structure than its bulk counterpart. Important effects include segregation of impurities at grain boundaries, diffusion of impurities along grain boundaries, accelerated electromigration near grain boundaries, scattering of charge carriers by grain boundaries, etc. Such effects are exacerbated by the current trend to utilize even thinner films with submicron lateral dimensions.

Of course, the most obvious way to eliminate problems associated with grain boundaries in thin films is to forsake polycrystalline films altogether and concentrate exclusively on monocrystalline films. Although this approach is sometimes feasible, generally necessary control of fabrication conditions and limited selection of available materials and substrates render such an approach impractical. Monocrystalline thin films can, however, provide a standard by which less perfect films may be compared. For example, diffusion of undesirable chemical elements, which would be negligible in perfect crystalline materials, is greatly facilitated by short-circuit paths, such as grain boundaries. Moreover, the extent of diffusion along grain boundaries is strongly dependent on the degree of misorientation between neighboring grains and the inclination of the boundary plane (anisotropy). The effect of grain boundaries is even more profound in thinner films, for not only is the diffusion length shortened, but also the grain size is characteristically of the order of the film thickness, so that density of available short-circuit paths is increased accordingly. Therefore, the extent of diffusion along grain boundaries in thin films is measured by the product of the amount of material traversing the film thickness by grain boundary diffusion and the density of grain boundaries. Other effects, such as surface degradation and occurrence of localized mechanical stress, may also be important, but the most severe impediment to desirable properties is attributed to short-circuit interdiffusion and impurity segregation.

Given that monocrystalline thin films provide a standard to which less perfect films are compared but, on the other hand, polycrystalline films are in everyday use, it is logical to attempt to bridge the gap between ideal and practical use of thin films by investigating structure and properties of grain boundaries in a controlled manner. Recently, new techniques have been developed to produce bicrystalline thin films containing preselected grain boundaries of known characteristics. These films are amenable to detailed structural characterization by transmission electron microscopy (TEM) and associated diffraction techniques, as well as to measurement of certain engineering properties. Moreover, it is possible to investigate anisotropy of these properties, thus providing an opportunity to ameliorate the usefulness of polycrystalline materials by controlled (preferred) orientation of the constituent grains. Therefore, a review of structure and properties (characterization) of bicrystalline thin films provides a logical transition between the preceding articles in this volume devoted to monocrystalline thin films and the succeeding articles devoted to polycrystalline and amorphous thin films.

It was mentioned previously that carefully prepared thin-film specimens are amenable to direct examination by TEM. This particular aspect also provides an opportunity for a significant advance in fundamental knowledge because, as in bulk materials, details of grain boundary structure must provide the key to concomitant properties, and the ability to reveal such structure is increasing rapidly through advances in high-resolution TEM. Only a decade or two ago, this technique was a relatively unknown tool for characterization of microstructure, but now images of individual atoms can be revealed (Krivanek *et al.*, 1977). Because it is certain that a fundamental understanding of the relationships between structure and properties of thin films will benefit greatly from further advances in this rapidly developing field, preparation of specimens for and characterization of grain boundaries by high-resolution TEM are emphasized throughout the remainder of this article.

The purpose of this article, therefore, is to review important aspects of the structure and properties of grain boundaries in thin films and how these phenomena are interrelated by focusing attention on details of grain boundary structure in relatively pure materials, as elucidated by either theoretical or experimental investigations on bicrystalline specimens. Accordingly, the remainder of this article is divided into several sections: First, structure and properties of grain boundaries are reviewed in Sections II and III, respectively. Thereafter, production of bicrystalline thin films and techniques for characterization of concomitant grain boundary structure are described in Sections IV and V, respectively. The structure, properties, production and characterization of bicrystalline thin films are then integrated by reviewing a representative selection of recent experimental results in Section VI. Lastly, the present state of the art is summarized in Section VII and a prognostication of future developments is ventured in Section VIII. It is hoped that consideration of bicrystalline thin films in this manner will help to unify the accompanying articles of this volume and to provide valuable insight for further developments of this important subject.

II. Structure of Grain Boundaries

As mentioned in Section I, many properties of polycrystalline materials are intimately related to atomic structure of grain boundaries. The purpose of this section is to review current models of grain boundary structure and to define associated parameters in order to provide background for analysis of recent experimental results, as presented in succeeding sections. First, purely geometric models and concepts, based on crystallography of the unrelaxed lattice, and then energetic models and concepts, based on minimization of the free energy of a grain boundary, are reviewed. Further details are provided in recent articles by Gleiter and Chalmers (1972), Christian (1975), Pumphrey (1976), Smith and Pond (1976), and Balluffi (1979).

A. *Geometric Models*

The earliest and most logical attempts to characterize grain boundary structure were based on purely geometric concepts, involving misorientation of two identical lattices (grains) with respect to one another. Three degrees of freedom are necessary to fully define this misorientation; e.g., rotation by a given angle about a given axis, if at least one point is common to both lattices, and two more degrees of freedom are necessary to define the boundary plane. However, if one lattice is rigidly translated with respect to the other, three additional degrees of freedom are required. Therefore, details of grain boundary structure depend on a large number of independent variables (Goux, 1974). Generally, a given boundary is defined by a relative rotation of two adjacent grains θ and an inclination of the boundary plane ϕ about a common crystallographic axis ω. Rotations of this type represent a tilting of one lattice with respect to the other if the boundary normal is perpendicular to ω, and a twisting of one lattice with respect to the other if the boundary normal is parallel to ω. Thus, given values of θ and ω define a so-called tilt boundary, twist boundary, or some combination thereof, depending on the specific inclination of the grain boundary plane. Several geometric models, based on these elementary concepts, are reviewed in the following paragraphs.

Early models of grain boundary structure were based on dislocation theory, wherein a given (low-angle) grain boundary is represented by a regular array of dislocations (Read, 1953). The density of dislocations in the boundary is related to the angle of misorientation θ about a common crystallographic axis ω by the expression (Amelinckx, 1958).

$$\mathbf{B} = 2(\omega \times \mathbf{s})\sin(\theta/2) \qquad (1)$$

where $\mathbf{B}$ denotes the sum of Burgers vectors of all dislocations intersecting an arbitrary unit vector $\mathbf{s}$, aligned in the plane of the boundary. For special cases where ω is aligned parallel to the boundary plane (symmetrical tilt boundary) or perpendicular to the boundary plane (twist boundary), Eq. (1) reduces to the expression

$$d = \mathbf{b}/[2 \sin(\theta/2)] \qquad (2)$$

where d denotes the spacing between adjacent dislocations in a parallel array of edge dislocations or a cross grid of screw dislocations characterized by Burgers vector $\mathbf{b}$. In certain cases, however, the dislocation arrays described by Eqs. (1) and (2) may not represent the most stable (lowest-energy) configuration, especially when ω is aligned along high-index crystallographic directions. Therefore, certain dislocation arrays may decompose into more complex configurations, characterized by different values of d (Rey and Saada, 1976; Saada, 1979).

The description of grain boundary structure in terms of dislocation arrays can, in principle, be extended to any value of θ. However, as θ increases, the spacing between dislocations decreases to the point where elastic strain fields of each dislocation effectively cancel one another, thus leaving only the highly disordered dislocation cores to define the boundary plane. At this point, it becomes a moot issue whether or not a grain boundary corresponds to a discrete array of dislocations, since principles of linear elasticity are no longer applicable.

The misorientation limit for which dislocations in a grain boundary are no longer identical to lattice dislocations probably depends on the property being measured. Experimental results on the energy of tilt and twist boundaries in copper (Gjostein and Rhines, 1959) show a discrepancy with theory for a misorientation of about 6°. More recently, extended cores of edge dislocations in a 5° tilt boundary have been revealed by high-resolution TEM in germanium (Bourret and d'Anterroches, 1979). In view of these results, it is important to distinguish between isolated dislocations and dislocations in a grain boundary, since mutual interaction between nearby dislocations can alter their associated strain fields and core structure. In spite of these uncertain possibilities, Eqs. (1) and (2) adequately describe the configuration of dislocation networks in numerous metals, ceramics, and oxides (cf. Gervais *et al.*, 1979).

The first general description of high-angle grain boundary structure was proposed by Kronberg and Wilson (1949), who noted that certain rotations of one lattice (grain) with respect to the other about a common atomic position produce perfect coincidence between a subset of atoms of the two lattices. The actual structure is then defined by eliminating atoms from one lattice on one side of the boundary and atoms from the other lattice on the other side of the boundary. Although these boundaries are formed by rigid rotations of one lattice with respect to the other and exclude the possibility of lattice translation and/or atomic relaxation, the coincidence site lattice (CSL) theory identifies important concepts which apply for all types of grain boundaries, and therefore will be described further in the following paragraphs.

Basic properties of the CSL (Brandon *et al.*, 1964; Brandon, 1966; Ranganathan, 1966) can be identified by considering a common rotation axis ω in a cubic system. A CSL is then generated at values of θ given by the expression

$$\theta_{CSL} = 2 \tan^{-1}[(n/m)\omega^2] \tag{3}$$

where n and m are integers, and the corresponding reciprocal volumetric density of coincidence sites is given by the expression

$$\Sigma = n^2 + m^2\omega^2 \tag{4}$$

where, by convention, Σ is repeatedly reduced by a factor of 2 until an odd integer is obtained. The largest nontrivial density of coincidence lattice sites in cubic systems is for $\Sigma = 3$, which corresponds to a rotation of 70.5° about the [110] axis or 60° about the [111] axis; a complete list of misorientation angles and rotation axes is presented elsewhere (Pumphrey, 1976).

It should be noted that the CSL does not identify the grain boundary plane, but merely defines the axis of rotation and angle of misorientation, which give rise to a certain density of coincidence sites; i.e., only three of the possible eight parameters necessary to fully define a grain boundary are specified. The boundary itself, therefore, is characterized by another parameter Γ, which denotes the planar density of coincidence lattice sites normalized by the lattice parameter of the perfect lattice. Values of Γ may range from near zero for high-index planes to values exceeding unity for certain common twin orientations. Since regions of good fit in the CSL model are centered about coincidence sites and represent a state of minimum configurational energy, it is expected that a (planar) grain boundary, characterized by a large value of Γ, should also represent a state of minimum configuration energy (Brandon *et al.*, 1964). Therefore, it may be energetically favorable for a grain boundary to adjust its local inclination (facet) in order to assume a planar configuration characterized by a large value of Γ. Recent experimental results and further consideration of this topic are presented in Section VI.

A typical example of a CSL is presented in Fig. 1, wherein (001) faces of two fcc lattices are depicted after a rotation of 53.1° (equivalent to 36.9°) about a common [001] axis, which intersects an atomic site of both lattices (any solid circle). The CSL (super-lattice of all solid circles) is defined by coincidence of atoms of lattice I (crosses) and atoms of lattice II (open circles), and is characterized by $\Sigma = 5$. Certain high-density planes, separating lattices I and II, are also indicated. For this particular angle of misorientation, the highest-density plane corresponds to the {210} twin and is characterized by $\Gamma = 0.92$. It should be noted, however, that the CSL can be destroyed by an infinitesimal rotation of one lattice with respect to the other; therefore, the CSL lattice parameter and density of coincidence sites are discontinuous functions of θ.

The actual rigid-sphere configuration associated with a grain boundary in the CSL, depicted in Fig. 1, is presented in Fig. 2a for a symmetric [001] direction, corresponding to a {210} twin. However, since this particular configuration involves overlapping neighboring atoms of each lattice, it is evident that some degree of relaxation must occur. One possible type of relaxation involves a rearrangement of atoms in the core of the boundary without disturbing the CSL, whereas another type involves a rigid translation of one lattice with respect to the other (Gleiter and Chalmers, 1971). Configurations resulting from these types of relaxation are illustrated in

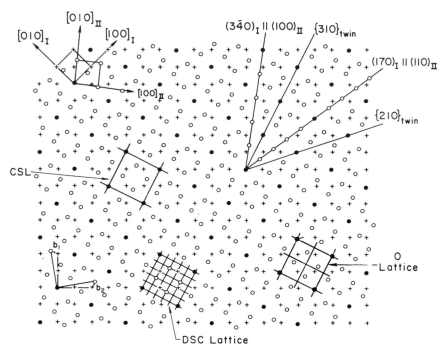

Fig. 1. Coincidence site lattice (CSL), produced by rotation of two fcc lattices (○, ×) by 53.1° about the common [001] axis (●) and characterized by $\Sigma = 5$. In addition, sections of the corresponding O lattice (for $(a/2)\langle 1\bar{1}0 \rangle$ Burgers vectors) and DSC lattice, as well as planes (directions) characterized by a high density of coincidence sites, and Burgers vectors of the DSC lattice are depicted. Note that periodicities of the O and DSC lattices correspond to one-half and one-fifth $(1/\Sigma)$ that of the CSL, respectively.

Fig. 2b and c, respectively. Regardless whether or not perfect coincidence between the two lattices has been destroyed, the periodicity of the boundary p is unchanged. Rigid-body translations have been observed experimentally (Pond *et al.*, 1974; Pond, 1977) and by computer simulation (Pond and Vitek, 1977). For the case of [001] twist boundaries, however, local atomic relaxations have been observed without rigid-body translations (Bristowe and Crocker, 1978). At present, it is not known whether grain boundaries are generally characterized by local rearrangement of atoms or rigid-body translations. It is known, however, that some sort of relaxation must accompany rigid rotation of one lattice with respect to the other. Models of grain-boundary structure which incorporate some sort of relaxation, are reviewed in the following paragraphs.

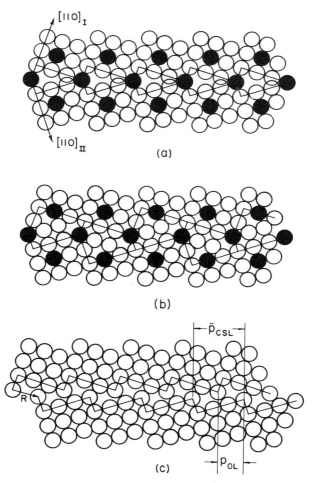

Fig. 2. Rigid-sphere models of a 36.9° [001] coincidence boundary, corresponding to the {210} twin depicted in Fig. 1, wherein three possible atomic configurations are illustrated: (a) unrelaxed and untranslated boundary, wherein considerable overlap of adjacent atoms is apparent, (b) relaxed and untranslated boundary, wherein overlap has been eliminated by rearrangement of atoms near the boundary, and (c) unrelaxed and translated boundary, wherein overlap has been eliminated by displacement of one lattice with respect to the other by a translation vector **R**. All boundaries are characterized by the periodicity of the coincidence site lattice p_{CSL} rather than that of the O lattice p_{OL}.

Basic concepts of the CSL have been formalized by Bollman (1970), and further elucidated by Smith and Pond (1976) and Bollmann (1977). This formalism is based on the principle that one lattice can be transformed to another by a general linear homogeneous transformation, corresponding to a rotation, dilation, shear, or some combination thereof. The ensemble of all origins of such a transformation is termed the O lattice. These origins denote regions of best atomic register and, as such, do not necessarily correspond to actual atomic sites. Moreover, they are not uniquely defined by the angle of misorientation and, therefore, must be specified by some other criterion as well; e.g., minimization of the density of dislocation cores in the boundary. Unlike the CSL, however, the O lattice parameter varies continuously with angle of misorientation and, for symmetric tilt or twist boundaries, is defined by Eq. (2). Since the O lattice denotes regions of best atomic fit, relaxations are localized between O lattice points and assume the periodicity of the O lattice. For small angles of misorientation, these relaxations correspond to individual dislocations, characterized by lattice Burgers vectors; hence such relaxations are termed primary relaxations. Moreover, for any angle of misorientation, the periodicity of atomic relaxations is given by the O lattice parameter, rather than by the purely geometric periodicity corresponding to the CSL lattice parameter. Since the atomic configurations about O lattice points are not necessarily identical, however, periodicity of the grain boundary is given by the CSL lattice, rather than by the O lattice parameter (cf. Fig. 2). A section of the O lattice derived from dislocations characterized by $(a/2)\langle 1\bar{1}0 \rangle$ Burgers vectors is illustrated in Fig. 1.

Small deviations from exact coincidence orientation may be accommodated by yet another set of relaxations (Brandon *et al.*, 1964). These relaxations are determined by a linear homogeneous transformation corresponding to small deviations from perfect coincidence $\Delta\theta$ (Warrington and Bollman, 1972; Bollman, 1977). Again, origins of this transformation do not necessarily correspond to actual atomic sites but, rather, to a set of translation vectors which conserve periodicity of the CSL. The ensemble of points defined by these vectors is termed the displacement shift complete (DSC) lattice, and also represents a superlattice of the CSL. For small deviations from coincidence, misfit is accommodated by relaxations corresponding to dislocations characterized by DSC lattice vectors. Such relaxations are termed secondary relaxations. The spacing between secondary relaxations is given by an expression similar to Eq. (2) by replacing the lattice Burgers vector by the DSC Burgers vector b^{DSC} and θ by $\Delta\theta$. A table of all observed secondary relaxations is presented elsewhere (Dingley and Pond, 1979).

A section of the DSC lattice is also illustrated in Fig. 1, wherein DSC lattice Burgers vectors are denoted by b_1 and b_2, corresponding to the smallest translation vectors of the DSC lattice, and, in this particular case, are given by $(a/10) \langle 310 \rangle$. The DSC lattice is also characterized by a third (DSC) Burgers vector b_3, which does not lie in the plane of the boundary. The magnitudes of b_1 and b_2 are related to the size of the CSL lattice parameter a^{CSL} by the expression a^{CSL}/Σ. Thus, as Σ approaches infinity, b_1 and b_2 tend to zero, and, in this limit, the misregister between grains may be described in terms of plane matching, wherein b_3 corresponds to the interplanar spacing (Pumphrey, 1972). Further details concerning the DSC lattice are presented elsewhere (Grimmer *et al.*, 1974; Ishida and McLean, 1973, 1974; Brokman, 1981).

The geometric models of grain boundary structure considered in this section are based on rigid rotations and translations of one lattice with respect to the other followed by some form of local relaxation, usually associated with either lattice (primary) or grain boundary (secondary) dislocations. Geometric models may also involve other structural units, such as ensembles of grain boundary terraces and ledges, partial grain boundary dislocations, facets, and stair-rod dislocations (Balluffi, 1979). Moreover, segregation of impurities at grain boundaries and possible grain boundary (phase) transformations further complicate attempts to characterize dislocation structure. Nevertheless, appreciation of grain boundary structure has advanced significantly in recent years due to comparison of geometric models with experimental results, and now such models provide a fairly reliable description of the atomic structure of grain boundaries. Other models, based primarily on thermodynamic (energetic) principles, are reviewed in the following section.

B.   Energetic Models

The structure of grain boundaries can be described formally by a regular network of dislocations, characterized by lattice Burgers vectors and spacings given by Eq. (2). Based on this principle, the energy of various low-angle grain boundaries has been computed by linear elasticity theory (Read and Shockley, 1950) and compared with experimental results (Gjostein and Rhines, 1959). More recently, the elastic strain field of dislocation networks has been analyzed by the method of surface dislocation density tensors (Rey and Saada, 1976; Saada, 1979). This analysis is very general and includes all possible dislocation networks, such as serrated boundaries and partial grain boundary dislocations separated by stacking faults. However, as mentioned earlier, all analyses based on linear elasticity are not applicable for high-angle grain boundaries, wherein the dislocation core energy exceeds that of the associated elastic strain fields. Nevertheless, energy and stability of low-angle [001] tilt boundaries in germanium have been successfully analyzed by this method (Bourret and Desseaux, 1979).

A more general approach for determination of atomic structure of any grain boundary according to energetic principles is through use of high-speed computational techniques (Christian, 1975; Harrison *et al.*, 1976). In this approach, the initial configuration corresponds to a grain boundary, characterized by angles of misorientation and inclination about a specified rotation axis, separating two unrelaxed (perfect) lattices. This configuration is then allowed to relax according to a preselected algorithm in order to determine the lowest-energy grain boundary structure. The interaction between atoms is effected by appropriate central force potentials and the resulting potential energy is computed by a summation of pairwise interaction energies. This approach provides a powerful tool to ascertain atomic structure of grain boundaries; however, results are very sensitive to the choice of interatomic potential, the actual relaxation algorithm, and assumed boundary conditions.

In addition to previously mentioned limitations of computer modeling, only highly periodic grain boundaries, corresponding to small values of Σ, have been investigated to date. Nevertheless, important results recently have been obtained on atomic relaxations of tilt (Smith *et al.*, 1977; Pond and Vitek, 1977) and twist (Bristowe and Crocker, 1978; Ingle and Crocker, 1980) boundaries. These results generally support earlier (geometric) models of grain boundary structure.

Various models have been reviewed in this section in order to reflect present-day understanding of the atomic structure of grain boundaries. Analysis of this structure depends on the extent that geometric or energetic principles are applicable. Therefore, grain boundaries are usually classified as low-angle boundaries, where principles of linear elasticity are applicable, random high-angle boundaries, and special boundaries, where geometrical concepts are applicable. Selected properties of materials containing such boundaries are reviewed in the following section.

III. Properties of Grain Boundaries

The properties that grain boundaries impart to materials are intimately related to grain boundary structure, as reviewed in Section II. The purpose of Section III is to review important properties of grain boundaries, not only in order to emphasize relationships between structure and properties but also to provide background for a review of recent experimental results, as presented in Section VI. Although a complete review of grain boundary properties is well beyond the space limitations of this article, brief descriptions of chemical, kinetic, electrical, and other properties are included herein in order to emphasize selected fundamental relationships between structure and properties of thin films. More complete reviews are provided elsewhere (Gleiter and Chalmers, 1971; Cotterill and Mold, 1976; Poate *et al.*, 1978; Haessner, 1978).

A. Chemical Properties

Chemical properties of grain boundaries are associated with bulk and interfacial phase relationships, as dictated by classical laws of thermodynamics, and represent such diverse phenomena as distribution of solute atoms near grain boundaries (segregation), formation of other phases near grain boundaries (precipitation), and nonequilibrium effects near grain boundaries (diffusion). Obviously, the particular distribution of solute atoms in the vicinity of such grain boundaries strongly affects concomitant properties.

One of the most fundamental relationships describing distribution of solute atoms near a grain boundary is based on the principle that the free energy of a solid is altered by an amount U_B when a given solute atom is transferred from the bulk material to a given grain boundary. The term U_B is known as the solute atom–grain boundary binding energy and results in attraction when $U_B < 0$ and repulsion when $U_B > 0$. In either case, a concentration gradient is established which just balances the effect of the interaction, thus allowing the concentration at a distance x from the boundary to be calculated by the general expression

$$c(x) = c(\infty)\exp[-U(x)/kT] \qquad (5)$$

where $c(\infty)$ denotes the concentration of solute atoms at an infinite distance from the grain boundary, $U(x)$ denotes the solute atom–grain boundary interaction energy for a solute atom separated from the grain boundary by a distance x, k denotes Boltzmann's constant, and T denotes absolute temperature. The maximum absolute value at $U(x)$ obtains at the grain boundary ($x = 0$), which is termed the solute atom–grain boundary binding energy $U(0) \equiv U_B$. The quantity U_B depends not only on the solute and solvent atom species but also on precise details of grain boundary structure. It should be noted that Eq. (5) is strictly valid for dilute solutions and must be modified when the atomic fraction of solute atoms is no longer small compared to unity. Moreover, analysis of segregation effects becomes much more complex when more than one chemical species is present, since affinity of one species for a grain boundary could be affected by the presence of another.

Equation (5) demonstrates that the concentration of solute atoms at a given grain boundary may greatly exceed the bulk value if $U_B < 0$, especially at intermediate temperatures, where some degree of diffusion occurs but the randomizing effect of entropy is not severe. The macroscopic relationship between segregation of solute atoms and grain boundary energy γ is given by a modified form of the Gibbs adsorption equation as

$$c(0) = -(1/kT)\, \partial\gamma/\partial \ln c(\infty) \qquad (6)$$

Obviously, the amount of solute at grain boundaries not only depends on the temperature and overall concentration but also on the character of the grain boundary and grain size. For example, segregation of solute atoms at grain boundaries characterized by small values of Σ is much less pronounced than segregation at random high-angle grain boundaries (Hondros, 1976). This result is generally attributed to the better atomic register (low γ) associated with coincidence grain boundaries. Moreover, variations of grain boundary structure could promote precipitation and formation of other phases, even when the appropriate phase diagrams specify complete solid solubility. A review of interfacial segregation and modification of engineering properties therefrom is presented elsewhere (Johnson and Blakely, 1979).

B. Kinetic Properties

Kinetic properties of grain boundaries may be divided into two classes: (1) diffusion of solute atoms along stationary grain boundaries and (2) diffusion of solute atoms along moving grain boundaries. In the former case, it is realized that grain boundaries provide short-circuit paths for rapid diffusion of solute atoms at surprisingly low temperatures. This particular effect is enhanced in thin films not only by small film dimensions but also by characteristically small grain size (Balluffi and Blakely, 1975).

The problem of short-circuit diffusion has been considered in detail by a number of investigators who were able to obtain analytical expressions for the amount of solute transported along a given grain boundary by assigning a characteristic width to the boundary δ. This characteristic width is related to grain boundary structure, although, at present, functional relationships between δ and θ, ϕ, Σ, and Γ are not fully appreciated (Martin and Perraillon, 1975). The first quantitative solution of the grain boundary diffusion problem was obtained by Fisher (1951) and later modified by Whipple (1954). In both treatments, the grain boundary is approximated by a uniform, isotropic continuum, characterized by a unique diffusion coefficient D_b, which is much larger than the corresponding lattice diffusion coefficient D_l. Although exact mathematical solutions to the diffusion equations may be obtained, it is sufficient here to note that a characteristic parameter β, given by the expression

$$\beta = (D_b/D_l)(\delta/\lambda) \tag{7}$$

where λ denotes grain size (diameter), characterizes the diffusion process (Gupta *et al.*, 1978). Two limiting cases are suggested by Eq. (7): (1) when $\beta \gg 1$, mass transport is effected solely by volume diffusion, i.e., $D_b \ll D_l$ and/or $\lambda \gg \delta$; or (2) when $\beta \gg 1$, mass transport is effected solely by grain boundary diffusion, i.e., $D_b \gg D_l$ and $\lambda \rightarrow \delta$. Since the activation energy for grain boundary diffusion is less than that for lattice diffusion, mass transport by grain boundary diffusion is facilitated by relatively low temperatures and small grain sizes. Moreover, such transport is very sensitive to grain boundary structure. Since certain properties of grain boundaries are indeed so sensitive to concomitant grain boundary structure, it is possible to manipulate such structure in order to optimize important engineering properties. For example, undesirable interdiffusion in polycrystalline thin films may be suppressed by producing preferred orientations, corresponding to low-angle or coincidence grain boundaries.

A further complication arises when the temperature and/or driving force (mobility) is sufficient to promote grain boundary migration. Unlike diffusion of solute atoms along the boundary, this phenomenon involves diffusion of solvent atoms across the boundary due to an energy difference between adjacent grains, rather than due to a concentration gradient. Values of grain boundary velocity, however, are often limited by diffusion of solute atoms either parallel or perpendicular to the grain boundary and/or surface-pinning effects (Bauer, 1974, 1975). As in previous cases, these effects are sensitive to the degree of grain boundary anisotropy (Haessner, 1978). Grain boundary diffusion is also enhanced in moving boundaries (Smidoda *et al.*, 1978). In other cases, diffusion of solute along grain boundaries promotes grain boundary migration—a process known as diffusion-induced grain boundary migration (Cahn and Balluffi, 1980).

Some of the most important kinetic properties of grain boundaries have been summarized in the preceding paragraphs, such as rapid (short-circuit) diffusion of solute atoms along grain boundaries and dependence of such diffusion on anisotropy of grain boundary structure. These properties, especially as related to grain boundary structure, are considered further in Section VI.

C. *Electrical Properties*

Although grain boundaries affect many diverse properties of bulk polycrystalline materials, a certain subset of properties becomes more important in thin films. Since thin films are often used to conduct an electrical current, it is natural that the effect of grain boundaries on electrical properties represents an important subject in thin-film technology. In the following paragraphs, selected electrical properties, such as scattering of electrons by grain boundaries and electromigration, are considered, with special emphasis on relationships to grain boundary structure.

The most fundamental electrical property associated with thin films is scattering of electrons by free surfaces and grain boundaries. The first effect becomes significant when the film thickness is less than the electron mean free path, which is especially important at low temperatures, whereas the second effect becomes significant when the density of grain boundaries is large. As a general rule, the disordered grain boundary region scatters electrons to a greater extent than an equivalent volume of perfect material. The fractional change (increase) in electrical resistance due to grain boundaries may then be approximated by the expression

$$\Delta R/R = \zeta\delta/(\lambda + \zeta\delta) \tag{8}$$

where ζ is a constant which provides a measure of grain boundary resistance. Since ζ varies between ~ 100 for high-angle random grain boundaries and 5 for low-angle and coincidence grain boundaries, $\Delta R/R$ is negligible for the usual bulk polycrystalline specimens ($\lambda \sim 10^6\delta$) but increases measurably for characteristic grain sizes of very thin films ($\lambda \sim 10^2\delta$). Therefore, it is obvious that electrical resistivity due to grain boundaries in thin films is a sensitive function of grain boundary structure. More detailed reviews of grain boundary scattering, due to both boundary structure and shape of the associated Fermi surface, are presented elsewhere (Van der Voort and Guyot, 1971; Martin and Truchot, 1974).

Another important property which is strongly affected by the presence of grain boundaries in thin films is electromigration. Electromigration is related to either localized variations in grain size or flux divergence at grain boundary triple junctions. Obviously, this latter effect is sensitive to the transport of matter along grain boundaries (δD_b) and, therefore, to grain boundary structure. Due to the fact that grain boundary structure is a sensitive function of misorientation angle, it is unlikely that the net atomic flux at any triple junction truly vanishes. The undesirable phenomenon of flux divergence may be suppressed by addition of a chemical element which segregates at grain boundaries, thus diminishing the effect of structure on transport properties. This diminution is especially striking when a few percent of copper is added to aluminum. Further details concerning electromigration and related phenomena are presented elsewhere (d'Heurle and Ho, 1978).

Electrical properties are also indirectly affected by kinetic processes, such as accelerated grain boundary diffusion. For example, when two dissimilar materials are brought into intimate contact, impurity segregation and/or intermetallic phase formation occur at the original interface. In polycrystalline materials, such effects also occur at grain boundaries, thus contributing to degradation of electrical properties. This degradation is especially severe in thin films, not only because of abnormally small grain size, but also because excess Joule heating, which further accelerates the degradation process, is generated locally. Moreover, the extent of mass transport along grain boundaries is strongly dependent on grain boundary structure, increasing from coherent twin boundaries to random high-angle grain boundaries.

Consideration of effects of grain-boundary structure on concomitant electrical properties could continue, but it is sufficient for the purpose of this article to indicate the intimate relationships which obtain between grain boundary structure and concomitant properties. Other important engineering properties, which are also dependent on grain boundary structure, are briefly mentioned in the following section.

D. *Other Properties*

Grain boundaries affect many diverse properties of materials. For example, the mechanical properties of bulk specimens are affected by grain size. In thin films, however, bulk mechanical properties are less important due to the fact that such films are generally not intended to support a mechanical load. Nevertheless, mechanical strength does play an important role due to secondary considerations resulting from the fact that all thin films are in intimate contact with a substrate or neighboring film. Temperature variations of a substrate, for example, can produce a strain in the attached film given by the expression

$$\epsilon = \sigma/G = \Delta\alpha \, \Delta T \qquad (9)$$

where σ, G, $\Delta\alpha$, and ΔT denote, respectively, stress, shear modulus, differential thermal expansion coefficient between film and substrate, and temperature change. It is not unusual that values of the thermal expansion coefficient for a metallic thin film differ by a factor of 5 from those of a semiconductor substrate, so that a 200°C temperature change could produce a strain of 10^{-4}. Since the equivalent stress often exceeds the corresponding yield stress, repeated heating and cooling cause thermal fatigue and eventual mechanical failure. In turn, the fracture stress is affected by grain size. Grain boundary sliding is also greatly reduced in low-angle and special grain boundaries due to the more orderly atomic structure (Lagarde

and Biscondi, 1974). Many such problems in thin-film technology are related to control of transmission of stress between dissimilar materials.

Other properties related to grain boundary structure in thin films include
Josephson tunneling, dynamics of magnetic bubbles, flux pinning in superconductors, and selected optical properties. More detailed discussion of
these and other properties are presented elsewhere (Chaudhary and Mathews, 1972; Gleiter and Chalmers, 1972; Murr, 1975).

IV. Preparation of Bicrystalline Thin Films

In previous sections, structure and properties of grain boundaries have
been reviewed without regard to actual specimen preparation. This section
is devoted to a short review of preparation of specimens containing grain
boundaries, with special emphasis on experimental techniques which allow
close control of important variables, such as angle of misorientation θ, plane
of grain boundary inclination ϕ, and control of specimen dimensions. Since
characterization of grain boundary structure has been achieved mainly
through application of TEM and related techniques, preparation of (thin-
film) specimens for subsequent examination by TEM will receive special
emphasis, with only passing reference to techniques for preparation of
specimens for optical microscopy, field-ion microscopy, and x-ray diffraction. Moreover, this review will focus on preparation of well-defined bicrystalline specimens, rather than preparation of polycrystalline specimens
for less-controlled examination of grain boundary structure.

A. Thinning of Bulk Specimens

The most common technique for examination of well-defined grain
boundary structure is by production of bulk bicrystalline specimens and
subsequent modification of dimensions to produce the desired configuration.
Generally, bulk bicrystalline specimens may be produced by either (1)
growth in the solid state, (2) growth from the melt, or (3) bonding of
monocrystalline specimens. The first technique involves controlled deformation of a polycrystalline specimen followed by annealing to promote
controlled recrystallization and grain growth. The resulting microstructure
consists of either large grains with random orientations (Ishida *et al.*, 1969;
Howell *et al.*, 1975) or preferred grains produced by growth selection of
grain boundaries characterized by large nucleation and/or growth rates
(Lücke, 1974). Consequently, grain boundaries can only be investigated
by observation of a large number of random boundaries or observation of

certain preferred boundaries. For example, for thin wires of small tip radius, required for examination of grain boundaries by field-ion microscopy, only growth from the solid state is permissible, but even then recrystallization texture limits examination to a few special grain boundaries (Loberg and Norden, 1973). In other cases, small specimen size severely hampers specimen preparation.

Whenever possible, it is desirable to produce bicrystalline specimens with preselected angles of misorientation and inclination. The most common method for producing such specimens is by direct growth from the melt, whereby bicrystalline specimens are grown by controlled solidification of two appropriately oriented seed crystals. Such techniques are generally classified as the Bridgman technique, wherein controlled solidification occurs from an appropriate bicrystalline seed by translation of a temperature gradient (Levy, 1969; Horton *et al.*, 1974), or the Czochralski technique, wherein two appropriately oriented seeds are retracted slowly from the melt. This latter technique has been used successfully for preparation of ionic (Cosandey, 1978) and covalent (Bourret and Desseaux, 1979) bicrystals.

Another, more specialized, technique for preparation of bicrystalline specimen is by direct bonding of monocrystalline specimens (usually by sintering) to produce a bicrystalline specimen containing a grain boundary with desired angles of misorientation and inclination (Föll and Ast, 1978; Sun and Balluffi, 1979). For most materials, joining must be effected under carefully controlled conditions to avoid contamination, oxide formation, and formation of excessive imperfections at the interface. Therefore, this particular technique is rather limited in application. It does represent, however, the principal technique for production of interphase boundaries with desired angles of misorientation and inclinations (Hwang *et al.*, 1980).

In all of the aforementioned techniques, thin films of desired (uniform) thickness are then produced by cutting and thinning procedures, so that the boundary plane may be observed at any desired angle relative to the incident electron beam by TEM and associated diffraction effects. Of course, grain boundaries in thin films may be investigated by many other techniques, but such techniques are generally capable of determining chemical composition and chemical-composition profiles rather than details concerning grain boundary structure.

B. Epitaxial Growth

In order to circumvent numerous and tedious procedures for thinning bulk bicrystalline specimens, it is desirable to modify the techniques reviewed in Section IV,A, so that bicrystalline thin films, amenable for sub-

sequent examination by TEM, can be produced directly. The first and most
extensive successful implementation of this approach was achieved through
modification of the joining of monocrystalline specimens (films) (Schober
and Balluffi, 1969; Tan *et al.*, 1976). This procedure involves production
of monocrystalline thin films by epitaxial growth on suitably prepared
substrates of NaCl. Two such films, still attached to their respective substrates, are then bonded (sintered) face to face with a desired angle of
misorientation. A bicrystalline thin film is thus produced which contains
a grain boundary of preselected misorientation and inclination. The NaCl
substrates are then dissolved in distilled water in order to free the resultant
bicrystalline film for examination by TEM. Advantages of this technique
are that (1) a variety of boundaries may be produced with relative ease
and (2) the boundary is aligned perpendicular to the incident electron
beam, thus facilitating examination of grain boundary structure (Balluffi
et al., 1972a, 1975).

An example of a grain boundary produced by the aforementioned technique is presented in Fig. 3, wherein a [001] twist boundary in gold, characterized by an angle of misorientation $\theta = 1.1°$, is pictured. The boundary

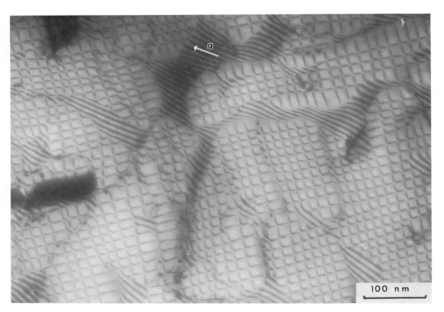

Fig. 3. Low-angle twist boundary in gold, produced by a rotation of 1.1° about the common
[001] axis and imaged by a diffraction vector $\mathbf{g} = (200)$. The boundary is composed of two
perpendicular sets of screw dislocations, characterized by Burgers vectors $\mathbf{b} = (a/2) \langle 1\bar{1}0 \rangle$
and mean spacings of ∼15 nm.

is composed of a cross grid of screw dislocations characterized by Burgers vector of the type $(a/2)$ $\langle 110 \rangle$ and a spacing of 20 ± 5 nm, in good agreement with a value of 15 nm computed from Eq. (2). The irregular patches correspond to regions of imperfect bonding produced during the sintering process. In this particular configuration, grain boundary area is maximized and film thickness can be varied so that such specimens are amenable to characterization by other techniques as well (e.g., x-ray diffraction).

A complementary technique for production of bicrystalline thin films involves production of such films directly from the vapor phase by deposition and subsequent epitaxial growth (Cosandey et al., 1975, 1978a). In this technique, bicrystals of NaCl are first produced by rotation of two seed crystals by a desired angle of misorientation about a common [001] axis and by growth of corresponding bicrystals from the melt by the Czochralski technique. Bicrystalline thin films of silver are then produced by vapor deposition and subsequent epitaxial growth on cleaved (001) surfaces of the NaCl bicrystals, and bicrystalline thin films of gold are produced on the silver films by a similar process of vapor deposition and epitaxial growth. In this manner, exact misorientation of grains and essential characteristics of the grain boundary, such as preferred inclination and dislocation misfit structure, are transmitted from the underlying substrate to these films. Prior to and during the early stages of deposition, the NaCl substrates are irradiated with low-energy electrons. This process improves the quality of the epitaxial films by increasing the number of nucleation sites as well as the degree of epitaxy (Cosandey et al., 1979). The gold films are then removed from their substrates by dissolution of NaCl and silver in distilled water and dilute nitric acid, respectively, and prepared for examination by TEM. Resulting grain boundaries are aligned normal to the specimen surface (parallel to the incident electron beam) and are characterized by a unique value of θ about a common [001] axis, which is also aligned normal to the specimen surface. The high degree of perfection of these boundaries, uniform and controlled thickness, and optimum inclination of the boundary plane for lattice-fringe imaging make these specimens ideally suited for many investigations involving high resolution of grain boundary structure (Cosandey et al., 1978b).

An example of a grain boundary produced by this latter technique is presented in Fig. 4, wherein a [001] tilt boundary in gold, characterized by an angle of misorientation of 10°, is pictured. The boundary is composed of an array of edge dislocations characterized by Burgers vector $(a/2)$ $\langle 110 \rangle$ and a spacing of 1.65 nm, in good agreement with a value of 1.66 nm computed from Eq. (2). In this particular configuration, grain boundary inclination is optimized for lattice-fringe imaging, investigation of mass

Fig. 4. Low-angle tilt boundary in gold, produced by a rotation of 9.5° about a common [001] axis. The boundary is composed of a set of parallel edge dislocations, characterized by Burgers vector $\mathbf{b} = (a/2) \langle 1\bar{1}0 \rangle$ and mean spacing of 1.8 nm (Cosandey *et al.*, 1978a).

transport along the boundary, and investigation of other phenomena which vary as a function of distance from the boundary.

Thin-film specimens may also be prepared by other techniques, such as sputtering or chemical vapor deposition (Tu and Lau, 1978). The purpose of this section, however, has been to review the most successful techniques for production of specimens for subsequent controlled examination of grain boundary structure. Methods for such examination are described in the following section.

V. Characterization of Grain Boundary Structure

Grain boundary structure may be characterized by a number of diverse techniques, depending on the type of material, specimen configuration, and desired level of resolution. The purpose of this section is to review some of the most common techniques, which are classified as (1) optical microscopy, (2) field-ion microscopy, (3) transmission electron microscopy, (4) diffraction techniques, and (5) indirect techniques. Selected recent experimental results obtained by application of these techniques are then presented in Section VI.

A. *Optical Microscopy*

Until recently, optical microscopy has played a dominant role in identification, examination, and characterization of grain boundaries. Initially, it was discovered that proper chemical or thermal etching of a suitably prepared surface could reveal intersection of grain boundaries with free surfaces. Therefore, general grain boundary topology (DeHoff and Rhines, 1968) and crystallographic dependence of preferred inclinations (Bishop *et al.*, 1971) can be determined by various sectioning techniques. In this manner, the energy of grain boundaries in many materials has been measured and compared with various models of grain boundary structure (see Section II). Even though such observations are limited to the intersection of a grain boundary with an external surface, the relative simplicity of this technique has led to a wealth of information concerning character and concomitant properties of grain boundaries in many diverse classes of materials.

One of the first applications of optical microscopy to determination of precise atomic structure of grain boundaries was through resolution of individual dislocations in a grain boundary by an etch-pit technique (Dash, 1957). Observations of the spacing between these etch pits and the angle of misorientation between neighboring grains in germanium provided the first unambiguous confirmation of the structure of low-angle grain boundaries (Vogel *et al.*, 1953), as described in Section II. Later, such techniques were applied to metals and ceramics as well. These techniques are, however, limited by the fact that resolution of spacing between etch pits is a few microns, so that the corresponding angle of misorientation between grains is limited to a few seconds. Therefore, only the dislocation structure of very low-angle grain boundaries can be resolved by this technique.

The structure of higher-angle grain boundaries may be characterized indirectly in certain circumstances, wherein boundaries assume preferred inclinations, corresponding to certain crystallographic planes, usually termed grain boundary facets. The frequency of occurrence of such facets as a function of angles of misorientation and inclination can be related to a so-called Wulff plot, which depicts grain boundary energy as a function of angle(s) of misorientation and/or inclination. Cusps in such plots signify a potential facet inclination and, therefore, provide information concerning grain boundary structure. Many results have been reported concerning energy, structure (Bishop *et al.*, 1971; Hartt *et al.*, 1974; Pumphrey, 1976; Goodhew *et al.*, 1978), and frequency of such facets as a function of θ and ϕ (Viswanathan and Bauer, 1973; Masteller and Bauer, 1979). These results demonstrate that grain boundaries often facet on a macroscopic scale.

Even though a wealth of information has been obtained by optical microscopy, interpretation of such information eventually depends on details beyond the ultimate limit of resolution; namely, the wavelength of visible light. However, due to the intimate relationship between observed properties and grain boundary structure, it is often necessary to interpret experimental results in terms of unresolvable structural details. Therefore, results based solely on optical microscopy, no matter how numerous and precise, cannot possibly provide a complete description of relationships between structure and properties of grain boundaries. It is for this reason that such coarse methods must be supplemented by high-resolution techniques, as described in the following paragraphs.

B.   Field-Ion Microscopy

The technique of field-ion microscopy (FIM) involves ionization of an inert gas at the tip of a specimen by a large electrostatic field and subsequent acceleration of this ion to a phosphorescent screen, where an image of high magnification is produced. Such images consist of concentric ring patterns, corresponding to ledges bounding certain crystallographic planes at the tip of the specimen. Thus, grain boundaries and other lattice imperfections may be observed by deviations from perfect symmetry of the ring patterns at the atomic level of resolution.

Although, the CSL description of grain boundary structure was first verified by FIM (Brandon *et al.*, 1964), the precise atomic configuration cannot be fully determined because only a small fraction ($\sim$15%) of all surface atoms are revealed and, moreover, preferred evaporation may occur at the grain boundary, thus obscuring true grain boundary structure. Further, FIM is primarily limited to high-melting-point metals, wherein field ionization occurs before field evaporation. Systematic investigation of grain boundary structure also is precluded by specimen dimensions, which limit results to occasional observations of random grain boundaries. Accordingly, characterization of grain boundary structure by FIM, since its advent about two decades ago, has primarily been limited to random grain boundaries in selected bcc metals. Further details concerning applications of FIM to the characterization of grain boundaries may be found elsewhere (Loberg and Norden, 1976).

C.   Transmission Electron Microscopy

Although the atomic structure of certain surfaces can be resolved by FIM, transmission electron microscopy (TEM) provides a more general approach for resolution of internal structure in a variety of materials. In general, this approach involves transmission of an incident electron beam through a thin foil (specimen) utilizing one of three principal techniques:

(1) Bright- or dark-field strain-contrast microscopy, wherein a single beam passes through the objective aperture in order to form a resultant image.

(2) Interference or phase-contrast microscopy, wherein two or more beams are recombined, in order to form a resultant interference image.

(3) Diffraction techniques, wherein the periodic nature of the lattice is displayed in reciprocal space.

The first two (image-forming) techniques are described in this section, whereas general diffraction techniques are described in Section V,D.

Theories of image formation by either bright- or dark-field TEM are now rather well developed, and considerable theoretical and practical information is presented in treatises by Hirsch *et al.* (1965) and Edington (1976). The ultimate resolution of closely spaced defects, such as arrays of dislocations, depends on many factors, such as instrument resolution, specimen configuration, and specimen thickness. Resolution can be increased by use of the weak-beam technique, wherein defects are imaged in the dark field by a weakly excited diffracted beam (Cockayne *et al.*, 1969; Cockayne, 1973). If intensity of the diffracted beam is sufficiently weak and other reflections are not strongly excited, weak-beam TEM is well suited for characterization of grain boundary structure because (1) a narrow image close to the core of the defect is produced and (2) the effective extinction distance is reduced, thus giving rise to many thickness fringes in the boundary and to a more precise determination of boundary topography (Jones *et al.*, 1976). In addition to inclination of the grain boundary plane, rotation axis and angle of misorientation can be determined with great accuracy using Kikuchi lines (Ishida, *et al.*, 1977).

The Burgers vector of grain boundary dislocations can also be identified by the conditions

$$\mathbf{g} \cdot \mathbf{b} = \mathbf{g} \cdot \mathbf{b} \times \mathbf{u} = 0 \qquad (10)$$

where $\mathbf{g}$ denotes the appropriate diffraction vector, $\mathbf{u}$ denotes the dislocation sense, and $\mathbf{b}$ denotes the Burgers vector, which define conditions for which the resultant image vanishes (Edington, 1976). However, for dislocations characterized by small Burgers vectors, such as those which accommodate small angular deviations from coincidence orientations, a large error may be associated with Eq. (10), especially for anisotropic materials. Moreover, contrast associated with secondary dislocations decreases as Σ increases (see Section II, A) so that Burgers vectors are more commonly identified by noting sense and spacing of the corresponding dislocations. It should be noted also that Eq. (10) can be satisfied by several different Burgers vectors. For general grain boundaries, computer image matching can be applied (Forwood and Humble, 1975; Mori and Ishida, 1978) or, if computer programs are not available, Burgers vectors of grain boundary dislocations may be determined by comparison of geometrical models of grain boundary structure, as specified by Eq. (1), with the conditions expressed by Eq. (10) (Clark and Smith, 1978).

Unlike strain-contrast microscopy, interference-contrast or phase-contrast microscopy involves formation of an image by recombination of two or more beams. When only two beams are recombined, a lattice-fringe image is produced which reflects the periodicity of the lattice in one dimension only, whereas when three or more beams are recombined, a lattice-crystal image is produced which reflects the periodicity of the lattice in two dimensions. In principle, the resulting images correspond exactly to the projected atomic planes or positions, but, due to aberrations in the optical system of the microscope, the intensity and position of such images are a sensitive function of specimen thickness, orientation, degree of defocus, and certain characteristics of the microscope itself (Cowley, 1975, 1976).

Experimental results are also affected by the resolution limit of the microscope. For high-voltage microscopes with a point-to-point resolution limit of 0.2 nm, the image formed by axial illumination and recorded at the Scherzer defocus distance may be easily interpreted, since a one-to-one correspondence exists between object and image (Krivanek et al., 1977). An example of an image formed by high-resolution, high-voltage microscopy is presented in Fig. 5, wherein a twin in a thin film of gold is pictured on a {110} plane (Ichinose and Ishida, 1981). The configuration of the atoms is clearly visible and atoms at the twin boundaries are undisturbed, thus confirming the existence of a perfectly coherent interface.

For lower-voltage microscopes (e.g., 100 kV), point-to-point resolution is increased to about 0.3 nm due to an increase in the electron wavelength. Therefore, only materials characterized by a lattice spacing greater than 0.3 nm may be examined by axial illumination. In addition, resulting images are very sensitive to the amount of defocus and foil thickness (Spence et al., 1978; Spence and Kolar, 1979; Desseaux et al., 1977), so that image simulation is required to determine optimum experimental conditions.

For most metals or whenever knowledge of the exact atomic configuration is unavailable, microscope aberrations may be reduced and resolution increased to better than 0.2 nm by use of tilted illumination. Although lattice-fringe images produced in this manner may not correspond exactly to lattice planes, considerable information, such as grain boundary periodicity and Burgers vectors of grain boundary dislocations, may be obtained (Cockayne et al., 1971; Cosandey et al., 1978b). An example of a lattice-fringe image of a [001] 10° tilt boundary in gold is presented in Fig. 6, wherein the beam is tilted so that the optical axis is midway between the transmitted beam and the (200) diffracted beams of both grains. The resulting image, therefore, consists of a set of fringes perpendicular to the diffraction vector and is characterized by a periodicity identical to that of the corresponding lattice planes. Some fringes terminate at the boundary

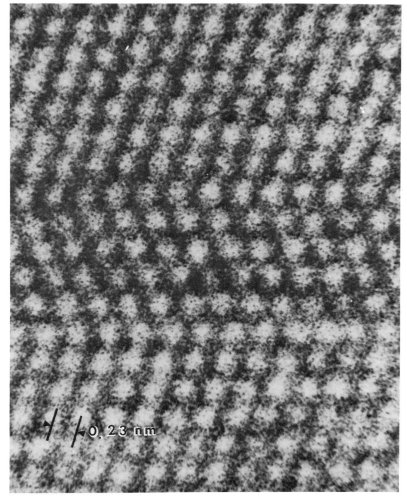

Fig. 5. Multibeam lattice-crystal image of a {111} microtwin intersecting a {110} plane in gold. (Courtesy of Ichinose and Ishida, 1981.)

plane, corresponding to end-on dislocations characterized by the Burgers vector $(a/2)[1\bar{1}0]$.

In summary, the structure of grain boundaries may be characterized at high resolution incorporating principles of lattice-fringe and crystal-fringe imaging. Special experimental conditions, however, must be satisfied in order to obtain images free of artifacts and the highest possible resolution.

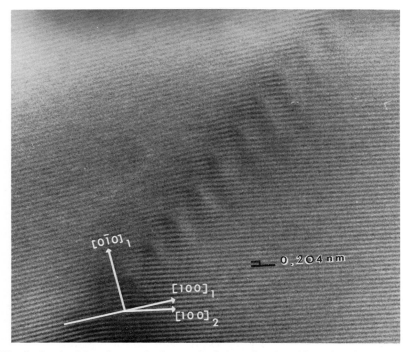

Fig. 6. Lattice-fringe image of a low-angle tilt boundary in gold, produced by a rotation of 10.0° about the common [001] axis. Spacing between adjacent (200) fringes is 0.204 nm. (Courtesy of Cosandey *et al.*, 1978b.)

These conditions include utilization of thin-film specimens with a uniform thickness of ≤10 nm, imaging of lattice planes parallel to the optical axis and at the exact Bragg condition, alignment of imaged defects parallel to the incident electron beam (in order to produce uniform projected image), and adjustment of the amount of focus to produce maximum lattice-fringe contrast. Moreover, additional conditions must be satisfied in order to produce satisfactory crystal-fringe images, such as uniform phase change over the area necessary to image the defect and accurate defocusing. Recent experimental results involving these imaging techniques are presented in Section VI.

D. Diffraction Techniques

Only recently have diffraction techniques been applied to characterization of grain boundary structure. These techniques are based on the principle that a periodic array of dislocations gives rise to extra characteristic reflections in reciprocal space (Balluffi *et al.*, 1972b). In the case of electron diffraction, the structure of [001] twist boundaries in gold has been investigated extensively by Sass *et al.* (1975). Since extra reflections were observed to occur in the reciprocal lattice of the O lattice, it was concluded that [001] twist boundaries are characterized by a periodicity identical to that of the O lattice. Results associated with electron diffraction are often complicated by double diffraction, which is promoted by high electron energy and the associated large radius of the Ewald sphere. For investigations of grain boundary structure, such effects can be minimized if the boundary plane is inclined relative to the incident electron beam (Carter *et al.*, 1979).

In contrast to electron diffraction, x-ray diffraction techniques are not severely affected by double diffraction. Therefore, the structure of grain boundaries has been characterized more frequently by this latter technique (Gaudig and Sass, 1979; Guan and Sass, 1979). In addition to determination of grain boundary periodicity, it is also possible to determine the grain boundary structure factor and displacement field near and far removed from the boundary from the relative intensity of the diffracted beams (Sass, 1980). However, large grain boundary area and long exposure time necessitate preparation of two monocrystalline thin-film specimens by epitaxial growth and subsequent bonding to produce a grain boundary of desired misorientation (Schober and Balluffi, 1969). Use of high-intensity synchrotron radiation and special detectors may facilitate characterization of grain boundary structure by x-ray diffraction (Sass, 1980).

Since foil and boundary both are of finite thickness, diffraction spots are elongated along the foil normal for crystal diffraction and along the boundary normal for grain boundary diffraction. Therefore, it is possible to measure grain boundary thickness by either x-ray or electron diffraction from measurement of elongation and shape of the diffracted beam (Budai *et al.*, 1979). The diffraction pattern and bright-field images of an end-on tilt boundary in Al_2O_3 are pictured in Fig. 7, wherein elongated grain boundary diffraction spots are clearly visible. The length of these spots is inversely related to grain boundary thickness, which, in turn, is equal to grain boundary periodicity (Carter *et al.*, 1980). Diffraction techniques, therefore, not only enable measurement of grain boundary periodicity but also the extent of lattice distortion in the neighboring grains.

The techniques presented thus far are classified as direct techniques, since results are either in the form of a direct image of the grain boundary or a diffraction pattern which is directly related to grain boundary structure. Nevertheless, these techniques are limited by availability of special instrumentation and/or specimen configuration. Therefore, more complete knowledge of grain boundary structure may be obtained by application of

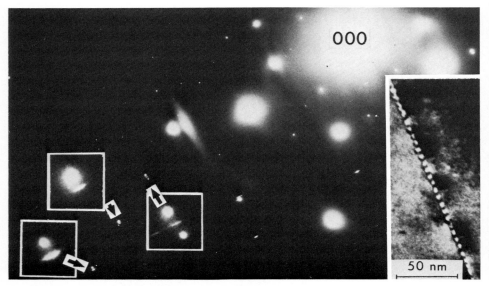

Fig. 7. Strain-contrast and electron diffraction patterns of a low-angle tilt boundary in Al$_2$O$_3$. Lengths of diffraction spots are inversely proportional to the boundary thickness, which also corresponds to boundary periodicity. (Courtesy of Carter *et al.*, 1979.)

several techniques. This approach is especially useful when combined with information obtained from more indirect results, as reviewed briefly in the following section.

E. Indirect Techniques

Although grain boundary structure is usually characterized by one or more of the direct techniques mentioned previously, valuable supplementary information can be obtained from various indirect techniques. These techniques, in effect, are sensitive to some phenomenon which itself is dependent on grain boundary structure, such as impurity segregation and precipitation at grain boundaries, impurity or self-diffusion along grain boundaries, grain boundary sliding, grain boundary migration, or fracture along grain boundaries.

Perhaps some of the earliest investigations of grain boundary structure were based on the fact that diffusion along low-angle grain boundaries could be related to dislocation structure (Balluffi, 1968). In this manner it was concluded that short-circuit diffusion depended on the nature of the core region and alignment of the dislocation array relative to the direction of mass transport. Electrical resistivity also may provide an indication of dislocation structure, both through scattering of electrons by various grain boundaries and, indirectly, through detection of grain boundary diffusion (Bauer and Jordan, 1978). Segregation of impurities at grain boundaries also provides an indication of grain boundary structure. These impurities are normally detected either by indirect methods, such as x-ray diffraction, measurement of grain boundary energy and electrical properties, and metallographic examination, or by direct methods, such as autoradiography, energy-loss spectroscopy, and surface analysis techniques. These and other methods are reviewed in a recent article by Joshi (1979). Measurements of grain boundary mobility may also be related to grain boundary structure (Viswanathan and Bauer, 1973; Masteller and Bauer, 1979).

The aforementioned techniques generally involve measurement of properties of a polycrystalline aggregate, wherein correlation with explicit grain boundary structure is not possible. More definite indirect techniques involve preparation of bicrystalline (or tricrystalline) specimens, wherein rotation axis and angles of misorientation and inclination are carefully defined. Such techniques involve grain boundary diffusion (Hoffman, 1956; Love and Shewman, 1963), grain boundary precipitation (Le Coze and Biscondi, 1974), grain boundary sliding (Biscondi and Goux, 1975), grain boundary energy (Hasson and Goux, 1971; Hermann et al., 1976), grain boundary (diffusional) creep (Yeager and Gleiter, 1978), grain boundary segregation (Boos and Goux, 1970), grain boundary flux pinning (Yetter, 1980), and grain boundary mobility (Viswanthan and Bauer, 1973; Masteller and Bauer, 1979). In general, these techniques have been applied to bulk specimens rather than to thin films.

Many other techniques may also be applied to indirect determination of grain boundary structure, such as electron spectroscopy for chemical analysis, secondary ion mass spectrometry, and Rutherford backscattering (Mayer and Poate, 1978). The purpose of this section, however, is merely to indicate the wide variety of techniques available for the characterization of grain boundary structure and the relative merits of each. Recent experimental results stemming from application of these techniques are reviewed in the following section.

VI. Recent Experimental Results

The numerous details presented in previous sections concerning structure, properties, and characterization of grain boundaries, as well as specimen preparation, now provide a basis for interpretation of recent experimental results. These results are divided into three classifications: (1) low-angle grain boundaries, characterized by arrays of well-defined dislocations, (2) high-angle grain boundaries, characterized by complex atomic core structure, and (3) special grain boundaries, characterized by special orientation relationships between adjacent grains. Since considerable effort has been devoted to these topics during recent years, a selection of experimental results, which reflects the present state of knowledge, is presented herein. Additional details are presented elsewhere (Pumphrey, 1976; Balluffi, 1979).

A. Low-Angle Grain Boundaries

Grain-boundary structure was first elucidated in terms of regular arrays of well-defined dislocations in low-angle boundaries (see Section II,A) and verified by measuring spacing between etch pits as a function of misorientation angle in germanium (Vogel et al., 1953). Since then, numerous examples of dislocation networks in low-angle grain boundaries have been reported (Amelinckx, 1958; Amelinckx and Dekeyser, 1959; Gervais et al., 1979), which agree well with predictions of Eqs. (1) and (2).

The structure of low-angle grain boundaries was investigated as a function of misorientation angle for [001] tilt boundaries in aluminum (Levy, 1969) and more recently for [001] and [011] tilt and twist boundaries in gold (Schober and Balluffi, 1970, 1971). For pure tilt boundaries, only one set of dislocations is necessary in order to accommodate deviation from perfect coincidence (Levy, 1969; Schober and Balluffi, 1971; Balluffi et al., 1972a), whereas, for pure twist boundaries, two coplanar sets of screw dislocations are required. For twist boundaries in gold, [001] boundaries are composed of a regular orthogonal network of screw dislocations, whereas [110] and [111] boundaries are composed of a hexagonal network of screw dislocations (Goodhew et al., 1976). Still more complicated dislocation networks are observed in mixed boundaries. Indeed, primary grain boundary dislocations in silicon have been observed to dissociate into partial dislocations separated by stacking faults in [111] twist boundaries in silicon (Föll and Ast, 1979), in [110] tilt boundaries in germanium (Bourret and Desseaux, 1979), and in [001] and [011] tilt boundaries in gold (Darby and Balluffi, 1977). In all cases, however, these networks must be consistent with Eqs. (1) and (2) if an equilibrium configuration obtains, even though grain boundary energy might be reduced further by certain dislocation reactions.

An example of a dislocation network in silicon is presented in Fig. 8, wherein alternate intrinsic and extrinsic stacking faults are formed at dislocation nodes. Occasionally, these dislocations have been observed to react

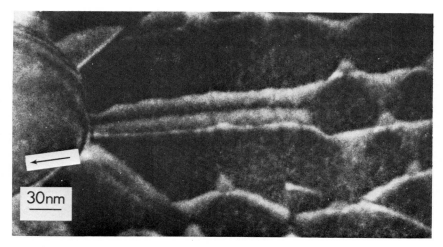

Fig. 8. Weak-beam image of a low-angle twist boundary in silicon, produced by a rotation of 0.4° about a [111] axis. Dislocations have reacted to form double ribbons, representing intrinsic and extrinsic stacking faults. The ⟨111⟩ reflection, used to image the defects, is indicated by an arrow. (Courtesy of Föll and Carter, 1979.)

with amorphous patches at the interface to form intrinsic–extrinsic double stacking faults. By assuming a balance between dislocation line energy and stacking fault surface energy, intrinsic and extrinsic stacking fault energies may be estimated. In this particular case, the intrinsic fault energy is about 15% greater than the extrinsic energy (Föll and Carter, 1979).

Formation of partial dislocations has not been observed directly in tilt boundaries in gold, but serrated configurations are observed whenever the tilt axis is not parallel to the {111} plane. These configurations favor dissociation into partial dislocations on {111} planes (Darby and Balluffi, 1977), although the extent of such dissociation decreases with increasing angle of misorientation. Similar effects have been reported for dissociated [111] twist boundaries in silicon (Föll and Ast, 1979).

Four different dislocation structures have been observed for low-angle grain boundaries in germanium (Bourret and Desseaux, 1979): (1) an array of sessile edge dislocations, (2) an array of dissociated 60° (mixed) dislocations, (3) an array of three identical Frank partial dislocations, and (4) an array of three partial dislocations characterized by global Burgers vector $(a/2)\langle211\rangle$. These general results are consistent with the analysis of Rey and Saada (1976), as described briefly in Section II,A. A multibeam lattice-crystal image of a dissociated 60° (mixed) dislocation ($\mathbf{b} = (a/2)\langle110\rangle$) in germanium is illustrated in Fig. 9. The dissociation reaction gives rise to partial edge and 30° (mixed) dislocations, characterized by $\mathbf{b}$

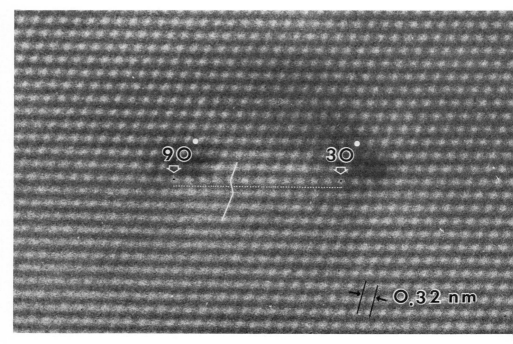

Fig. 9. Multibeam lattice-crystal image of a dissociated 60° dislocation intersecting a {110} plane in germanium, wherein partial dislocations, corresponding to 30° and edge (90°) character, are indicated by arrows and separated by an intrinsic stacking fault, indicated by the dotted line. (Courtesy of Bourret and Desseaux, 1979.)

$= (a/6) \langle 211 \rangle$ and separated by an intrinsic stacking fault. The intrinsic stacking fault energy is estimated from separation between partial dislocations to be 100 mJ/m^2 (Bourret and Desseaux, 1979).

Dependence of grain boundary precipitation kinetics on orientation and inclination relationships also provides valuable information on grain boundary structure. For example, the density and morphology of precipitates on grain boundaries in aluminum alloys are dependent on grain boundary energy, as dictated by the CSL (Le Coze *et al.*, 1973). More recent investigations by high-resolution TEM of grain boundary precipitation in aluminum alloys have revealed that intrinsic grain boundary defects significantly affect the precipitation sequence by assisting emerging precipitates in establishing low-energy habit planes with at least one grain (Gronsky and Furrer, 1981). Typical examples of precipitation at low-angle tilt boundaries in these alloys are presented in Fig. 10. The alignment of small particles in Fig. 10a is due to the fact that the boundary plane is parallel to a (220) plane of one grain, whereas the particles are aligned with their

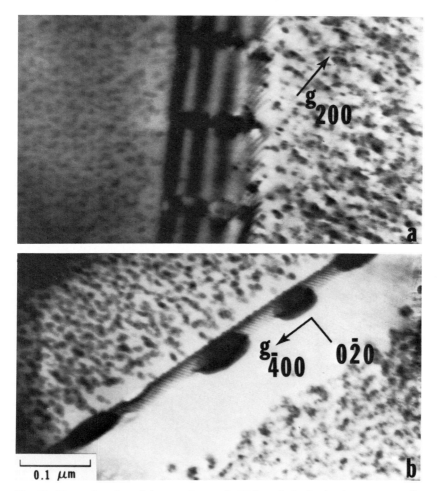

Fig. 10. Formation of precipitates at low-angle tilt boundaries in aluminum–copper alloys, wherein (a) precipitates are oriented parallel to the boundary plane when it is inclined along a (220) plane of one grain and (b) precipitates are oriented perpendicular to the boundary plane when it is inclined along a more closely packed (020) plane of one grain. (Courtesy of Gronsky and Furrer, 1981.)

longitudinal dimension transverse to the dislocations comprising the more closely packed boundary parallel to the $(0\bar{2}0)$ plane.

From the aforementioned discussion, it is evident that experimental results on the structure of low-angle grain boundaries are in general agreement with the geometric models described in Section II,A, although, in some cases, dissociation of dislocation networks and/or individual dislocations further reduces the overall grain boundary energy. In general, agreement is best for low-angle boundaries ($\theta < 10°$) and decreases as the mutual interaction between neighboring dislocations increases (with increasing θ). The more complex case of (random) high-angle grain boundaries is considered in the following section.

B. High-Angle Grain Boundaries

In principle, description of low-angle grain boundaries may be extended to high-angle grain boundaries. In reality, however, relaxations which occur at the boundary may be quite different from those which occur near the core of isolated dislocations. Thus, overlap of dislocation cores may lead to entirely new structures which cannot be predicted from the description of low-angle grain boundaries. Nevertheless, certain primary relaxations at grain boundaries, be it due to "dislocations" or other defects, are observed for boundaries characterized by all angles of misorientation.

Detection of these primary relaxations by standard strain-contrast microscopy at large angles of misorientation becomes difficult because contrast decreases with increasing θ (Schober and Balluffi, 1970; Föll and Ast, 1978). Moreover, moiré fringes, produced at normal incidence by interference between diffracted beams from each grain, often obscure primary relaxations. In order to overcome these difficulties, the periodic nature of high-angle grain boundaries has been investigated primarily by diffraction techniques (Sass, 1980). Primary relaxations have been detected over the entire range of misorientation angle in [001] twist boundaries in gold from extra reflections on electron diffraction patterns, which correspond to reciprocal points of the O lattice (Sass et al., 1975). The O lattice was then imaged directly by interference-contrast microscopy, wherein the diffracted beam responsible for these extra reflections is recombined with the transmitted beam in order to form an interference image. In this manner, periodic primary relaxations have been detected for angles of misorientation up to 25° (Tan et al., 1975). Similar effects have been obtained by x-ray diffraction for [001] tilt boundaries (Guan and Sass, 1979) and [001] tilt boundaries (Gaudig and Sass, 1979). These results indicate that the observed periodicity corresponds to that of the O lattice and that associated grain boundary relaxations occur between O lattice points. Recent results also indicate that grain boundary thickness (i.e., extent of long-range distortion), corresponds to grain boundary periodicity (Budai et al., 1979). This thickness also corresponds to the periodicity of the O lattice.

The structure of low- and high-angle [001] tilt boundaries in bicrystalline thin films of gold has recently been investigated by high-resolution TEM

(Cosandey et al., 1978b; Cosandey and Bauer, 1981). Typical results are presented for a 27.5° [001] tilt boundary in Fig. 11, wherein lattice-fringe and corresponding bright-field images are pictured. The resultant grain boundary periodicity is determined to be 0.58 nm from either the mean spacing between terminating fringes or from the associated strain-contrast pattern. Similar results were obtained for a large range of misorientation angles. Since these results are in excellent agreement with Eq. (2) and the O lattice theory, it is concluded that primary grain boundary relaxations occur between points of the O lattice and are characterized by a periodicity equal to that of the O lattice. For low-angle grain boundaries, these relaxations correspond to individual lattice dislocations.

As mentioned in previous sections, anisotropy of grain boundary structure often causes grain boundary faceting. A typical example of such faceting is illustrated in Fig. 12, wherein a random [011] grain boundary in tungsten is revealed by FIM (Ishida and Smith, 1974). It is evident that

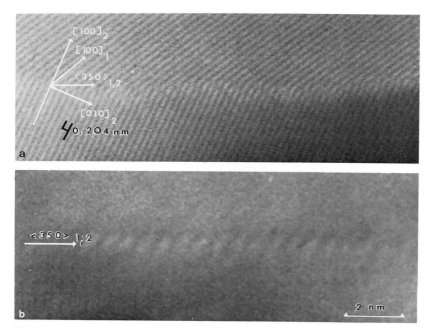

Fig. 11. Lattice-fringe (a) and bright-field (b) images of a high-angle tilt boundary in gold, produced by a rotation of 27.5° about the common [001] axis. The lattice-fringe image is produced using tilted illumination and the (200) fringes are characterized by a separation of 0.204 nm. The resultant boundary periodicity is determined to be 0.58 nm from either the mean spacing between terminating fringes or from the associated strain-contrast pattern. (Courtesy of Cosandey and Bauer, 1981.)

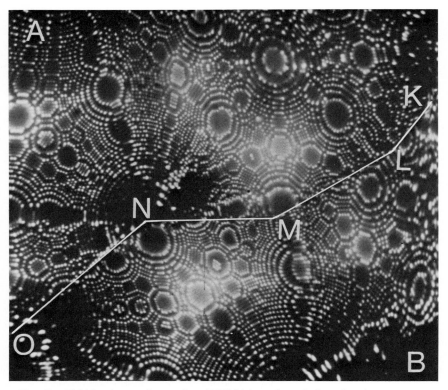

Fig. 12. Field-ion image of a random [001] high-angle grain boundary in tungsten separating crystals A and B, wherein four facets (O–N, N–M, M–L, and L–K) are visible. (Courtesy of Ishida and Smith, 1974.)

this boundary is composed of four facets (O–N, N–M, M–L, and L–K). These observations are consistent with the grain boundary morphologies observed on a macroscopic (Bishop *et al.*, 1971; Weins and Weins, 1972) and microscopic (Sargent, 1968; Cosandey and Bauer, 1980) scale. Matching of (011) planes across the grain boundary is also evident. In addition, both lattice and grain boundary dislocations may be revealed by this technique (Brandon *et al.*, 1964; Loberg and Norden, 1976).

 Characterization of the atomic structure of high-angle grain boundaries may also be achieved through computational techniques, as mentioned in Section II,B. Despite considerable effort, characterization of grain boundary structure by computational techniques and computer modeling is not always reliable due to the arbitrary choice of interatomic potentials, boundary conditions, and relaxation algorithms. Nevertheless, new and improved understanding of grain boundary structure is now emerging through large-scale computation and careful correlation with experimental results (Pond and Vitek, 1977). Future emphasis should be directed to correlation between computer simulations of grain boundary structure and direct crystal-fringe imaging. Precise atomic potentials could then be formulated with greater confidence, giving rise to a deeper understanding of grain boundary structure in general.

The results presented in this section strongly indicate that primary grain boundary relaxations are intimately related to the O lattice, regardless of angle of misorientation or inclination of the boundary plane. Although only a limited number of grain boundaries have been investigated to date, it is likely that these conclusions are quite general, since grain boundary periodicity as small as 0.5 nm has been detected (Sass *et al.*, 1975; Cosandey and Bauer, 1981). Characterization of the structure of special grain boundaries is more complicated, however, as discussed in the following section.

C. Special Grain Boundaries

In addition to low- and high-angle grain boundaries, certain grain boundaries may be classified as special grain boundaries when concomitant structure is dictated by special orientation–inclination relationships (e.g., twin and coincidence boundaries). In general, coincidence boundaries are expected to occur only at precise angles of misorientation, corresponding to small values of the reciprocal CSL density Σ. Whenever θ deviates by a small amount from these values, however, a high degree of coincidence can be preserved by occurrence of secondary relaxations, as described in Section II. Recent experimental results on these special boundaries are presented in this section, with special emphasis on agreement with theory, as reviewed previously in Section II,A.

Despite considerable progress over the past decade in characterization of special grain boundaries, many questions still remain unresolved. One question concerns the range over which secondary dislocations may exist, since the Burgers vector of such dislocations decreases with increasing Σ until a point is reached whereat characterization of grain boundary structure in terms of secondary dislocations is no longer physically meaningful. The smallest Burgers vector thus far detected is $(a/82) \langle 41, 4, 5 \rangle$ (i.e., $b = 0.51a$) for a $\Sigma = 41$ tilt boundary in aluminum (Dingley and Pond, 1979). Another question concerns spacing and core structure of secondary dislocations, since, for sufficiently large $\Delta\theta$, the unique structure associated with special grain boundaries can no longer be preserved.

Compared to experimental results available on primary grain boundary relaxations, even fewer results are available on secondary relaxations, espe-

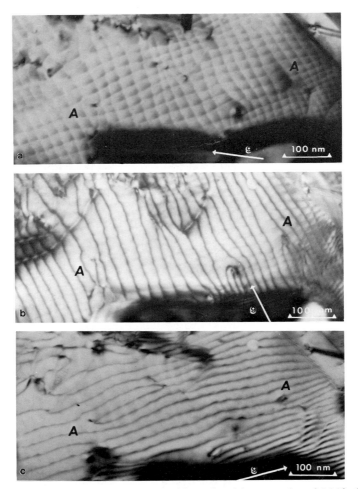

Fig. 13. High-angle twist boundary in gold, produced by a rotation of 36.9° about the common [001] axis and imaged by diffraction vectors **g** of (a) (0$\bar{2}$0), (b) (3$\bar{1}\bar{1}$), and (c) (13$\bar{1}$). The boundary is composed of two perpendicular sets of screw dislocations, characterized by Burgers vector $(a/10) \langle 310 \rangle$ and mean spacing of 2.5 nm. (Courtesy of Hwang *et al.*, 1980.)

cially concerning structural variation as a function of θ and Σ. The most complete investigation to date has been conducted on a variety of tilt and twist boundaries in gold (Balluffi *et al.*, 1972a, 1975). In all cases, deviations from perfect coincidence are accommodated by a periodic array of secondary dislocations, whose spacing is given by Eq. (2) with θ replaced by $\Delta\theta$. More complex dislocation networks occur whenever the boundary

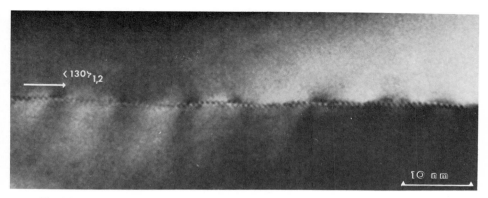

Fig. 14. Near-coincidence tilt boundary in gold, produced by a rotation of 38.5° about the common [001] axis. Diffraction conditions are given by $\mathbf{g} = (200)$ for both grains and resultant boundary periodicities are determined to be 0.62 and 7 nm from the superposed strain-contrast patterns. (Courtesy of Cosandey and Bauer, 1981.)

plane does not correspond to a symmetric inclination (Bollmann *et al.*, 1972). A typical example of the resulting (secondary) dislocation structure of $\Sigma = 5$, [001] twist boundaries is presented in Fig. 13, wherein a cross grid of screw dislocations, characterized by Burgers vector $\mathbf{b} = (a/10)$ $\langle 310 \rangle$, is pictured. The Burgers vectors of the secondary dislocations have been determined by use of Eq. (10). The interaction and/or absorption of dislocations by grain boundaries provides another method to investigate the fine structure of grain boundary dislocations (Pond and Smith, 1977; Darby *et al.*, 1978). In Fig. 13, lattice dislocations have interacted with the boundary (cf. regions marked by A) and dissociated into three secondary dislocations according to the reaction $(a/2) [1\bar{1}0] \rightarrow (a/10) [310] + 2(a/10) [1\bar{3}0]$. By a simple analysis of dislocation reactions, it is therefore possible to analyze and determine Burgers vectors of secondary dislocations. For a general interface, three noncoplanar Burgers vectors are necessary to accommodate deviations from perfect coincidence.

In some cases, complex relaxations have been observed in special grain boundaries. For example, primary dislocations have been detected in [001] twist boundaries (Sass *et al.*, 1975) and in [001] tilt boundaries (Cosandey and Bauer, 1981) in gold over a range of misorientations, wherein secondary dislocations have also been detected (Balluffi *et al.*, 1972a). Recently, the structure of special grain boundaries in bicrystalline thin films of gold has been examined by high-resolution TEM (Cosandey and Bauer, 1981). A typical example of the results is presented in Fig. 14, wherein the structure of a nominal $\Sigma = 5$, 36.9° [001] tilt boundary is pictured. Two periodic strain-contrast patterns are discernible: one (small spacing) due to an array of primary relaxations and the other (large spacing) due to an array of secondary relaxations, which accommodate small deviation ($\Delta\theta = 1.6°$) from perfect coincidence. Thus, primary and secondary relaxations may occur concurrently near coincidence orientations. In this case, secondary relaxations may be described by an independent array of dislocations, by a modulation of the spacing of primary relaxations, or by a periodic variation of the core structure of primary relaxations.

Fewer observations of secondary relaxations have been reported in nonmetallic materials. Recently, secondary dislocation networks have been observed for $\Sigma = 5$, [001] twist boundaries in MgO, which are characterized by Burgers vector, $(a/5) \langle 210 \rangle$, rather than that previously reported for gold (Sun and Balluffi, 1979). This difference is attributed to the nature of bonding in metallic and ionic solids. On the other hand, the character of secondary dislocations associated with $\Sigma = 3$, [111] twist boundaries in silicon (Föll and Ast, 1979) is similar to that observed in metals.

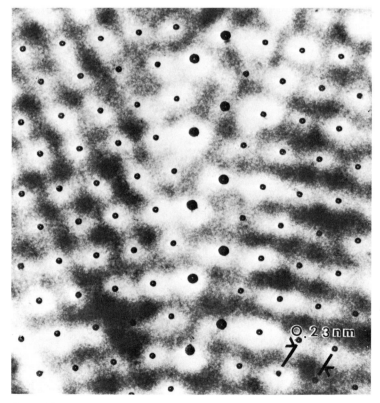

Fig. 15. Multibeam lattice-crystal image of a $\Sigma = 11$ coincidence tilt boundary in gold, corresponding to a rotation of 50.5° about the common [011] axis. (Courtesy of Ichinose and Ishida, 1981.)

It is evident that improved understanding of secondary relaxation mechanisms is necessary in order to fully characterize the structure of special grain boundaries. A step in this direction has recently been achieved through direct resolution of atomic structure of special grain boundaries by high-voltage, high-resolution TEM (Krivanek *et al.*, 1977; Ichinose *et al.*, 1978). A typical example of the detail achievable by such methods is presented in Fig. 15, wherein the structure of a $\Sigma = 11$, [110] tilt boundary in gold, produced by a rotation of 50.5° about the [110] axis, is pictured (Ichinose and Ishida, 1981). This boundary is characterized by a periodicity of 0.42 nm and by an atomic arrangement which does not deviate appreciably from that of the perfect crystal.

The relative energy of grain boundaries and their structure can be determined indirectly from the occurrence of facets, as mentioned previously in Section II. Using this technique, the first experimental observation of the CSL description was obtained (Brandon *et al.*, 1964). Since then, faceting has been observed in numerous metals and alloys (Sargent, 1968; Pumphrey, 1976; Goodhew *et al.*, 1976; Masteller and Bauer, 1978; Cosandey and Bauer, 1980). It is now generally recognized that boundaries characterized by small values of Σ and Γ possess lower energy, but, in general, there is no direct and obvious relationship between boundary energy and low periodicity (Hermann *et al.*, 1976; Masteller and Bauer, 1978). More recently, Cosandey and Bauer (1980) have shown that faceting of [001] tilt boundaries is better described by the O lattice, wherein low-energy boundaries contain the highest density of O lattice sites, which, in turn, correspond to the best atomic register between two crystals. Nevertheless, further research is necessary to fully elucidate the atomic structure and energy of grain boundaries. The principal limitation of all geometrical models arises from the fact that only coincident atoms, periodicity, or best atomic fit are considered, without regard to the exact atomic configuration of all atoms defining the grain boundary (Hermann *et al.*, 1976).

In spite of imperfect appreciation of grain boundary structure, significant advances have occurred during recent years, primarily through high-resolution TEM. Some of these advances include verification that the width of grain boundaries is limited to one or two atomic diameters, that primary relaxations occur between points of the O lattice for all grain boundaries, regardless of angles of misorientation and/or inclination, that secondary relaxations accommodate slight deviations from exact coincidence orientations, and that primary and secondary relaxations occur concurrently in grain boundaries close to coincidence orientations. Future advances not only depend on higher resolution of grain boundary structure but also on further development of capabilities to produce specimens containing grain boundaries with preselected angles of orientation and inclination. Some of these advances are suggested in Section VIII.

VII. Summary

This particular article has attempted to demonstrate that important engineering properties of materials are related to the presence of grain boundaries and, more importantly, to details of the atomic structure of these grain boundaries. Although such relationships obtain for all classes and sizes of crystalline materials, the relative importance of grain boundaries increases for the case of thin polycrystalline films, not only because slight modifications of structure often represent large fractional changes in properties, but also because the density of grain boundaries is generally larger in thin films. Accordingly, it is especially important to appreciate relationships between structure and properties of grain boundaries in such films. These factors will become even more important as thinner films with small lateral dimensions are utilized in rapidly advancing technological areas.

Given that properties and behavior of polycrystalline thin films are related to grain boundary structure, it is important to characterize such structure at the highest possible level of resolution. Therefore, a large fraction of this article has been devoted to methods of characterization of grain boundary structure in thin films and recent experimental results involving TEM and related techniques. Through such experiments, several purely geometrical concepts, such as the CSL, the O lattice, and grain boundary dislocations, have been verified by high-resolution TEM. Moreover, the concepts and descriptions developed herein may readily be applied to the study of interfaces separating dissimilar materials, such as interphase boundaries, epitaxial growth, and semicoherent systems, which are of great importance in the use of thin films for device applications.

VIII. Perspective

Over the past half century, the concept of a grain boundary has evolved dramatically—from an amorphous film several hundred angstroms in thickness, to a disordered structure several atomic diameters in thickness, to a structure characterized by significant order and periodicity for all angles of misorientation. Such improved understanding has primarily evolved from advanced experimental techniques, especially at increasingly higher levels of resolution. Therefore, it is only natural to anticipate further progress along these lines as the limits of resolution are extended. Indeed, new and exciting discoveries are virtually assured as the technology of high-resolution TEM and related techniques continue to advance. Indeed, the latest generation of microscopes are now equipped with x-ray and energy-loss spectrometers which allow quantitative chemical analysis at a very high level of resolution (~ 10 nm). Thus, TEM has evolved into an analytical technique as well as a technique for examination of microstructure at high levels of resolution.

Advancement of the state of the art might proceed along the following lines: First, highly perfect bicrystalline thin films must be produced with preselected angles of misorientation and inclination. These films can then be further characterized by high-resolution and lattice-image TEM in order to determine atomic positions accurately. Results may then be compared with those from computer modeling. Finally, the fine details of grain boundary structure may then be applied to predict properties of individual grain boundaries and, eventually, of polycrystalline aggregates. Results can also be extended to interfaces between dissimilar materials.

In the past decade, primarily due to advances in high-resolution TEM, appreciation of grain boundary structure has leapfrogged appreciation of grain boundary properties. In the next decade, it is anticipated that this lag will be diminished as high-resolution techniques and detailed knowledge of grain boundary structure are applied to such important subjects as segregation of impurities to grain boundaries, mass transport along grain boundaries, and precipitation at grain boundaries. Examination of highly perfect bicrystalline thin films, prepared under carefully controlled experimental conditions, will certainly play an important role in advancing the understanding of these and related topics.

Acknowledgments

The authors express appreciation to those colleagues who have furnished photographs for this article and to the National Science Foundation for partial support under Grant DMR76-11373.

References

Amelinckx, S. (1958). *Acta Metall.* **6**, 34.
Amelinckx, S., and Dekeyser, V. (1959). *Solid State Phys.* **8**, 325.
Baïlon, J.-P., Daniel, J. S., Dickson, J. I., and Dorlot, J.-M., eds. (1974). *Grain Boundaries, Metall. Inst. Q.* **13**.

Balluffi, R. W. (1968). *Phys. Status Solidi* **42**, 11.
Balluffi, R. W. (1979). *In* "Interfacial Segregation" (W. C. Johnson and J. M. B. Blakely, eds.), p. 193. American Society for Metals, Cleveland, Ohio.
Balluffi, R. W., and Blakely, J. M. (1975). *Thin Solid Films* **25**, 363.
Balluffi, R. W., Komem, Y., and Schober, T. (1972a). *Surf. Sci.* **31**, 68.
Balluffi, R. W., Sass, S. L., and Schober, T. (1972b). *Philos. Mag.* **26**, 585.
Balluffi, R. W., Goodhew, P. J., Tan, T. Y., and Wagner, W. R. (1975). *J. Phys.* **36**, C4-17.
Bauer, C. L. (1974). *Can. Metall. Q.* **13**, 303.
Bauer, C. L. (1975). *Proc. Bolton Landing Conf. Grain Boundaries Eng. Mat., 4th* p. 55.
Bauer, C. L., and Jordan, A. G. (1978). *Phy. Status Solidi* **A47**, 321.
Biscondi, M., and Goux, C. (1975). *J. Phys.* **C4**, 36.
Bishop, G. H., Hartt, W. H., and Bruggeman, G. A. (1971). *Acta Metall.* **19**, 36.
Bollmann, W. A. (1970). "Crystal Defects and Crystalline Interfaces." Springer-Verlag, Berlin and New York.
Bollmann, W. (1977). *Acta Cryst. A* **33**, 730.
Bollmann, W., Michaut, B., and Sainfort, G. (1972). *Phys. Status Solidi* **A13**, 637.
Boos, J. Y., and Goux, C. (1970). *C.R. Acad. Sci. Paris* **271**, 978.
Bourret, A., and Desseaux, Y. (1979). *Philos. Mag.* **A39**, 405.
Bourret, A., and D'Anterroches, C. (1979). *Proc. Annu. Meet. Electron Microsc. Soc. Am., 37th* p. 388.
Brandon, D. G. (1966). *Acta Metall.* **14**, 1479.
Brandon, D. G., Ralph, R., Ranganathan, S., and Wald, M. S. (1964). *Acta Metall.* **12**, 813.
Bristowe, P. D., and Crocker, A. G. (1978). *Philos. Mag.* **A38**, 487.
Brokman, A. (1981). *Acta Cryst.* **A37**, 500.
Budai, Y., Gaudig, W., and Sass, S. L. (1979). *Philos. Mag.* **A40**, 757.
Cahn, J. W., and Balluffi, R. W. (1980). *Acta Metall.* **29**, 493.
Carter, C. B., Donald, A. M., and Sass, S. L. (1979). *Philos. Mag.* **A39**, 533.
Carter, C. B., Donald, A. M., and Sass, S. L. (1980). *Philos. Mag.* **A41**, 467.
Chadwick, G. A., and Smith, D. A. (1976). "Grain Boundary Structure and Properties." Academic Press, New York.
Chaudhary, P., and Matthews, R. W., eds. (1972). *Proc. Int. Conf. Struct. Prop. Grain Boundaries Interf., Surf. Sci.* **31**.
Christian, J. W. (1975). "Theory of Transformation in Metals and Alloys," Part I, p. 350. Pergamon, Oxford.
Clark, W. A. T., and Smith, D. A. (1978). *Philos. Mag.* **A38**, 367.
Cockayne, D. J. H. (1973). *J. Microsc.* **98** (2), 116.
Cockayne, D. J. H., Ray, I. L. F., and Whelan, M. J. (1969). *Philos. Mag.* **20**, 1265.
Cockayne, D. J. H., Parsons, J. R., and Hoelke, C. W. (1971). *Philos. Mag.* **24**, 139.
Cosandey, F. (1978). PhD. thesis, Carnegie-Mellon University.
Cosandey, F., and Bauer, C. L. (1980). *Acta Metall.* **28**, 601.
Cosandey, F., and Bauer, C. L. (1981). *Philos. Mag.* **A44**, 391.
Cosandey, F., Kang, S. K., and Bauer, C. L. (1975). *J. Phys.* **36**, C4-367.
Cosandey, F., Komem, Y., and Bauer, C. L. (1978a). *Phys. Status Solidi* **A48**, 555.
Cosandey, F., Komem, Y., Bauer, C. L., and Carter, C. B. (1978b). *Scr. Metall.* **12**, 577.
Cosandey, F., Komem, Y., and Bauer, C. L. (1979). *Thin Solid Films* **59**, 165.
Cotterill, P., and Mould, P. R. (1976). "Recrystallization and Grain Growth in Metals." Surrey Univ. Press, London.
Cowley, J. M. (1975). "Diffraction Physics." North-Holland Publ., Amsterdam.
Cowley, J. M. (1976). *Annu. Rev. Mat. Sci.* **53**.
Darby, T. P., and Balluffi, R. W. (1977). *Philos. Mag.* **36**, 53.

Darby, T. P., Schindler, R., and Balluffi, R. W. (1978). *Philos. Mag.* **A37**, 245.

Dash, W. C. (1957). "Dislocations and Mechanical Properties of Crystals" (J. D. Fisher, W. G. Johnston, R. Thompson, and T. Vreeland, Jr., eds.). Wiley, New York.

DeHoff, R. T., and Rhines, F. N. (1968). "Quantitative Microscopy." McGraw-Hill, New York.

Desseaux, J., Renault, A., and Bourret, A. (1977). *Philos. Mag.* **35**, 357.

d'Heurle, F. M., and Ho, P. S. (1978). Thin Films—Interdiffusion and Reactions, p. 243. Wiley, New York.

Dingley, D. J., and Pond, R. C. (1979). *Acta Metall.* **27**, 667.

Edington, J. W. (1976). "Practical Electron Microscopy in Materials Science." Van Nostrand-Reinhold, Princeton, New Jersey.

Fisher, J. C., (1951). *J. Appl. Phys.* **22**, 74.

Föll, H., and Ast, D. G. (1978). *Proc. Int. Congr. Electron Microsc.*, *9th, Toronto* **1**, 418.

Föll, H., and Ast, D. G. (1979). *Philos. Mag.* **A40**, 589.

Föll, H., and Carter, C. B. (1979). *Philos. Mag.* **A40**, 497.

Forwood, C. T., and Humble, P. (1975). *Philos. Mag.* **31**, 1025.

Gaudig, W., and Sass, S. L. (1979). *Philos. Mag.* **A39**, 725.

Gervais, A., Tertian, L., Deschamps, Y., and Kokim, D. (1979). *Acta Metall.* **27**, 499.

Gjostein, N., and Rhines, R. N. (1959). *Acta Metall.* **7**, 319.

Gleiter, H., and Chalmers, B. (1971). *Philos. Mag.* **23**, 1541.

Gleiter, H., and Chalmers, B. (1972). *Prog. Mat. Sci.* **16**.

Goodhew, P. J., Darby, T. P., and Balluffi, R. W. (1976). *Scr. Metall.* **10**, 495.

Goodhew, P. J., Tan, T. Y., and Balluffi, R. W. (1978). *Acta Metall.* **26**, 557.

Goux, C. (1974). *Can. Metall. Q.* **13**, 9.

Grimmer, H., Bollmann, W., and Warrington, D. H. (1974). *Acta Cryst.* **A30**, 197.

Gronsky, R., and Furrer, P. (1981). *Metall. Trans.* **12A**, 121.

Guan, D. Y., and Sass, S. L. (1979). *Philos. Mag.* **A39**, 293.

Gupta, D., Campbell, D. R., and Ho, P. S. (1978). "Thin Films—Interdiffusion and Reactions." p. 161. Wiley, New York.

Haessner, F. (1978). "Recrystallization of Metallic Materials." Riederer-Verlag, Stuttgart.

Harrison, R. J., Bruggeman, G. A., and Bishop, G. H. (1976). *In* "Grain Boundary Structure and Properties, " (G. A. Chadwick and D. A. Smith, eds.), p. 45. Academic Press, New York.

Hartt, W. H., Bishop, G. H., and Bruggeman, G. A. (1974). *Acta. Metall.* **22**, 971.

Hasson, G., and Goux, C. (1971). *Scr. Metall.* **5**, 889.

Hermann, G., Gleiter, H., and Bäro, G. (1976). *Acta Metall.* **24**, 353.

Hirsch, P. B., Howie, A., Nicholson, R. B., Pashley, P. W., and Whelan, M. J. (1965). "Electron Microscopy of Thin Crystals." Butterworths, London.

Hoffman, R. (1956). *Acta Metall.* **4**, 97.

Hondros, E. D. (1976). *In* "Grain Boundary Structure and Properties" (G. A. Chadwick and D. A. Smith, eds.), p. 265. Academic Press, New York.

Horton, C. A. P., Silcock, G. M., and Kegg, G. R. (1974). *Phys. Status Solidi* **A26**, 215.

Howell, P. R., Jones, A. R., and Ralph, B. (1975). *J. Mat. Sci.* **10**, 1351.

Hwang, M., Laughlin, D. E., and Bernstein, I. M. (1980). *Acta Metall.* **28**, 621.

Ichinose, H., and Ishida, Y. (1978). *Proc. Int. Congr. Electron Microsc.*, *9th, Toronto* **1**, 412.

Ichinose, H., and Ishida, Y. (1981). *Philos. Mag.* **A43**, 1253.

Ingle, K. W., and Crocker, A. G. (1980). *Philos. Mag.* **42A**, 713.

Ishida, Y., and McLean, M. (1973). *Philos. Mag.* **27**, 1125.

Ishida, Y., and McLean, M. (1974). *Philos. Mag.* **30**, 453.

Ishida, Y., and Smith, D. A. (1974). *Scr. Metall.* **8**, 293.

Ishida, Y., Hasegawa, T., and Noyota, F. (1969). *J. Appl. Phys.* **40.**

Ishida, Y., Mori, M., and Iida, F. (1977). *Acta Metall.* **25,** 815.

Johnson, W. C., and Blakely, J. M., eds. (1979). "Interfacial Segregation." Am. Soc. for Metals, Metals Park, Pennsylvania.

Jones, A. R., Howell, P. R., and Ralph, B. (1976). *Phys. Status Solidi* **A33,** 107.

Joshi, A. (1979). *In* "Interfacial Segregation" (W. C. Johnson and J. M. Blakely, eds.). Am. Soc. for Metals, Metals Park, Pennsylvania.

Krivanek, O. L., Isoda, S., and Kobayashi, K. (1977). *Philos. Mag.* **36,** 931.

Kronberg, M. L., and Wilson, F. H. (1949). *Trans. AIME* **85,** 501.

Lagarde, P., and Biscondi, M. (1974). *Can. Metall. Q.* **13,** 245.

Le Coze, J., and Biscondi, M. (1974). *Can. Metall. Q.* **13,** 59.

Le Coze, J., Biscondi, M., and Goux, C. (1973). *C.R. Acad. Sci. Paris C* **276,** 479.

Levy, J. (1969). *Phys. Status Solidi* **31,** 193.

Loberg, B., and Norden, H. (1973). *Acta Metall.* **21,** 213.

Loberg, B., and Norden, H. (1976). *In* "Grain Boundary Structure and Properties" (G. A. Chadwick and D. A. Smith, eds.), p. 1. Academic Press, New York.

Love, G. R., and Shewmon, P. G. (1963). *Acta Metall.* **11,** 899.

Lücke, K. (1974). *Can. Metall. Q.* **13,** 261.

McLean, D. (1957). "Grain Boundaries in Metals." Claredon, Oxford.

Martin, G., and Perraillon, B. (1975). *J. Phys.* **36,** C4–165.

Martin, G., and Truchot, P. (1974). *Can. Metall. Q.* **13,** 111.

Masteller, M. S., and Bauer, C. L. (1978). *Philos. Mag.* **A38,** 697.

Masteller, M. S., and Bauer, C. L. (1979). *Acta. Metall.* **27,** 483.

Mayer, J. W., and Poate, J. M. (1978). *In* "Thin Films—Interdiffusion and Reactions" (J. M. Poate, K. N. Tu, and J. W. Mayer, eds.), p. 119. Wiley, New York.

Mori, M., and Ishida, Y. (1978). *Scr. Metall.* **12,** 11.

Murr, L. E. (1975). "Interfacial Phenomena in Metals and Alloys." Addison-Wesley, Reading, Massachusetts.

Poate, J. M., Tu, K. N., and Mayer, J. W. (1978). "Thin Films—Interdiffusion and Reactions. Wiley, New York.

Pond, R. C. (1977). *Proc. R. Soc. London A* **357,** 471.

Pond, R. C., and Smith, D. A. (1977). *Philos. Mag.* **26,** 353.

Pond, R. C., and Vitek, V. (1977). *Proc. R. Soc. London A* **357,** 543.

Pond, R. C., Smith, D. A., and Clark, W. A. T. (1974). *J. Microsc.* **102,** 309.

Pumphrey, P. H. (1972). *Scr. Metall.* **6,** 107.

Pumphrey, P. H. (1976). *In* "Grain Boundary Structure and Properties" (G. A. Chadwick and D. A. Smith, eds.), p. 139. Academic Press, New York.

Ranganathan, S. (1966). *Acta Cryst.* **21,** 197.

Read, W. T. (1953). "Dislocations in Crystals." McGraw-Hill, New York.

Read, W. T., and Shockley, W. (1950). *Phys. Rev.* **78,** 275.

Rey, C., and Saada, G. (1976). *Philos. Mag.* **33,** 825.

Saada, G. (1979). *Acta Metall.* **27,** 921.

Sargent, C. M. (1968). *Metall. Trans.* **242,** 1188.

Sass, S. L. (1980). *J. Appl. Crystallogr.* **13,** 109.

Sass, S. L., Tan, T. Y., and Balluffi, R. W. (1975). *Philos. Mag.* **31,** 559.

Schober, T., and Balluffi, R. W. (1969). *Philos. Mag.* **20,** 511.

Schober, T., and Balluffi, R. W. (1970). *Philos. Mag.* **21,** 109.

Schober, T., and Balluffi, R. W. (1971). *Phys. Status Solidi* **B44,** 103.

Smidoda, K., Gottschalk, W., and Gleiter, H. (1978). *Acta Metall.* **26,** 1833.

Smith, D. A., and Pond, R. C. (1976). *Int. Metall. Rev.* **205,** 161.

Smith, D. A., Vitek, V., and Pond, R. C. (1977). *Acta Metall.* **25,** 475.

Spence, J. C. H., O'Keefe, M. A., and Iijima, S. (1978). *Philos. Mag.* **A38,** 463.

Spence, J. C. H., and Kolar, H. (1979). *Philos. Mag.* **A39,** 59.

Sun, C. P., and Balluffi, R. W. (1979). *Scr. Metall.* **13,** 757.

Tan, T. Y., Sass, S. L., and Balluffi, R. W. (1975). *Philos. Mag.* **31,** 575.

Tan, T. Y., Hwang, J. C. M., Goodhew, P. J., and Balluffi, R. W. (1976). *Thin Solid Films* **33,** 1.

Tu, K. N., and Lau, S. S. (1978). *In* "Thin Films—Interdiffusion and Reactions" (J. M. Poate, K. N. Tu, and J. W. Mayer, eds.). Wiley, New York.

Van Der Voort, E., and Guyot, P. (1971). *Phys. Stat. Solidi* **B67,** 465.

Viswanathan, R., and Bauer, C. L. (1973). *Metall. Trans.* **4,** 2645.

Vogel, F. L., Pfann, W. G., Corey, H. E., and Thomas, E. E. (1953). *Phys. Rev.* **90,** 498.

Warrington, D. H., and Bollman, W. (1972). *Philos. Mag.* **25,** 1195.

Watler, J. L., Westbrook, J. H., and Woodford, D. A. (1975). *Proc. Bolton Landing Conf. Grain Boundaries Eng. Mat., 4th.*

Weins, M. J., and Weins, J. J. (1972). *Philos. Mag.* **26,** 885.

Whipple, R. T. P. (1954). *Philos. Mag.* **45,** 1225.

Yeager, W., and Gleiter, H. (1978). *Scr. Metall.* **12,** 675.

Yetter, W. E. (1980). Ph.D. thesis, Cornell University.

5

Mechanical Properties of Thin Films on Substrates

MASANORI MURAKAMI, TUNG-SHENG KUAN,

IBM Thomas J. Watson Research Center
Yorktown Heights, New York

and

ILAN A. BLECH

Department of Materials Engineering
Technion-Israel Institute of Technology
Haifa, Israel

I. Introduction

Thin films are widely used in modern miniaturized electronic devices. One of the major concerns with these devices is the mechanical stability of their thin films. The purpose of the present chapter is to review the up-to-date studies in the mechanical properties of thin films deposited onto rigid substrates. There are two kinds of stress (or strain) in thin films: one is *intrinsic* stress, which is observed in as-deposited films, and the other is *thermal* stress, which is introduced in films upon a temperature change after the film deposition is completed. Generally, the intrinsic stress is significantly large in films with high melting points and the thermal stress becomes important in films with low melting points. A review of intrinsic stress is not given here, to avoid duplication with a number of earlier articles on this topic (Hoffman, 1966, 1974; Campbell, 1966, 1970; Kinosita, 1972).

In this chapter we shall review the mechanical properties of thermally strained films. Throughout the discussion we will use illustrative data obtained from Pb and Pb-alloy thin films deposited onto Si substrates. From the theoretical and experimental viewpoints, Pb has the following advantages:

(a) Its physical parameters (e.g., coefficients of thermal expansion, diffusion and elastic constants) are known for a wide temperature range from the melting temperature down to liquid He temperature. These parameters are necessary for establishing theoretical models.

(b) Pb has a relatively large thermal expansion coefficient and large x-ray and electron scattering factors. Thus, it is possible to measure accurately the thermal strain values in extremely thin films by x-ray diffraction techniques.

(c) Pb films can be prepared with various grain sizes and film thicknesses. This makes it easy to sort out the effect of microstructure on the mechanical properties.

(d) Pb has a very low intrinsic stress in the as-deposited state and the effects of the intrinsic stress can be ignored.

(e) Pb-alloy films are currently used in experimental Josephson devices. Thus, the mechanical stability of Pb thin films reviewed here could be directly correlated with the device reliability.

Note that the studies on Pb films reviewed here can be extended to other metal films.

II. Biaxial Strain Model

When a thin film is deposited onto a rigid substrate at temperature T_1 and the temperature is then changed to T_2, a thermal strain (ϵ_{therm}) is introduced into the film. The ϵ_{therm} (parallel to the film surface) is given by

$$\epsilon_{\text{therm}} = \int_{T_2}^{T_1} (\alpha_{\text{film}} - \alpha_{\text{sub}}) \, dT \qquad (1)$$

where α_{film} and α_{sub} are the linear thermal expansion coefficients of the film and the substrate, respectively.

In a thin film bonded to a substrate, it is difficult to measure directly the elastic strain ϵ'_{11} (or ϵ'_{22}) parallel to the film surface. (The subscripts "ii" denote the directions of orthogonal axes: "11" and "22" are directions parallel to the film surface and "33" is the one normal to the film surface.) The strain ϵ'_{33} (normal to the film surface) is experimentally measurable by an x-ray diffraction technique, whereas the stresses σ'_{11} or σ'_{22} can be measured by the cantilever beam technique. The values of ϵ'_{33}, σ'_{11}, or σ'_{22} can be related to other strain or stress components by a so-called biaxial strain model. This model is briefly reviewed below. When the principal axes (ii) coincide with the $\langle 100 \rangle$ crystal directions, the strains ϵ_{ij} are related to the stresses σ_{ij} by

$$\epsilon_{ij} = S_{ijkl}\sigma_{kl} \qquad (2)$$

where the S_{ijkl} are the compliances calculated from the elastic constants, and i, j, k, and l are the integers 1, 2, or 3. For an arbitrary (hkl) oriented crystal Eq. (2) also holds, which becomes

$$\epsilon'_{ij} = S'_{ijkl}\sigma'_{kl} \qquad (3)$$

where the transformed compliance S'_{ijkl} is given by (Nye, 1972)

$$S'_{ijkl} = a_{im}a_{jn}a_{ko}a_{lp}S_{mnop}$$

The rotation matrix $a_{\theta\varphi}$ is written

$$a_{\theta\varphi} = \begin{pmatrix} \cos\varphi & -\sin\varphi & 0 \\ \cos\theta\sin\varphi & \cos\theta\cos\varphi & -\sin\theta \\ \sin\theta\sin\varphi & \sin\theta\cos\varphi & \cos\theta \end{pmatrix}$$

where φ and θ are rotation angles. To solve Eq. (3) for the strain in a thin film bonded to a substrate, six boundary conditions are required (Vook and Witt, 1965; Witt and Vook, 1968, 1969). Since the film is biaxially strained, $\epsilon'_{11} = \epsilon'_{22}$. The stresses acting on the film are applied at the film–substrate interface, and consequently all tensile and shear stress components in directions normal to the film surfaces are zero, which means that $\sigma'_{31} = \sigma'_{32} = \sigma'_{33} = 0$. Because the film is assumed to adhere rigidly to the substrate, $\epsilon'_{12} = 0$. Using these assumptions, all the necessary equations for relating the measured strain or stress components to unknown components can be rewritten as

$$\epsilon'_{11} = S'_{1111}\sigma'_{11} + S'_{1122}\sigma'_{22} + S'_{1112}\sigma'_{12} \tag{4a}$$

$$\epsilon'_{22} = S'_{2211}\sigma'_{11} + S'_{2222}\sigma'_{22} + S'_{2212}\sigma'_{12} \tag{4b}$$

$$\epsilon'_{12} = S'_{1211}\sigma'_{11} + S'_{1222}\sigma'_{22} + S'_{1212}\sigma'_{12} \tag{4c}$$

$$\epsilon'_{33} = S'_{3311}\sigma'_{11} + S'_{3322}\sigma'_{22} + S'_{3312}\sigma'_{12} \tag{4d}$$

Applying the conditions $\epsilon'_{11} = \epsilon'_{22}$ and $\epsilon'_{12} = 0$ to Eqs. (4a)–(4c), the stresses σ'_{12} and σ'_{22} can be expressed as a function of σ'_{11} by

$$\sigma'_{12} = \frac{f_2(S'_{ijkl})}{f_1(S'_{ijkl})}\, \sigma'_{11} \tag{5a}$$

$$\sigma'_{22} = \frac{f_3(S'_{ijkl})}{f_1(S'_{ijkl})}\, \sigma'_{11} \tag{5b}$$

where

$$f_1(S'_{ijkl}) = S'_{1112}S'_{1222} - S'_{1122}S'_{1212} + S'_{1212}S'_{2222} - (S'_{1222})^2$$

$$f_2(S'_{ijkl}) = -S'_{1111}S'_{1222} + S'_{1112}S'_{1122} - S'_{1112}S_{2222} + S'_{1122}S'_{1222}$$

$$f_3(S'_{ijkl}) = S'_{1111}S'_{1212} - (S'_{1112})^2 + S'_{1211}S'_{2212} - S'_{1212}S'_{2211}$$

Inserting Eqs. (5a) and (5b) into Eqs. (4), the strains ϵ'_{11} and ϵ'_{33} are also expressed as a function of σ'_{11} by

$$\epsilon'_{11} = \epsilon'_{22} = f_4(S'_{ijkl})\sigma'_{11} \tag{6a}$$

$$\epsilon'_{33} = f_5(S'_{ijkl})\sigma'_{11} \tag{6b}$$

where functions f_4 and f_5 can be derived from Eqs. (4) and (5). From Eqs. (5) and (6) it is clear that if one of the values ϵ'_{11}, ϵ'_{33}, σ'_{11}, or σ'_{22} is experimentally determined, the other values can be calculated for a biaxially strained film with any crystallographic orientation.

The relations given by Eqs. (5) and (6) are complicated because of the anisotropic character of the elastic constants. When a film has less anisotropy in elastic constants, the isotropic approximation is applicable to the film. In this case ϵ'_{11}, ϵ'_{33}, and σ'_{11} are given by

$$\epsilon'_{11} = \epsilon'_{22} = -[(1 - \nu)/2\nu]\epsilon'_{33} \tag{7a}$$

$$\sigma'_{11} = \sigma'_{22} = -(E/2\nu)\epsilon'_{33} \tag{7b}$$

where ν is Poisson's ratio and E is Young's modulus. It should be noted that the stress σ'_{11} or σ'_{22} has no crystal orientation dependence if the anisotropy in elastic constants is weak.

III. Strain Relaxation Mechanisms

When thermal strain is introduced into a metal film, the stress in the film can be relaxed by several deformation (or strain relaxation) mechanisms which may operate simultaneously. But the strain relaxation rate of each mechanism is different and strongly dependent on the applied stress and temperature. The dominant relaxation mechanism at a given temperature and applied stress is the one which has the fastest relaxation rate. Ashby (1972) and Frost and Ashby (1973) developed the idea of constructing deformation mechanism maps for bulk materials. The map predicts the dominant mechanism of plastic flow for a given condition.

It is useful to construct a map for a Pb thin film before we discuss the details of several strain relaxation mechanisms. Four possible strain relaxation mechanisms were taken into account for the calculations: dislocation glide, dislocation climb, Harper–Dorn creep, and diffusional creep. The constitutive equations and a review of the mechanisms were given by Frost and Ashby (1973). They treated steady-state flow of the bulk materials and related the tensile strain rate and the tensile stress. The equations used to calculate the relaxation rates of different mechanisms in thin films are reviewed below.

A. Defectless Flow

Under a sufficiently high stress, planes of atoms in the crystal can be lifted bodily over neighboring planes, producing permanent deformation. The value for the theoretical shear strength σ^{o}_{13} used here was $\mu/20$ (μ is the shear modulus), which is practically independent of temperature (Kocks *et al.*, 1974). Accordingly, the following constitutive relations are used:

$$\begin{aligned} \dot{\epsilon}_1 = \infty &\quad \text{for} \quad \sigma \geq \sigma_{TH} \\ \dot{\epsilon}_1 = 0 &\quad \text{for} \quad \sigma < \sigma_{TH} \end{aligned} \tag{8}$$

where $\dot{\epsilon}$ is the strain rate and σ_{TH} the tensile stress corresponding to the theoretical shear strength ($\sigma_{TH} = \sqrt{3}\sigma^{o}_{13}$).

B. Dislocation Glide

When the applied stress is reasonably high, dislocation glide is dominant in fcc and hcp crystals. The glide in these crystals is affected by the presence of obstacles such as impurities, solute atoms, other dislocations, or precipitates. For such crystals, the flow stress is proportional to $\mu b/l$, where l is the obstacle spacing and b is the Burgers vector. We adopt here the empirical law for the rate equation (Kocks *et al.*, 1974)

$$\dot{\epsilon}_2 = \dot{\epsilon}_0(\sigma/\sigma_0)^{\Delta F/kT}$$

where σ_0 is the flow stress at the absolute zero temperature, ΔF is the total free energy required to overcome the obstacles without any aid from external stresses and is taken to be $0.5\mu b^3$, k is Boltzmann's constant, and T is the absolute temperature.

C. Dislocation Climb

At temperatures above $0.3 T_m$ (T_m is the material's melting temperature) dislocations acquire a new degree of freedom: they can climb as well as glide. If a gliding dislocation is held up by discrete obstacles, a little climb may release it, allowing it to glide to the next set of obstacles where the process is repeated. The rate equation for this climb-controlled creep is given by (Frost and Ashby, 1973)

$$\dot{\epsilon}_3 = A_3(\mu b/kT)D_g(\sigma/\mu)^{n+2} \tag{9}$$

where A_3 and n are constants, and D_g is the grain boundary diffusion coefficient, which is given by $D_g = D_{0g} \exp(-Q_g/kT)$. At temperatures above $0.6 T_m$ climb is generally lattice diffusion-controlled. Thus, the above rate equation is rewritten as

$$\dot{\epsilon}_4 = A_4(\mu b/kT)D_l(\sigma/\mu)^n \tag{10}$$

where the volume diffusion coefficient D_l is given by $D_l = D_{0l} \cdot \exp(-Q_l/kT)$.

D. Harper–Dorn Creep

Based on experimental evidence that at sufficiently low stresses, dislocation creep operates with a strain rate linearly proportional to σ, the rate equation is given by

$$\dot{\epsilon}_5 = A_5(\mu b/kT)D_l(\sigma/\mu) \tag{11}$$

where A_5 is a constant. For bulk materials, Harper–Dorn creep rates would be much higher than those of either the dislocation creep or diffusion creep discussed below. However, for a thin film with small grain sizes, $\dot{\epsilon}_4$ and $\dot{\epsilon}_3$ are greater than $\dot{\epsilon}_5$.

E. Diffusional Creep

Diffusional flow of single atoms either by bulk (volume) transport or by grain boundary transport leads to the viscous creep of a polycrystal. When bulk diffusion dominates, the creep is called Nabarro–Herring creep ($\dot{\epsilon}_6$) (Nabarro, 1948; Herring, 1950); when boundary diffusion dominates, it is called Coble creep ($\dot{\epsilon}_7$) (Coble, 1963). (The details of the diffusional creep will be described in Section V.) The constitutive equations for thin films are given by (Gibbs, 1966)

$$\dot{\epsilon}_6 = A_6 \frac{\mu}{kT} \frac{\Omega}{gh} D_l\left(\frac{\sigma}{\mu}\right) \tag{12}$$

$$\dot{\epsilon}_7 = A_7 \frac{\mu}{kT} \Omega \frac{\delta}{gh^2} D_g\left(\frac{\sigma}{\mu}\right) \tag{13}$$

Here A_6 and A_7 are constants, g is the grain size, δ is the effective width of a boundary for diffusional transport ($\simeq 2b$), h is the film thickness, and Ω is the atomic volume ($\simeq 0.7b^3$).

F. Other Mechanisms

For thin films, strain relaxation by twinning, or by diffusion at the film surface or at the film–substrate interface (Chaudhari, 1974), may be important. Although twins have been observed in as-deposited Pb films (Matthews et al., 1977), twin formation does not appear to be an important strain relaxation mechanism upon cooling. Diffusion at the surface of Pb films considered here is also negligible due to the presence of a native oxide layer on the Pb. Diffusion at the film–substrate interface may be similarly restricted due to the reaction of the first layer of Pb atoms with O_2 remaining on the substrate surface after substrate cleaning in an oxygen glow discharge. In preparing the deformation mechanism map, it was assumed that negligible strain relaxation occurs by these processes.

G. Construction of Map

A deformation mechanism map calculated for a 0.5-μm-thick Pb film is shown in Fig. 1. The average grain size (g) of the film was measured

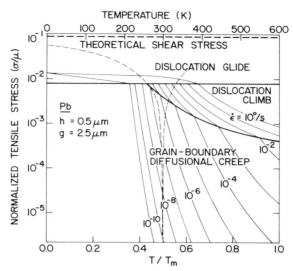

Fig. 1. A calculated deformation mechanism map for a Pb thin film with $h = 0.5$ μm and $g = 2.5$ μm. (After Murakami, 1978b.)

to be 2.5 μm, and the flow stress (σ_0) was calculated from the strain measured at 4.2 K to be 2×10^9 dyn/cm² (Murakami, 1978a).

In this map the dominant strain relaxation mechanism, i.e., the one with the greatest strain relaxation rate, at any given point in the normalized stress–temperature space, was determined using the rate equations (8)–(13). The boundaries between the fields of two different mechanisms were defined by equating the rate equations for the two dominant mechanisms and solving for stress as a function of temperature.

From this map, it is noted that the dislocation glide mechanism is dominant at high stress levels and that the grain boundary diffusional creep is dominant at low stress and at low temperature regions. The volume diffusional creep field which appears in the bulk material's deformation map at high temperatures (Ashby, 1972) does not appear in the present map. This is due to small grain sizes, which greatly increase the importance of grain boundary diffusional creep.

In this map, the expected tensile or compressive stress levels in a Pb thin film that is deposited onto a Si substrate at room temperature and then cooled down to 4.2 K or heated up to 400 K are plotted by dashed curves in Fig. 1. The tensile and compressive stresses are introduced into the film upon cooling and heating, respectively. The stress levels were calculated for a (111)-oriented film using Eqs. (1) and (6a), assuming that there is no strain relaxation occurring upon cooling or heating, i.e., $\epsilon'_{11} = \epsilon_{\text{therm}}$. It is noted that the strain relaxation mechanism with relaxation rate greater than 10^{-6} s^{-1} is predicted to be dislocation glide during the cooling process or diffusional creep during the heating process above room temperature. The details of these two mechanisms are described in the following sections.

IV. Strain Relaxation by Dislocation Glide

A. *Observation of Dislocations*

From the deformation mechanism map analysis, it was predicted that dislocation glide is the dominant strain relaxation mechanism in Pb thin films at temperatures below room temperature. The prediction was supported by scanning (Caswell *et al.*, 1963; Lahiri, 1975) and transmission electron microscopy (TEM) experiments in which surface steps or dislocations were observed during low-temperature thermal cycling.

Dislocation motion was observed *in situ* by TEM in a 0.2-μm-thick Pb film which was deposited at room temperature onto a Si_3N_4 substrate and then cooled to 100 K (Kuan and Murakami, 1982). The micrographs shown in Fig. 2a and b were taken from the same sample area at room temperature and at 100 K, respectively. It can be seen from Fig. 2 that the as-deposited Pb film contains very few dislocations at room temperature; however, upon cooling a high density of dislocations was introduced into the grains.

The observed dislocation behavior is shown schematically in Fig. 3. Some observations suggested that the dislocations emanate from grain boundaries and then glide across the grains during cooling on {111} planes that are either parallel or inclined to the film surface. All the dislocation motions are confined in each grain by the native surface oxide, the substrate, grain boundaries, and twin boundaries. These dislocations were observed only in grains with grain sizes larger than 0.6 μm. The dislocation density was not affected by the grain sizes and was measured to be ~10^{10} cm^{-2}. The observed dislocation density can account for the value of strain relaxation which was measured by the x-ray diffraction technique (Murakami, 1978a).

In the repeated-thermal-cycling experiments, most of the dislocation glide events were found to be reversible. Dislocations induced upon cooling disappeared during the heating period; and others appeared and moved on another set of glide planes during the next cooling process. Therefore, the dislocation density did not increase appreciably with the number of thermal cycles, which resulted in almost no work hardening following upon thermal cycling.

Fig. 2. Transmission electron micrographs for a 0.2-μm-thick Pb film at room temperature (a) and at 100 K (b). (After Kuan and Murakami, 1982.)

B.   Film Strength Models Using Dislocation Theory

Several models for thin film strength were developed based on dislocation theory. Thin films bonded to rigid substrates will usually support a higher strain than the bulk material. The tensile stress in Pb thin films at 4.2 K

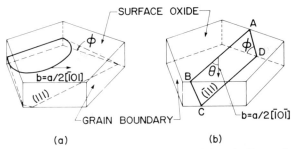

Fig. 3. Dislocation slip planes parallel (a) and inclined (b) to the film surface. (After Kuan and Murakami, 1982.)

was found to be close to the theoretical limit of the shear strength of Pb (Murakami, 1978a). In seeking an explanation of the observed high stress supported in the film, several thin-film strength models have been proposed. These models are reviewed below and we compare the stress levels predicted by the models and those obtained in the experiments.

1.   MODEL USING FORCE CRITERION

When stress is applied to a film, dislocations are generated and they glide to relax the stress. If the applied stress is smaller than the yield stress, the dislocations are pinned by obstacles. In thin films possible obstacles could be the film surface and the film–substrate interface when grain sizes are larger than the film thickness. A dislocation pinned at the film surface and at the interface is schematically shown in Fig. 4 with a force normal to the dislocation. Here, F_1 is the force applied on the dislocation slip plane along the slip direction and F_2 is the force arising from the dislocation line tension $T = \mu b^2/2$ (b is the Burgers vector and μ is the shear modulus of the film). F_1 is given by

$$F_1 = \sigma''_{31} b \, dS$$

where σ''_{31} is the resolved shear stress and dS is the segment of the dislocation line. F_2 is given by

$$F_2 = 2T\alpha \sin(d\theta/2) \simeq 2T\alpha(d\theta/2) = \mu b^2 \alpha(dS/h)$$

where h is the film thickness and α is given by $\cos \theta_0$ (θ_0 is the angle between the dislocation glide direction and the tangent to the dislocation line at the obstacle). When the two forces are balanced $F_1 = F_2$. Thus, the minimum resolved shear stress σ''_{31} (on the dislocation slip plane along the slip direction) required to propagate the dislocation is given by

$$\sigma''_{31} = \alpha\mu b/h \qquad (14)$$

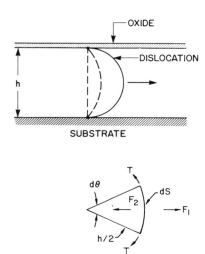

Fig. 4. Schematic illustration of a dislocation line pinned at the film surface and at the film–substrate interface.

The measured stress levels supported by the Pb films are larger than the yield stress values predicted by Eq. (14) by a factor of 3–4 (Murakami, 1979). The same discrepancy was also found in other metal films not attached to a substrate (Hoffman, 1966). Equation (14) could fit the experimental data by assuming a pinning distance shorter than h (Menter and Pashley, 1959). However, no pinning obstacles separated by distances shorter than h were observed in the *in situ* TEM experiment (Kuan and Murakami, 1982). Also the yield stress in Pb films was found to have a strong grain size dependence which Eq. (14) failed to describe. The most obvious shortcoming of Eq. (14) is that it ignores the difference in dislocation line tension resulting from the different shear moduli of the oxide and the substrate.

2. Model Using Work Hardening Effect

Ronay (1979) developed a strength model using existing work hardening theory to explain the high yield strength (σ_F) of Pb thin films. In this model the main obstacle to dislocation motion was considered to be the stress field of other dislocations. The stress field of arrays of dislocations is given by $\sigma_F = \alpha \mu b \rho^{1/2}$, where α is a dimensionless constant whose value ranges from $\frac{1}{2}\pi$ to 1 and ρ is the dislocation density. This model assumes that the films are nonuniformly strained and that the high tensile stress observed in thin films bonded to substrates is due to increases in the (geometrically necessary) dislocation density (Cottrell, 1964) in thin films. The density is directly related to the gradients of plastic shear strain $\Delta\epsilon$ (Kroner, 1961). In the case of a gradient of slip in the x direction on a single slip system, the density of the geometrically necessary dislocations is given by

$$\rho^G = \frac{1}{b}\frac{\partial\Delta\epsilon}{\partial x}$$

In a thin film, if the strain is assumed to be completely relaxed at the film surface and grain boundaries, the gradient of $\Delta\epsilon$ is very large along directions both parallel and normal to the film surface, because the film thickness and grain size are very small.

This model assumes that the moving dislocations in the film have to overcome (1) the Peierls stress (σ_s), (2) the long-range stress field of geometrically necessary dislocations at the interface (σ_{GLR}), and (3) the short-range stress from geometrically necessary dislocations gliding on the intersecting slip systems (σ_{GSR}). The long-range stress field of geometrically necessary dislocations at the film–substrate interface is given by $\sigma_{GLR} = (1/\pi)\mu(b\epsilon/sh)^{1/2}$, where $s = \sin\theta$ (θ is the angle between dislocation slip plane and film surface).

If grain boundaries are regarded as obstacles to slip, the nonuniform deformation can be described in terms of gradients of slip with a wavelength equal to the grain size g. Deformation of a grain bonded to a substrate requires multiple slip. In multiple slip, dislocations move on intersecting slip systems and their crossing involves the formation of jogs, which requires additional stress. The applied stress necessary to overcome the short-range interactions between crossing dislocations is given by $\sigma_{GSR} = m\mu(2b\epsilon/g)^{1/2}$, where m is the Taylor orientation factor (Taylor, 1938). The yield stress is given by the sum of all the stress fields that dislocations have to overcome:

$$\sigma_y = \sigma_s + \frac{1}{\pi}\mu\left(\frac{b\epsilon}{sh}\right)^{1/2} + m\mu\left(\frac{2b\epsilon}{g}\right)^{1/2} \tag{15}$$

The yield stress σ_y is schematically plotted in Fig. 5 as a function of film thickness h for a given grain size g. The dashed horizontal line σ_T, is the maximum thermal shear stress σ_T introduced in the film upon cooling from 300 to 4.2 K, which was calculated using a strain value given by Eq. (1) (Murakami and Chaudhari, 1977). When $\sigma_y \geq \sigma_T$, or $h \leq h_c$, the film would support the maximum strain, and when $\sigma_y < \sigma_T$, or $h > h_c$, the film could be plastically deformed. Here, h_c is the critical thickness which is obtained by equating Eq. (15) to σ_T for a given g. A good agreement in the h_c values between theory and experiment was obtained for Pb films cooled from 300 to 4.2 K. However, the subsequent TEM results described above show that several assumptions used in this model are not justified for Pb films.

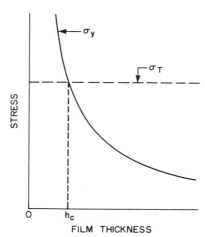

Fig. 5. Dependence of yield stress on film thickness at constant grain size. (After Ronay, 1979.)

For example, the geometrically necessary dislocations, whose density was assumed to be ~0.8×10^{10} cm^{-2} for $h = 0.2$ μm were not observed by TEM. Also, the assumed sharp strain gradient normal to the film surface was not found in the x-ray diffraction line broadening measurements (Murakami, 1978a).

3. MODEL USING ENERGY CRITERION

For a film deposited onto a substrate with different lattice spacing, misfit dislocations could result at the film–substrate interface when the film is thicker than a critical thickness. The critical thickness below which no misfit dislocations are present at the interface can be predicted by minimizing the total energy of the film with respect to the elastic strain. The total energy is the sum of elastic strain and misfit dislocation energies (Cherns and Stowell, 1976; Matthews, 1975).

Based on similar energy criterion considerations, Chaudhari (1979) developed a model to calculate the maximum elastic strain ϵ that can be supported in thin films bonded to the substrates. The model assumes that dislocations are generated in response to the uniform elastic strain. Following this approach, a more detailed evaluation of the yield stress of Pb films was recently carried out based on the dislocation behavior and density observed by TEM (Kuan and Murakami, 1982).

The total energy E of the film bonded to a substrate can be divided, for convenience, into two parts: $E = E_{\text{elast}} + E'_{\text{disloc}}$, where E_{elast} is the energy associated with a uniform elastic strain and E'_{disloc} is the energy of the dislocation strain field. These energies are considered in a rectangular volume of a grain of size g and thickness h, as shown in Fig. 6.

Assuming N dislocations have glided across the grain and relaxed the thermal strain level from ϵ_{therm} to an average level ϵ, the E_{elast} term is given by $E_{\text{elast}} = \frac{1}{2} Y\epsilon^2 g^2 h$, where Y is the Young modulus of the film. The energy E'_{disloc} is given by $E'_{\text{disloc}} = E_{\text{disloc}} N$, where E_{disloc} is the energy associated with each dislocation or dislocation loop present in the film (e.g., dislocation ABCD in Fig. 6).

If the film is not bonded to a substrate, the amount of strain each dislocation can relax is $\Delta\epsilon = b'/g$, where b' is the projection of the edge component of the Burgers vector on the film surface. For a film bonded to a rigid substrate, the determination of $\Delta\epsilon$ for each dislocation that glided to the film–substrate interface is much more complicated. If there is no strain relaxation at the interface except at the dislocation core region, we might expect that the amount of strain relaxed attains a maximum close to the dislocation and decreases as we move further away from the dislocation. The resultant $\Delta\epsilon$ for each dislocation could be approximated by $\Delta\epsilon = \bar{f} b'/g$, where the parameter $\bar{f}$ is the average displacement in units of the Burgers vector. The value of $\bar{f}$ ranges from 0 to 1 and is expected be a function of boundary conditions at the interfaces, the film thickness, elastic constants of the film and the substrate, and the dislocation density.

The number of dislocations is related to the strain by

$$N = (\epsilon_{\text{therm}} - \epsilon)/\Delta\epsilon = g(\epsilon_{\text{therm}} - \epsilon)/\bar{f} b'$$

Thus, the total energy E is expressed by

$$E = \frac{1}{2} Y\epsilon^2 g^2 h + \frac{(\epsilon_{\text{therm}} - \epsilon)}{b'\bar{f}} E_{\text{disloc}} g$$

$$= \frac{1}{2} Yg^2 h\left(\epsilon - \frac{E_{\text{disloc}}}{b'Y\bar{f}gh}\right)^2 + \frac{\epsilon_{\text{therm}} E_{\text{disloc}} g}{b'\bar{f}} - \frac{E_{\text{disloc}}^2}{2b'^2 Y\bar{f}^2 h}$$

In Fig. 7, E, E'_{disloc}, and E_{elast} are schematically shown as a function of ϵ.

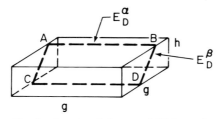

Fig. 6. A grain of size g and thickness h.

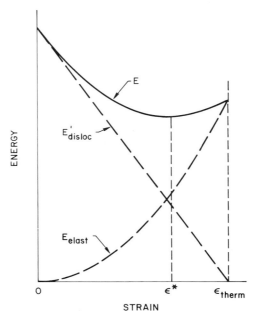

Fig. 7. Schematic illustration of energies E, E_{elast}, and E'_{disloc} as a function of elastic strain.

The strain ϵ^* at which E is at a minimum is given by

$$\epsilon^* = E_{\text{disloc}}/b'Y\bar{f}gh \tag{16a}$$

Equation (16a) means that when the energy associated with the dislocations is large, the deformation by dislocation glide is not favorable and, thus, the film can support higher strain elastically.

When the energy E_{disloc} represents the energies of the dislocation loop ABCD as shown in Fig. 6, E_{disloc} depends on the loop size, i.e., on grain size g and film thickness h. The energy E_{disloc} could be divided into two parts that are associated with dislocation pairs AB–CD and AC–BD, respectively, if the interaction energy between these two dislocation pairs is negligible. Then the energy E_{disloc} is expressed by

$$E_{\text{disloc}} \simeq E_{\text{D}}^{\alpha}g + E_{\text{D}}^{\beta}h$$

where E_{D}^{α} and E_{D}^{β} are energies per unit length of dislocation pairs AB–CD and AC–BD, respectively. Equation (16a) can be rewritten as

$$\epsilon^* \simeq \frac{1}{b'Y\bar{f}}\left(\frac{E_{\text{D}}^{\alpha}}{h} + \frac{E_{\text{D}}^{\beta}}{g}\right) \tag{16b}$$

For a film with $g \gg h$,

$$\epsilon^* \simeq E_D^\alpha / b' Y \bar{f} h \tag{17a}$$

and for a film with $g \ll h$,

$$\epsilon^* \simeq E_D^\beta / b' Y \bar{f} g \tag{17b}$$

The detailed calculation of E_D^α is described below, where we estimate the ϵ^* value supported in a film with $g \gg h$. In order to show the effects of surface oxide and substrate on the energy of dislocation, the calculation of E_D^α was carried out for the following different cases shown in Fig. 8: (a) a film without surface oxide on a substrate with the same shear modulus; (b) a film without surface oxide on a substrate with different shear modulus; (c) a film covered with a surface oxide layer on a substrate which has different shear modulus.

a. *Case (a).* Without a surface oxide layer, the dislocation segment AB at the film surface (a surface step) would have zero strain energy. All we have to consider is the energy of segment CD. Since the substrate is assumed to have the same shear modulus as the film, the line tension of the segment CD at distance h beneath the surface is given by (Hirth and

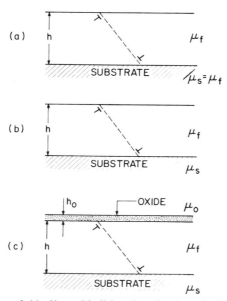

Fig. 8. Cross section of thin films with dislocation slip planes inclined to the film surface: (a) a film on a substrate with $\mu_s = \mu_f$, (b) a film bonded to the substrate with $\mu_s \neq \mu_f$, and (c) a film with surface oxide layer bonded to the substrate.

Lothe, 1968)

$$E_{\mathrm{D}}^{\alpha} = \frac{\mu_{\mathrm{f}} b^2}{4\pi} \left(\frac{1 - \nu \cos^2 \theta}{1 - \nu} \right) \ln \frac{\alpha h}{b}$$

where μ_{f} is the shear modulus of the film (and of the substrate), α is a constant ~ 2, θ is the angle between the dislocation line and the Burgers vector, and ν is Poisson's ratio.

b. Case (b). When the substrate and the film have different shear moduli, the strain energy of dislocation CD at the interface is modified to (Matthews, 1975)

$$E_{\mathrm{D}}^{\alpha} = \frac{\mu_{\mathrm{f}} b^2}{4\pi} (1 + k_{\mathrm{s}}) \left(\frac{1 - \nu \cos^2 \theta}{1 - \nu} \right) \ln \frac{\alpha h}{b}$$

where $k_{\mathrm{s}} = (\mu_{\mathrm{s}} - \mu_{\mathrm{f}})/(\mu_{\mathrm{s}} + \mu_{\mathrm{f}})$, and μ_{s} and μ_{f} are the shear moduli of the substrate and the film, respectively. The correction factor $1 + k_{\mathrm{s}}$ is plotted versus $\mu_{\mathrm{s}}/\mu_{\mathrm{f}}$ in Fig. 9. Here, it is seen that for a substrate with large shear modulus the energy of dislocation can increase to twice that of case (a) where μ_{s} is equal to μ_{f}.

c. Case (c). For a film covered with an oxide layer, the dislocation segment AB in Fig. 6 is pinned very close to the film–oxide interface (Head, 1953). To evaluate E_{D}^{α}, we have to include the self-energies and the interaction energy of the segments AB and CD. This can be calculated approximately by considering the total work done if we produce AB and

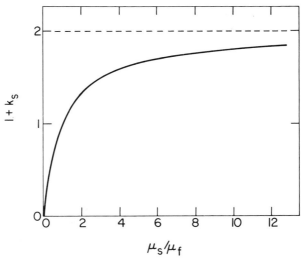

Fig. 9. Plot of $(1 + k_{\mathrm{s}})$ versus $\mu_{\mathrm{s}}/\mu_{\mathrm{f}}$.

TABLE I

STRENGTH AND POSITION OF IMAGES OF A
DISLOCATION AT DISTANCE x FROM FILM–OXIDE
INTERFACE DUE TO PRESENCE OF FILM–SUBSTRATE
INTERFACE, FREE SURFACE, AND FILM–OXIDE
INTERFACE

Position of images	Strength
$2h - x$	k_s
$-x$	k_o
$-(x + 2h_o)$	$-(1 - k_o^2)$
$-(x + 4h_o)$	$-(1 - k_o^2)k_o$
$-(x + 6h_o)$	$-(1 - k_o^2)k_o^2$
$-(x + 8h_o)$	$-(1 - k_o^2)k_o^3$
etc.	etc.

CD, each with opposite Burgers vectors, at the film–oxide interface, and then move CD against the interaction forces from AB and all the images to the film–substrate interface. This work is approximately equal to the total strain energy introduced by the presence of AB and CD at the two interfaces. (The extra stresses for the edge component due to the interface other than the images' stresses are ignored in the approximation.) The strength and position of the images of a dislocation at distance x from the film–oxide interface due to the presence of the film–substrate interface, the free surface (of the oxide layer), and the film–oxide interface are listed in Table I (Head, 1953). The images of images are not included here since their strengths are weaker and they are farther away from the film, and thus their energy contribution can be ignored without inducing any significant error. By integration of all the interaction forces from $x = b/\alpha$ to $x = h$, we can obtain the total energy of the dislocation pair AB and CD as

$$
E_D^\alpha = \frac{\mu_f b^2}{4\pi} \left(\frac{1 - \nu \cos^2 \theta}{1 - \nu} \right) \left\{ (k_s + k_o + 2)\ln \frac{\alpha h}{b} - 2k_s \ln 2 \right.
$$
$$
+ (1 - k_o^2)\left[\ln \frac{h + h_o}{h_o} + (k_o - 2) \ln \frac{h + 2h_o}{2h_o} \right.
$$
$$
\left. \left. + k_o^2 \ln \frac{h + 3h_o}{3h_o} + (k_o^3 - 2k_o) \ln \frac{h + 4h_o}{4h_o} + \cdots \right] \right\}
$$

where $k_o = (\mu_o - \mu_f)/(\mu_o + \mu_f)$, μ_o is the shear modulus of the oxide layer, and h_o is the thickness of the oxide layer.

Using a Pb film on a Si substrate as an example, the critical strain ϵ^*, under which the film starts to yield, was calculated for the above three cases. By comparing the strains in different cases, we can comprehend the effects of the surface oxide and the substrate on the yield strength of the film. The calculation assumes large grain size [Eq. (17a)] and uses $\mu_f = 1.36 \times 10^{11}$ dyn/cm^2 for Pb film [evaluated from the elastic constants listed in Waldorf and Alers (1962), using the Voigt average], $\mu_s = \mu_o = 6.4 \times 10^{11}$ dyn/cm^2, $\nu_{Pb} = 0.376$, $b' = b/2\sqrt{3}$, $b = 0.35$ nm, $h_o = 5$ nm, $\theta = 60°$, and $f = 0.6$. In case (c) 26 images were included, and the error caused by omitting higher-order images was estimated to be less than 0.3%.

These calculated strains were compared with the residual elastic strain measured in Pb films which were deposited on the Si substrates at room temperature and then cooled to 4.2 K (Fig. 10). These Pb films were deposited at a thickness of 1.0 μm at room temperature and then sputter-etch-thinned to various thicknesses down to 0.1 μm, so that they all have the same average large grain size ($\sim$4.5 μm). The calculated ϵ^* values for the case (c) are very close to the experimental data, suggesting that the rigid substrate and the surface oxide contribute significantly to the strength of the film.

In this model the energy criterion used is the necessary condition for dislocation glide to occur. The total reduction of the thermal strain energy due to the dislocation glide should be larger or at least equal to the total energy of the dislocation strain field. No consideration is taken of the energy to nucleate the dislocations or to propagate them across the grain.

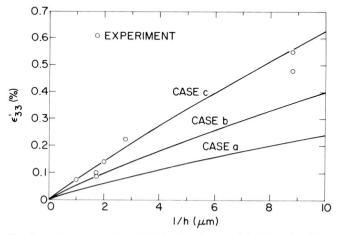

Fig. 10. Elastic strains supported at 4.2 K in films in cases (a), (b), or (c). The open circles are experimentally measured strain values. (After Kuan and Murakami, 1982.)

The details of the dislocation nucleation mechanism and the effects of grain size still remain to be explored.

C. Resolved Shear Stress in Biaxially Strained Thin Films

In polycrystalline films each individual grain has its specific crystal orientation. Dislocations slip only on particular sets of planes along certain directions. Thus, although each grain is subject to equal amounts of stress, some grains are expected to deform more preferably by dislocation glide than others.

The dislocation slip system is determined by the crystal structure. For fcc metals the slip system is the $\{111\}$ plane and the $\langle 110 \rangle$ direction. The resolved shear stress on the glide plane and in the slip direction produces a force on the dislocation. Thus, among all the glide planes and slip directions the one with the greatest resolved shear stress acting upon it will predominate in the slip process.

The resolved shear stress σ''_{31} along a specific slip direction $[\bar{1}10]$ on a (111) slip plane can be calculated from the component of the stress tensor σ'_{kl} using

$$\sigma''_{31} = r_{3k} r_{1l} \sigma'_{kl}$$

where r_{ij} is the rotation matrix element which depends on the crystal orientations, and the subscripts ij denote the directions of the orthogonal axes described in Section II.

Since the σ''_{31} value of a crystal with its surface plane parallel to (hkl) depends on the orientation of the two orthogonal axes on the (hkl) plane, the maximum σ''_{31} value can be determined by rotating these two axes around the axis normal to the (hkl) plane. The maximum value was plotted on the stereographic projection normal to the (111) glide plane and with the $[\bar{1}10]$ glide direction at the north pole (Fig. 11) (Murakami and Chaudhari, 1977). The slight shift toward the left side of the equicontour curves in Fig. 11 is due to the anisotropic character of the elastic constants of Pb. From the contour diagram the maximum σ''_{31} values are expected for grains whose surface planes are close to (011) or $(\bar{1}33)$. The low index planes $(\bar{1}11)$ and $(\bar{1}31)$ also have high σ''_{31} values. Thus, dislocation slip should occur first for $(\bar{1}33)$- or (011)-oriented grains and then for $(\bar{1}11)$- or $(\bar{1}31)$-oriented grains in biaxially strained polycrystalline films. The amount of strain relaxed (i.e., plastic strain) should also decrease with decreasing σ''_{31}, i.e., in the order of grain orientation: $\{110\} \approx \{331\} > \{111\} \approx \{311\}$.

Experimentally we can obtain a measure of the amount of plastic strain by defining a quantity $R = (\epsilon_{33}^{max} - \epsilon_{33})/\epsilon_{33}^{max}$, where ϵ_{33}^{max} is the maximum

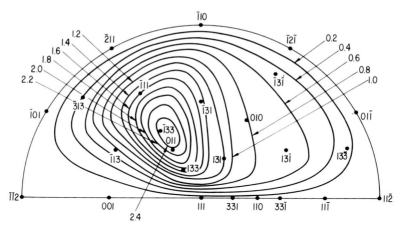

Fig. 11. A stereographic projection of equicontour curves of the resolved shear stresses σ''_{31} (10^9 dyn/cm^2). (After Murakami and Chaudhari, 1977.)

strain and ϵ'_{33} is the measured strain value. When $R = 0$, there is no plastic strain. This corresponds to the case for films with thickness of 0.1 or 0.2 μm. The R values for these thicknesses obtained at 4.2 K are given in Table II and are seen to be very small, as expected. When $R = 1$ (i.e., $\epsilon'_{33} \to 0$), the elastic strain in the film has relaxed entirely. Close to the elastic limit, R should correlate with σ''_{31}. As can be seen from the data in Table II, the experimental values of R at 150 K for the 0.5-μm-thick film decrease in the order $\{220\} \approx \{331\} > \{333\} \approx \{311\}$. This is in good qualitative agreement with the decreasing order of σ''_{31}. As the total strain is increased by going to lower temperatures, the agreement no longer holds; for example, at 4.2 K the decreasing order of $R(h = 0.5\ \mu\text{m})$ is $\{333\} > \{220\} \approx \{331\} > \{311\}$. This is believed to be due to the increasing importance of dislocation–dislocation interaction and possible operation of multiple slip

TABLE II

THE PARAMETERS $R = (\epsilon_{33}^{\max} - \epsilon'_{33})/\epsilon_{33}^{\max}$ AT 4.2 OR 150 K

(hkl)	$h = 0.1\ \mu\text{m}$ $T = 4.2$ K	$h = 0.2\ \mu\text{m}$ $T = 4.2$ K	$h = 0.5\ \mu\text{m}$ $T = 150$ K	$h = 0.5\ \mu\text{m}$ $T = 4.2$ K
(200)	—[a]	—[a]	—[a]	—[a]
(220)	−0.11	0.07	0.70	0.39
(311)	−0.11	−0.15	0.33	0.27
(331)	0.06	0.03	0.66	0.38
(333)	0.03	0.07	0.43	0.76

[a] Measurements could not be obtained due to interference by a Si x-ray diffraction peak.

systems when the applied stresses significantly exceed the critical resolved shear stress.

The result indicates that in polycrystalline films, the amount of strain supported elastically in each grain depends on the crystal orientation. The local deformation causes the strain nonuniformity in the film, which may produce mass flow from the strained to nonstrained regions.

V. Strain Relaxation by Diffusional Creep

As predicted and briefly explained in the deformation mechanism map of Pb thin films (Fig. 1), the strain could be relaxed by diffusional creep when a stress lower than the yield point is applied to films at temperatures above room temperature. Theories for diffusional creep have been established for bulk materials. As discussed below, these theories can be extended to explain the strain relaxation data obtained from thin films. Using these theories, it is also possible to obtain the diffusion coefficients from measurements of the strain relaxation rate.

A. Diffusional Creep Models

Diffusional creep in bulk materials relies on the redistribution of local vacancy concentrations in regions close to grain boundaries which are subject to stresses. When a compressive stress is applied to a bulk material, the vacancy concentration at grain boundaries normal to the stress direction decreases and the concentration at boundaries parallel to the stress direction increases. The local vacancy concentration difference between tensile and compressive grain boundaries is given by $\Delta C = 2C_0\sigma\Omega/kT$, where C_0 is the equilibrium vacancy concentration, σ is the applied stress, and Ω is the atomic volume. This concentration difference exists over a distance approximately equal to the grain size g. The resulting vacancy flux driven by the concentration gradient ($\Delta C/g$) leads to atomic flow as shown in Fig. 12. The corresponding creep rate $\dot{\epsilon}$ is related to the vacancy flux by

$$\dot{\epsilon} = A'_6\sigma\Omega D_l/g^2kT \qquad (18)$$

where A'_6 is a numerical constant depending on grain geometry and D_l is the volume diffusion coefficient. This equation, originally derived independently by Nabarro (1948) and Herring (1950), is called the Nabarro–Herring diffusional creep equation.

In this theory, diffusion was considered to occur only through the lattice.

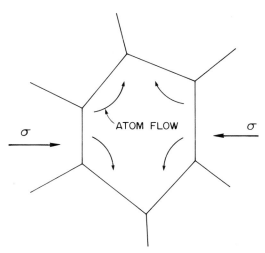

Fig. 12. Atom flows inside a grain of bulk material when the stress σ is applied.

However, material can also diffuse along grain boundaries. The diffusional creep contributed by this process was first recognized by Coble (1963), and the creep rate was given by

$$\dot{\epsilon} = A'_7 \sigma \Omega \delta D_g / g^3 kT \tag{19}$$

where δ is the grain boundary width, D_g is the grain boundary diffusion coefficient, and A'_7 is a constant. The main differences between the two creep equations (18) and (19) are the grain size dependence and the magnitude of the diffusion coefficients.

In Pb thin films, grain sizes usually are larger than the film thickness and the grains are columnar. When the film is under compression in the planar direction, the atoms flow from the grain boundaries to the film surface or to the film–substrate interface. The atom flows through the grain and along the grain boundaries are shown schematically in Fig. 13. The creep rate equations for thin films were first derived by Gibbs (1966). When the volume diffusion predominates, the creep rate analogous to Eq. (18) is given by Eq. (12), and when the grain boundary diffusion predominates, the creep rate equation analogous to Eq. (19) is given by Eq. (13).

B. Experimental Evidence to Support Diffusional Creep

When a Pb thin film was isothermally annealed at temperatures above room temperature, the thermal strain induced into the film was found to

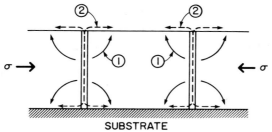

Fig. 13. Atom flows in a thin film under compressive stress σ through grains (1) or grain boundaries (2). (After Murakami and Kuan, 1980.)

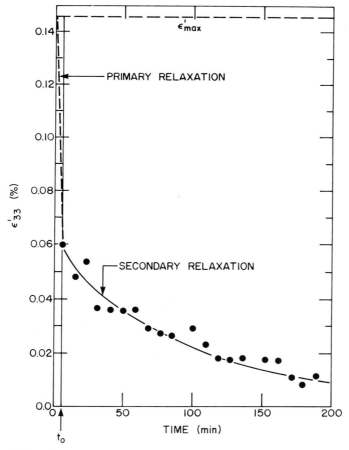

Fig. 14. Strain changes during isothermal annealing for a 0.2-μm-thick Pb film which was deposited at 298 K and then annealed at 350 K.

be relaxed at two distinguishable rates. A typical strain relaxation process is shown in Fig. 14 for a Pb thin film which was deposited at room temperature and then isothermally annealed at 350 K. The strains denoted by closed circles were measured by an x-ray diffraction technique. The maximum strain value ϵ'_{max} was calculated to be 0.146% when no strain relaxation was assumed upon heating. In Fig. 14 it is found that the strain was relaxed very quickly from ϵ'_{max} to 0.06% upon heating (primary relaxation process) and then relaxed at a much slower rate (secondary relaxation process) to the near-zero strain level.

If the relaxation process is diffusion-controlled, then we could determine the diffusion coefficient D from the measured strain relaxation rate. Before doing that, we must first identify the mechanisms behind the two relaxation processes.

1. PRIMARY STRAIN RELAXATION PROCESS

Since the rate of the primary relaxation process was extremely fast, the accurate rate could not be measured experimentally. When Pb or Pb-alloy films on the Si substrates are heated above room temperature, the films are under compressive stress. Excess atoms can diffuse from grain boundaries or from inside the grains to the stress free film surface to form hillocks. The hillock formation is observed in compressively stressed Pb films (Caswell *et al.*, 1963; Lahiri and Wells, 1969; Lahiri, 1970; Chaudhari, 1969, 1974; Ronay and Aliotta, 1980). In addition, when the annealing temperature is above the recrystallization temperature, grain growth can occur (Chaudhari, 1971; Murakami and Kuan, 1980).

An interesting SEM observation of hillocks was carried out by H.-C. W. Huang *et al.* (personal communication). They determined D values by measuring the growth rates of hillocks. A Pb-alloy film patterned into a line geometry was deposited onto Si substrate, and then a 0.2-μm-thick SiO was coated on the film, but leaving a hole at the center uncovered, as shown schematically in Fig. 15. When the sample was heated to 350

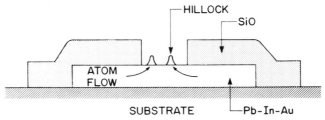

Fig. 15. Atom flows toward an opening in a film coated by a SiO layer.

K, the Pb alloy under the SiO coating was compressed and diffused toward the nearly stressfree window to form hillocks. The hillock volume was measured as a function of time by SEM during isothermal annealing at different temperatures. The hillock volume V was related to the diffusion coefficient D using the thin-slab diffusion equation (Shewmon, 1963)

$$V = \frac{8L\sigma_0}{D\pi^2} \sum_{n=0}^{\infty} \frac{1}{(2n + 1)^2} \left[1 - \exp \frac{-(2n + 1)^2 D\pi^2 t}{4L^2}\right]$$

where σ_0 is the stress at $t = 0$ and L is the length of the Pb film stripe. By using a trial-and-error technique, the D value was determined by fitting the calculated and experimental curves in V versus t plots. The D values determined were found to be close to the grain boundary diffusion coefficients. Thus, the excess atoms are believed to diffuse through grain boundaries to form hillocks. This is part of the evidence which leads to the conclusion that the primary strain relaxation mechanism in Fig. 14 is grain boundary diffusional creep.

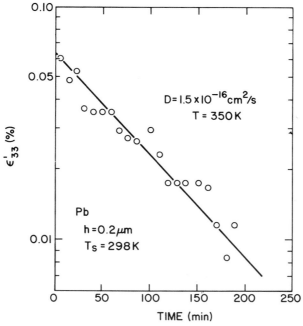

Fig. 16. Plot of ϵ'_{33} versus time for a 0.2-μm-thick Pb film which was deposited at 298 K and then annealed at 350 K. $D = 1.5 \times 10^{-16}$ cm^2/s. (After Murakami and Kuan, 1980.)

2.   SECONDARY STRAIN RELAXATION PROCESS

Since the relaxation rate was slow enough to be measurable, the secondary strain relaxation ($t > t_0$ in Fig. 14) was analyzed using the volume diffusional creep model (Murakami and Kuan, 1980). The atomic flow in a film under compression was shown schematically in Fig. 13 (labeled 1). The strain relaxation rate $\dot{\epsilon}_{11}$ (parallel to the film surface) is given by Eq. (13), which can be integrated to obtain

$$\ln \epsilon'_{11} = \ln \epsilon^0_{11} + (A_6 Y\Omega/ghkT)D_l t \qquad (20)$$

where ϵ^0_{11} is the strain at $t = 0$, t is the annealing time, and Y is Young's modulus ($\sigma'_{11} = Y\epsilon'_{11}$).

Equation (20) shows that the slope of a plot of $\ln \epsilon'_{11}$ versus t is proportional to the volume diffusion coefficient D_l. The isothermal changes in

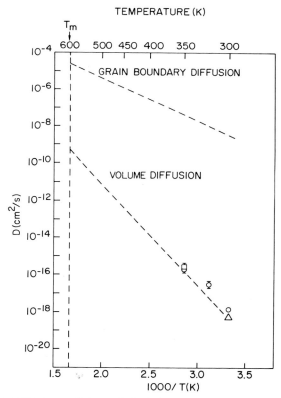

Fig. 17.   Diffusion coefficients of Pb. (After Murakami and Kuan, 1980.)

ϵ'_{33} are plotted as a function of t on a logarithm scale in Fig. 16. A linear relationship between $\ln \epsilon'_{33}$ and t was obtained in the plot. From the slope, the D_l value was calculated using Eq. (20). (The ϵ'_{11} values are easily calculated from ϵ'_{33}, since the ratio $\nu = \epsilon'_{33}/\epsilon'_{11}$ can be determined based on a biaxial strain model. However, to determine the D_l value, only the slope in the $\ln \epsilon'_{11}$ versus t plot is required. It is noted that the slope is not influenced by the multiplication factor ν.)

The D_l value obtained from the slope of Fig. 16 is plotted in Fig. 17. Also shown in this figure are the D_l values at 350, 320, and 300 K for films with various combinations of grain size and film thicknesses. The data for 300 K is obtained from a film under tensile strain (after cooling from 350 K). In Fig. 17, the D values which were determined from bulk Pb samples are shown by dashed lines for volume (Mehrer and Seeger, 1972) and grain boundary diffusion (Gupta and Kim, 1980). The D_l values determined from the secondary relaxation rate are found to agree well with the values for volume diffusion. Thus, the secondary relaxation rates of both compressive and tensile strains are believed to be controlled by volume diffusion.

VI. Strain at Grain Boundaries

There are several experimental results which suggest that strain occurs at grain boundaries. These results are reviewed below.

A. Strain Normal to Grain Boundaries

The strain introduced into a film upon cooling from 300 to 4.2 K was found to reach almost the calculated maximum value, i.e., the amount of strain relaxed was very small, when the average grain size is ~1 μm (Murakami, 1978b). However, the amount of elastically supported strain was observed to decrease slightly by further reducing the grain sizes for a given film thickness. This is believed to be due to strain occurring at grain boundaries.

Based on an assumption that there is strain at grain boundaries, the amount of strain can be calculated as below. Consider a film with a lateral grain size g_0 and assign a grain boundary width δ_0 at 4.2 K; the total maximum strain ϵ^m_{11} parallel to the film surface at this temperature can be expressed by

$$\frac{(\Delta g + \Delta \delta)}{(g_0 + \delta_0)} = \epsilon^m_{11}$$

where $\Delta g = g' - g_0$ and $\Delta\delta = \delta' - \delta_0$ (here g' and δ' are the strained grain size and boundary width, respectively). This equation can be rewritten as

$$\frac{\Delta g}{g_0} = \epsilon_{11}^m + \frac{\delta_0}{g_0}\left(\epsilon_{11}^m - \frac{\Delta\delta}{\delta_0}\right) \tag{21}$$

The value of $\Delta g/g_0$ corresponds to the strain ϵ_{11}' inside grains parallel to the film surface. The conventional x-ray diffraction technique measures the elastic strains ϵ_{33}' (inside grains) normal to the film surface. The strain ϵ_{11}' is given by $\epsilon_{11}' = 1.04\epsilon_{33}'$ since $\epsilon_{33}'/\epsilon_{11}'$ is 0.96 for (111)-oriented Pb grains at 4.2 K. The strains ϵ_{33}' at 4.2 K were measured for 0.2-μm-thick Pb films with average grain sizes smaller than 1.0 μm. Based on Eq. (21), the strain values ϵ_{11}' which were calculated from the measured ϵ_{33}' values are plotted versus an inverse of the average grain sizes in Fig. 18. The data points correspond rather closely to a straight line which intersects the vertical axis at 0.7%. This value corresponds to the strain in a single crystal, which was calculated assuming that there was no strain relaxation upon cooling

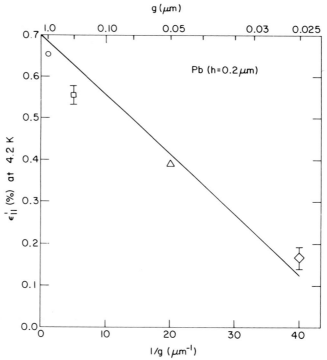

Fig. 18. Strain supported in 0.2-μm-thick Pb films with various grain sizes g.

from 300 to 4.2 K. From Eq. (21), the slope ϕ of this plot is given by $\phi = \delta_0(\epsilon_{11}^m - \Delta\delta/\delta_0)$. Thus, the strain $\Delta\delta/\delta_0$ at grain boundaries is

$$\Delta\delta/\delta_0 = \epsilon_{11}^m - \phi/\delta_0 \qquad (22)$$

Substituting into Eq. (22) the values $\epsilon_{11}^m = 0.70\%$, $\delta \sim 7$ Å, and $\phi = -1.5$ Å, $\Delta\delta/\delta_0$ is calculated to be about 21%. This result suggests that if strain occurs at grain boundaries and inside grains, the strain at grain boundaries could be as large as $\sim 20\%$.

B. Strain Parallel to Grain Boundaries

The strain ϵ_{33}' normal to the film surface is related to the strain ϵ_{11}' parallel to the film surface by

$$\epsilon_{33}' = -\nu(hkl)\epsilon_{11}' \qquad (23)$$

where $\nu(hkl)$ is Poisson's ratio for the biaxially strained film. The $\nu(hkl)$ value which is calculated from Eq. (6) is a function of elastic constants and crystal orientation. Thus, the $\nu(hkl)$ has a strong crystal orientation dependence if the material has anisotropic elastic constants.

The $\nu(hkl)$ values calculated for a Pb film which was cooled from 300 to 4.2 K are plotted on the upper half-sphere of the (111) stereographic projection as shown in Fig. 19 (Murakami and Chaudhari, 1977). The ν

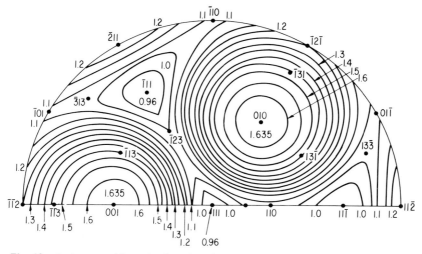

Fig. 19. A stereographic projection of equicontour curves of the strain ratio $-\epsilon_{33}'/\epsilon_{11}'$ for a biaxially strained Pb film at 4.2 K. (After Murakami and Chaudhari, 1977.)

TABLE III

Strains ϵ'_{33} Normal to the Film Surface ($T = 4.2$ K)

(hkl)		Theory		Experimental ϵ'_{33} (%)	
	ν	ϵ'_{33} (%) $(\epsilon'_{11} = 0.706\%)$	0.1 μm	0.2 μm
(200)	1.635	−1.15	—^{a}	—^{a}
(220)	1.094	−0.77	−0.86	−0.72
(222)	0.959	−0.68	−0.66	−0.63
(311)	1.457	−1.03	−1.14	−1.18
(331)	1.065	−0.75	−0.71	−0.73
(333)	0.959	−0.68	−0.65	−0.63

^{a} Measurements were not carried out.

values for any crystal orientation can be read off from this projection. It is seen that ν has a minimum value of 0.96 for (111) orientation and a maximum value of 1.635 for (100) orientation. The calculated $\nu(hkl)$ values for (200), (220), (222), (311), (331), and (333) orientations, whose interplanar spacing can be measured by an x-ray diffraction, are given in Table III. Using Eq. (23) and $\epsilon'_{11} = 0.706\%$, which was obtained from Eq. (1) for Pb on Si upon cooling from 300 to 4.2 K, the ϵ'_{33} values were calculated and listed in the third column of Table III. The strains in grains with different orientations were measured at 4.2 K for 0.1- and 0.2-μm-thick films. These thin films support almost the maximum strain. The measured ϵ'_{33} values are given in the last two columns of Table III. It is seen that the measured and calculated ϵ'_{33} values agree very well within experimental errors.

All these calculations and observations indicate that although the film is uniformly strained along planar directions, the strain normal to the film surface is different in grains with different crystal orientations. Thus, the grain boundaries between two differently oriented grains would be sheared in the direction normal to the film surface. A maximum shear strain at the grain boundaries is expected when a (100)-oriented grain is adjacent to a (111)-oriented grain.

VII. Strain and Stress at Film Edges

A. Review of Theory

In the previous sections, strain in a thin film with infinitely large surface area was described. The strain in such a film, thus, would not be influenced by the film edges. Here, effects of film edges on the strain and stress in a thin film which has a finite linewidth are described.

A film of thickness h and width L deposited on a substrate is schematically shown in Fig. 20. The same dimensionless x, y, z orthogonal axes used by Aleck (1949) were adopted here for convenience. Our axes notations "ii" used in the previous sections are also indicated for reference. It is assumed that at a temperature T the film is completely stressfree and the film is elastically isotropic. A stress or strain will be generated in the film upon changing the temperature to $T + \Delta T$. For a film of infinite extent in the X and Z directions, the stresses (σ_{11}, σ_{22}) on planar directions are given by Eq. (7b) for an elastically isotropic film. It is clear, however, that if the film is of finite width L, the stresses in the film will not remain uniform. For an example, it is expected that $\sigma_{11} = 0$ along the planes $X = \pm L/2$. The thermal stresses in a rectangular plate clamped along one edge were calculated by Aleck (1949). Aleck assumed $\sigma_{22} = 0$ (plane stress) for his calculation, which amounts to a very thin plate in the Z direction, but his calculations can be extended to films infinite in the Z direction. Aleck's calculation carried out for an elastically isotropic film will be briefly outlined here and several numerical errors in his calculations will be pointed out (Blech and Levi, 1981).

Following Aleck's reasoning, the stresses in a clamped plate can be calculated by superposition. First, the plate is assumed to be unclamped and will therefore deform due to the temperature change to

$$\epsilon_{11} = \Delta\alpha \, \Delta T$$

$$\epsilon_{33} = \Delta\alpha \, \Delta T$$

$$\epsilon_{13} = 0$$

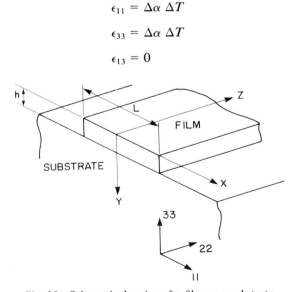

Fig. 20. Schematic drawing of a film on a substrate.

where $\Delta\alpha$ is the thermal expansion coefficient difference between the film and the substrate. Suppose now that a compressive stress $\sigma_{11} = Y\,\Delta\alpha\,\Delta T$ is applied to the plate. Then,

$$\epsilon_{11} = 0$$

$$\epsilon_{33} = \Delta\alpha\,\Delta T(1 - \nu)$$

$$\epsilon_{13} = 0$$

and the state of stress becomes

$$\sigma_{11} = -Y\,\Delta\alpha\,\Delta T$$

$$\sigma_{33} = 0$$

$$\sigma_{13} = 0$$

where Y is Young's modulus of the film. The plate is now cemented back onto the substrate; no forces are required to do so since $\epsilon_{11} = 0$ and $\epsilon_{13} = 0$. In reality, however, there are no normal stresses along the planes $X = \pm L/2$, and therefore a stress $\sigma_{11} = Y\,\Delta\alpha\,\Delta T$ must be applied on those planes in order to cancel the stress there. The problem of thermal stresses reduces to the problem of applying a uniform stress σ_{11} on the free edges $X = \pm L/2$.

The functional form of the stresses is assumed to be (with $x = X/h$ and $y = Y/h$, where X and Y are actual lengths, x and y are dimensionless)

$$\sigma_{11} = \sum_{i=1}^{3} f_i(x)y^{i-1}$$

Therefore from the equilibrium equations we obtain

$$\sigma_{13} = -\sum_{i=1}^{3} \frac{1}{i}\, y^i f_i'(x) \tag{24}$$

$$\sigma_{33} = \sum_{i=1}^{3} \frac{1}{i(i + 1)}\, y^{i+1} f_i''(x) \tag{25}$$

Equations (24) and (25) assure that $\sigma_{33} = \sigma_{13} = 0$ at $y = 0$.

According to the principle of least work, the stress field will be such that the elastic strain energy of the film will be minimized. The elastic strain energy E_{elast} is

$$E_{\text{elast}} = \frac{1}{Y} \int_{x=0}^{L/2h} \int_{y=0}^{1} [\sigma_{11}^2 + \sigma_{33}^2 + (2 + 2\nu)\sigma_{13}^2 - 2\nu\sigma_{11}\sigma_{33}]\, dx\, dy$$

Using the principles of the calculus of variations, it is possible to reduce the condition of minimum elastic strain energy to a set of three linear equations:

$$\sum_{j=1}^{3} a_{1j}f_j + b_{1j}f_j'' + c_{1j}f_j^{iv} = 0$$

$$\sum_{j=1}^{3} a_{2j}f_j + b_{2j}f_j'' + c_{2j}f_j^{iv} = 0 \qquad (26)$$

$$\sum_{j=1}^{3} a_{3j}f_j + b_{3j}f_j'' + c_{3j}f_j^{iv} = 0$$

where

$$a_{ij} = \frac{2}{i+j+1}$$

$$b_{ij} = -\frac{4}{ij(i+j+1)} - \frac{2\nu(i+j+2)}{ij(i+1)(j+1)}$$

$$c_{ij} = \frac{2}{ij(i+1)(j+1)(i+j+3)}$$

The condition that a solution of Eqs. (26) will be of the form

$$f_1 = A_1 \cosh \lambda x$$

$$f_2 = A_2 \cosh \lambda x$$

$$f_3 = A_3 \cosh \lambda x$$

requires the vanishing of the determinant

$$|a_{ij} + b_{ij}\lambda^2 + c_{ij}\lambda^4| = 0 \qquad (27)$$

Equation (27) produces six solutions for $\pm\lambda$:

$$\lambda_1 = 21.46929445$$

$$\lambda_2 = 6.55641247 + 2.811853236i$$

$$\lambda_3 = 6.55641247 - 2.811853236i$$

$$\lambda_4 = 2.580328004 + 1.339360994i \qquad (28)$$

$$\lambda_5 = 2.580328004 - 1.339360994i$$

$$\lambda_6 = 1.000579564$$

Corresponding to solutions (28), there will be six sets of A_1, A_2, and A_3. These will be written as A_{1j}, A_{2j}, and A_{3j}, where $j = 1, \ldots, 6$. Substituting

(28) into (26) yields

$$A_{21}/A_{11} = -9.25707015$$

$$A_{22}/A_{12} = -7.228832554 + 0.3938203841i$$

$$A_{23}/A_{13} = -7.228832554 - 0.3938203841i \qquad (29)$$

$$A_{24}/A_{14} = -4.275900625 + 0.5528040859i$$

$$A_{25}/A_{15} = -4.275900625 - 0.5528040859i$$

$$A_{26}/A_{16} = -0.1308266266$$

and

$$A_{31}/A_{11} = 13.29296812$$

$$A_{32}/A_{12} = 8.305571674 - 0.9943166057i$$

$$A_{33}/A_{13} = 8.305571674 + 0.9943166057i \qquad (30)$$

$$A_{34}/A_{14} = 3.137293505 - 0.4612713004i$$

$$A_{35}/A_{15} = 3.137293505 + 0.4612713004i$$

$$A_{36}/A_{16} = -0.778698474$$

It should be noted that several of the coefficients in Eqs. (28)–(30) are in error in Aleck's paper.

Finally, the A's are determined by the boundary conditions. In order to obtain a nondimensional solution, it is assumed the $\sigma_{11} = 1$ and $\sigma_{13} = 0$ along $x = \pm L/2h$ (rather than $\sigma_{11} = Y \, \Delta\alpha \, \Delta T$); therefore,

$$\sum_{j=1}^{6} A_{1j} \cosh(\lambda_j L/2h) = 1$$

$$\sum_{j=1}^{6} A_{2j} \cosh(\lambda_j L/2h) = 0$$

$$\sum_{j=1}^{6} A_{3j} \cosh(\lambda_j L/2h) = 0$$

$$\sum_{j=1}^{6} \lambda_j A_{1j} \sinh(\lambda_j L/2h) = 0$$

$$\sum_{j=1}^{6} \lambda_j A_{2j} \sinh(\lambda_j L/2h) = 0$$

$$\sum_{j=1}^{6} \lambda_j A_{3j} \sinh(\lambda_j L/2h) = 0$$

The stress in the clamped plate is finally

$$\frac{\sigma_{11}}{Y\,\Delta\alpha\,\Delta T} = \sum_{i=1}^{3}\sum_{j=1}^{6} A_{ij}\,y^{i-1}\,\cosh\lambda_j x - 1$$

$$\frac{\sigma_{13}}{Y\,\Delta\alpha\,\Delta T} = -\sum_{i=1}^{3}\sum_{j=1}^{6} A_{ij}\,\frac{y^{i}}{i}\,\lambda_j\,\sinh\lambda_j x \qquad (31)$$

$$\frac{\sigma_{33}}{Y\,\Delta\alpha\,\Delta T} = \sum_{i=1}^{3}\sum_{j=1}^{6} A_{ij}\,\frac{y^{i+1}}{i(i+1)}\,\lambda_j^2\,\cosh\lambda_j x$$

Thus far, the solutions (31) were based on the assumption that $\sigma_{22} = 0$, i.e., plane stress (of course, plane strain can also easily be considered). In reality, the case of more interest is not a plate but rather an elastic body with a depth in the Z direction about equal to its width L. This case has not been analyzed; instead it was assumed that σ_{22} has the form of σ_{11} and that the plane stress assumption is still valid. In this case the superposition consists of a plate with stresses $\sigma_{11} = \sigma_{22} = -Y\,\Delta\alpha\,\Delta T/(1-\nu)$, $\sigma_{33} = 0$; cemented onto a rigid substrate, and a stress $\sigma_{11} = Y\,\Delta\alpha\,\Delta T/(1-\nu)$ applied on the faces $x = \pm L/2h$. The resulting forms of the stress equations are the same as Eq. (31).

Figure 21 shows examples of (a) σ_{11}, (b) σ_{13}, and (c) σ_{33} as a function of x and y for $L/2h = 1.5$. The effect of the free edge on the stress is noted away from the edge. It is of interest to compare Fig. 21 with the corresponding figures in the articles by Aleck (1949) and Zeyfang (1971); the errors in the coefficients in the former references have a considerable effect on the stress curves.

B. *Average Stress, Strain, and Relaxed Volume in Thin Films*

1. AVERAGE STRESSES IN THIN FILMS

In the previous section, σ_{11}, σ_{33}, and σ_{13} were calculated for films of various $L/2h$. The advent of microlithography allows fabrication of films with very fine patterns. It is possible today to fabricate films with $L/h < 1$ using dry processing techniques. Such films will never, upon temperature excursions, be stressed at their center (at $x = 0$) as much as wide films ($L/h \gg 1$). It is therefore of interest to calculate the average stress $\bar{\sigma}_{11}$ at $x = 0$ for films of various L/h.

The average stress in the x direction at $x = 0$ is

$$\bar{\sigma}_{11} = \int_{y=0}^{1} \sigma_{11}(x = 0)\,dy$$

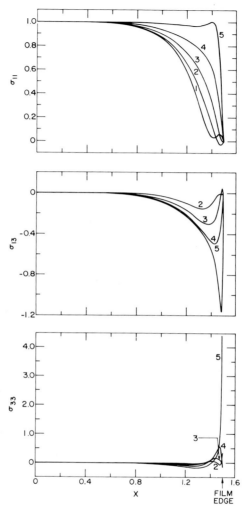

Fig. 21. Stresses normalized by a quantity $Y \, \Delta \alpha \, \Delta T / (1 - \nu)$ in clamped films with $L/2h = 1.5$ on a rigid substrate: (1) $y = 0$, (2) $y = 0.25$, (3) $y = 0.5$, (4) $y = 0.75$, (5) $y = 1$. (After Blech and Levi, 1982.)

And the relative average stress is

$$\frac{\bar{\sigma}_{11}}{Y \, \Delta \alpha \, \Delta T / (1 - \nu)} = f_1(0) + \frac{1}{2} f_2(0) + \frac{1}{3} f_3(0)$$

A plot of $(1 - \nu) \bar{\sigma}_{11} / (Y \, \Delta \alpha \, \Delta T)$ as a function of $L/2h$ can be seen in Fig. 22. Figure 22 shows that $\bar{\sigma}_{11}$ at the center of the film gets smaller as

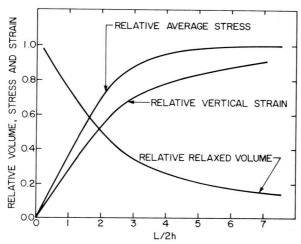

Fig. 22.   The relative average stress, strain, and relaxed volume as a function of $L/2h$ for adherent film.

$L/2h$ decreases; this comes about since the free edges, on which $\sigma_{11} = 0$, get closer to the center of the film when $L/2h$ decreases, thus reducing the stress at the center. For example, when $L/2h = 0.5$, $(1 - \nu)\bar{\sigma}_{11}/(Y\,\Delta\alpha\,\Delta T) \simeq 0.19$. Experimental verification of Fig. 22 will be published elsewhere.

2.   AVERAGE VERTICAL STRAIN IN THIN FILMS

So far, the average stress of a film was calculated. There is another pertinent quantity that can be both calculated and measured in films, namely the average vertical strain $\bar{\epsilon}_{33}$. The average vertical strain can be measured by x-ray diffraction.

Again, two extreme cases can be considered: films freely sliding on the substrate and perfectly adhering films. For adherent films $\bar{\epsilon}_{33}$ can be calculated as follows:

$$\bar{\epsilon}_{33} = \frac{1}{(L/2h)^2 Y} \int_{x=0}^{L/2h} \int_{z=0}^{L/2h} \int_{y=0}^{1} [\sigma_{33} - \nu(\sigma_{11} + \sigma_{22})]\, dx\, dy\, dz \quad (32)$$

In equilibrium the integral of σ_{33} must vanish. Also it can be assumed from symmetry considerations that the integral over σ_{11} equals that over σ_{22}. Equation (32) can be approximated by

$$\bar{\epsilon}_{33} = \frac{1}{(L/2h) Y} \int_{x=0}^{L/2h} \int_{y=0}^{1} (-2\nu\sigma_{11})\, dx\, dy$$

or in terms relative to the average vertical strain found in extended films

$$\frac{\bar{\epsilon}_{33}}{\bar{\epsilon}_{33}^0} = \frac{1}{(L/2h)} \int_{x=0}^{L/2h} \int_{y=0}^1 \frac{\sigma_{11}(1-\nu)}{Y \, \Delta\alpha \, \Delta T} \, dx \, dy \qquad (33)$$

where $\epsilon_{33}^0 = [2\nu/(1-\nu)] \, \Delta\alpha \, \Delta T$. Equation (33) is, of course, only approximate, since the two-dimensional solution has been used to determine $\bar{\epsilon}_{33}$ rather than the three-dimensional solution.

The relative vertical strain is plotted against $L/2h$ in Fig. 22. In the case of freely sliding films, $\bar{\epsilon}_{33} = 0$ since the entire stress is relieved.

3. Relaxed Volume in Thin Films

The maximum relaxed volume expected upon cooling or heating a film deposited on a substrate is given by

$$\frac{\Delta V^0}{V} = \epsilon_{11} + \epsilon_{22} = 2 \frac{(1-\nu)}{Y} \sigma_{11} = 2 \, \Delta\alpha \, \Delta T$$

For an adherent film the quantity $\epsilon_{11} + \epsilon_{22}$ can be estimated as

$$\frac{\Delta V}{\Delta V^0} = \frac{2\epsilon_{11}}{2 \, \Delta\alpha \, \Delta T} = \frac{(1-\nu)}{(L/2h)Y \, \Delta\alpha \, \Delta T} \int_{x=0}^{L/2h} \int_{y=0}^1 \sigma_{11} \, dx \, dy \qquad (34)$$

The result of Eq. (34) is shown in Fig. 22. It can be readily seen that adherent films with large linewidths, which correspond to large $L/2h$, will create far less relaxed volume than narrow lined films.

C. Comparison between Theory and Experiment

Equation (33) predicts that the average vertical strain $\bar{\epsilon}_{33}$ is maximum when L/h is infinite and decreases with decreasing L/h values. This means that film edges have a strong influence on the strain in the film when the linewidth is small and the influence is negligibly small when $L = \infty$.

The average strain ϵ_{33}' was measured by an x-ray diffraction technique for ϵ-phase Pb–Bi films with various L/h values (Murakami, 1982). These films were prepared by using a coevaporation technique from a single alloy source of Pb–29% Bi. The oxidized Si wafers were used as the substrates and the temperature was kept at 273 K. The films with 0.6 μm thickness were prepared. To prepare line-patterned films, the stencil lift-off technique

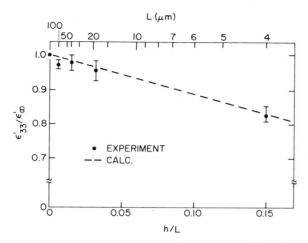

Fig. 23. Normalized average strain at 4.2 K of Pb–Bi films with various widths. (After Murakami, 1982.)

was used and the films with width range 4–100 μm were prepared. These films were cooled from 298 to 4.2 K and the strains were measured at 4.2 K. The strain of the film with $L = \infty$ (blanket film) was close to the maximum value (Basson *et al.*, 1982). The strain with finite L value was normalized by the one for $L = \infty$ and the normalized strain values are shown in Fig. 23. The theoretically predicted strain value is also shown by a dashed line in this figure. The experimental values are seen to fall on the theoretical curve, indicating that the films with finer width support less strain elastically.

VIII. Microstructures Which Affect Mechanical Properties of Thin Films

In the previous sections the dominant strain relaxation mechanism in Pb thin films was found to be dislocation glide or diffusional creep. The strain relaxation rate by the diffusional creep is significantly fast at temperatures above room temperature and is negligibly slow at low temperatures. The dislocation glide is considered to be the only important strain relaxation mechanism at low temperatures. In this section the effects of film microstructure on the dislocation behavior will be discussed.

A. Film Thickness and Grain Size

Film strength models described in Section IV,B predicted that the film strength could be increased by reducing the film thickness h and grain size g. Also, the TEM study indicated that grain boundaries, the native oxide layer on the film surface, and the film–substrate interface were effective barriers to dislocation motion (Kuan and Murakami, 1982). The film strength is, therefore, sensitive to h and g.

In order to study the effects of h and g on the strain at 4.2 K, Pb films with various combinations of h and g were prepared by using sputter-thinning, low-temperature deposition, or seeding techniques (Murakami, 1979). The strain at 4.2 K was measured and the strain ratios α of all samples were indicated on a h versus g plot in Fig. 24. The α values represent the measured strains for each sample normalized by the strain values of samples with $h = 0.1$ μm. Large α values indicate that the film supports most of the strain elastically. The approximate equistrain contour lines are shown by solid curves. This plot indicates that for $h < g/5$ the film thickness would control the film's strength, and that no significant

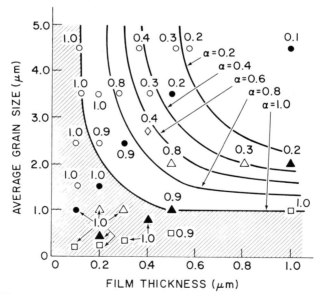

Fig. 24. The strain ratios α plotted on a film thickness versus grain size map: (●) Pb(A), (○) Pb(B), (□) Pb(C), (▲) Au + Pb(A), (△) Au + Pb(B), (◇) Pb + Au + Pb. (After Murakami, 1979.)

strain relaxation would be observed in the films with $g < 1$ μm or with $h < 0.15$ μm except for the small amount of strain at grain boundaries. The films shown in the shaded region in Fig. 24 can support elastically the thermal strain at 4.2 K. It should be noted that the critical sizes for inhibiting the strain relaxation are smaller for the film thickness than for the average grain size. This seems to indicate that the strain relaxation by dislocation glide was limited more efficiently by the grain size than by the film thickness.

However, since the x-ray technique measures the average strain of the film, the critical grain size could not be determined accurately by this technique. Thus, to determine the grain size effect, microscopic study is more useful. In a TEM study of a polycrystalline 0.2-μm-thick Pb film which was deposited at 300 K, dislocations were observed to be introduced into certain grains upon cooling to 100 K (Kuan and Murakami, 1982). The distances D between dislocations in each grain were measured from TEM micrographs and plotted in Fig. 25 as a function of grain size. It is noted that the D values are almost independent of grain size and the dislocation density calculated from the D value is close to 10^{10} cm^{-2} for $g \gtrsim 0.6$ μm. No dislocations were observed in grains smaller than 0.6 μm and these grains are believed to support the maximum strain elastically. The value of the critical grain size may also be influenced by impurities, film preparation techniques, i.e., by the actual grain boundary structure.

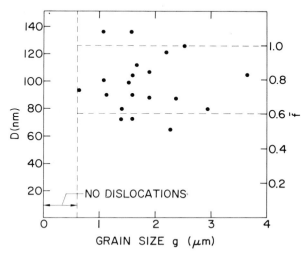

Fig. 25. Distances D between dislocations as a function of grain size g. (After Kuan and Murakami, 1982.)

B.   Crystal Defects

1.   MISFIT DISLOCATIONS

Pb-alloy films are often formed by depositing sequentially the Pb and alloying metal layers of desired thicknesses. If the lattice parameter mismatches between the layers are significantly large, misfit dislocations are formed at the interface between the layers to accommodate the misfit strain. Such misfit dislocations were observed in Pb–In films. Figure 26 shows a transmission electron micrograph of a Pb–In alloy film in which 0.16-μm-thick Pb and 0.04-μm-thick In were deposited sequentially at room temperature. If the Burgers vector of the dislocation is parallel to the film surface, the tensile thermal stress would exert no force on the dislocation. However, if the Burgers vector is inclined to the film surface as in the case of Pb–In film, the dislocation can glide when planar stress is applied to the film. The misfit dislocations in Pb–In films were observed to glide upon cooling from 300 to 100 K (T. S. Kuan, unpublished observations). The strain measured at 100 K by an x-ray diffraction technique was found to

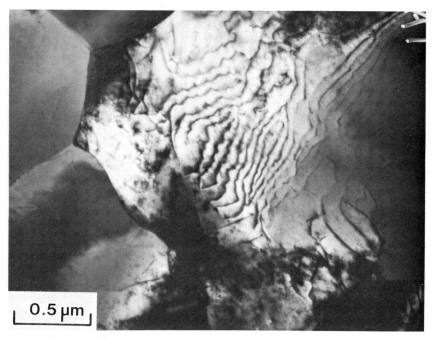

Fig. 26. Misfit dislocations observed in a layered Pb–In film. (After Kuan, 1980.)

be lower than that of Pb film with the same thickness and grain size. Thus, the presence of misfit dislocations can lead to more strain relaxation.

2. PRECIPITATES

Precipitates in a film which have the following characteristics are expected to improve the mechanical properties of the film:

(a) shear modulus of the precipitates is larger than that of the matrix,

(b) the lattice of the precipitates is coherent or semicoherent with the one of the matrix, and

(c) the dispersion of the precipitates is uniform inside the grains (it is desirable that the average distance between the precipitates be less than 10 nm).

To form such precipitates, solute atoms should be supersaturated and excess vacancies should be available in grains so that the atoms can diffuse and segregate at distances of ~ 10 nm. In bulk materials precipitates are formed by quenching from the liquid or single-solid phase region into the two-phase region and then by subsequently annealing at low temperature until the desired precipitate size is obtained (Kelly and Nicholson, 1963). However, this thermal treatment is difficult to apply to thin films. Even if thin films are successfully quenched, the quenched-in vacancies would not remain inside the grains, but would diffuse to sinks at grain boundaries, the film surface, or the film–substrate interface (Nicholson and Embury, 1963). Thus, it is difficult to form coherent precipitates inside the grains of polycrystalline thin films. Most of the precipitates would form at grain boundaries in the films. These precipitates, called discontinuous precipitates, are usually large and incoherent with grain lattice and could not increase the strength of the films. A technique to make fine coherent precipitates, such as Guinier–Preston zones, in thin films has not been established. Thus, no direct evidence of precipitate hardening in thin films has been obtained.

IX. Application

The studies reviewed here were carried out mainly to gain insights which might lead to the improvement of the mechanical stability of electrode materials used in Pb-alloy Josephson superconductive devices. The latter has exciting potential for use in ultra-high-speed computers (Anacker, 1979). They possess two key properties that are regarded as essential if the construction of such a computer is to be realized: fast switching speed and low power dissipation.

The junctions are made of several layers. A schematic cross section of such a junction device is shown in Fig. 27. The junction portions of the device consist of two superconductive electrodes separated by an ultrathin (6 nm) tunnel barrier. The junction regions are defined by windows in a thicker insulating layer.

Pb-alloy films are used for the electrode materials, because of their excellent electrical characteristics for Josephson devices (Ames, 1980; Kircher and Murakami, 1980): Pb or Pb alloys have a relatively high superconducting transition temperature; the thickness of the oxide tunnel barrier can be controlled to within one atomic layer in average thickness by growing them on Pb-alloy films; and the oxides have small dielectric constants which are required for the fast switching and resetting times of the junctions. A principal materials-related concern with Pb-alloy Josephson junctions is the reliability of the devices during thermal cycling between room and liquid He temperature (4.2 K), the temperature at which these devices are operated. The failure occurring in some Pb-alloy junctions during thermal cycling is believed to be caused by the rupture of the ultrathin tunnel barrier oxide when the strain induced by the thermal expansion coefficient mismatch between the Pb-alloy films and the Si substrate is relaxed by plastic deformation mechanisms.

As reviewed in this chapter when the strain was relaxed, microstructure changes such as dislocation slip steps, grain rotation, and hillock formation would be capable of causing the rupture of the tunnel barrier (Murakami *et al.*, 1979). As discussed before, the grain size and film thickness control strain relaxation upon cooling. The strain relaxation was reduced to near zero by reducing the grain size. Based on those results, a new, fine-grained Pb-In-Au alloy base electrode material was developed, and no evidence of the microstructure changes that could cause device failure was found after repeated cycles between 300 and 4.2 K (Murakami, 1981). The stress level supported at 4.2 K in the fine-grained Pb-In-Au films was found to be close to the theoretical shear strength of Pb and is believed to be the

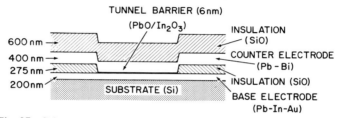

Fig. 27. Schematic cross section of a Pb-alloy Josephson junction device.

highest value obtained in thin films of soft materials. The use of such fine-grained Pb-alloy base electrode films in Josephson devices has significantly improved the ability of such devices to withstand repeated thermal cycling to 4.2 K (Huang *et al.*, 1981).

References

Aleck, B. J. (1949). *J. Appl. Mech.* **16**, 118.
Ames, I. (1980). *IBM J. Res. Dev.* **24**, 188.
Anacker, W. (1979). *IEEE Spectrum* **16**, 26.
Ashby, M. F. (1972). *Acta Metall.* **20**, 887.
Basson, J. H., Murakami, M., and Booyens, H. (1982). *J. Appl. Phys.* **53**, 337.
Blech, I. A., and Levi, A. A. (1981). *J. Appl. Mech.* **48**, 442.
Campbell, D. S. (1966). *In* "Basic Problems in Thin Films Physics" (R. Niedermayer and H. Mayer, eds.). Vandenhocck & Ruprecht, Göttingen.
Campbell, D. S. (1970). *In* "Handbook of Thin Film Technology" (L. I. Maissel and R. Glang, eds.). McGraw-Hill, New York.
Caswell, H. L., Priest, J. R., and Budo, Y. (1963). *J. Appl. Phys.* **34**, 3261.
Chaudhari, P. (1969). *IBM J. Res. Dev.* **13**, 197.
Chaudhari, P. (1971). *J. Vac. Sci. Technol.* **9**, 520.
Chaudhari, P. (1974). *J. Appl. Phys.* **45**, 4339.
Chaudhari, P. (1979). *Philos. Mag.* **39**, 507.
Cherns, D., and Stowell, M. J. (1976). *Thin Solid Films* **37**, 249.
Coble, R. L. (1963). *J. Appl. Phys.* **34**, 1679.
Cottrell, A. H. (1964). *In* "The Mechanical Properties of Matter." Wiley, New York.
Frost, H. J., and Ashby, M. F. (1973). *In* "A Second Report on Deformation Mechanism Maps." Naval Res. Report.
Gibbs, G. B. (1966). *Philos. Mag.* **13**, 589.
Gupta, D., and Kim, K. K. (1980). *J. Appl. Phys.* **51**, 2066.
Head, A. K. (1953). *Philos. Mag.* **44**, 92.
Herring, C. (1950). *J. Appl. Phys.* **21**, 437.
Hirth, J. P., and Lothe, J. (1968). *In* "Theory of Dislocations." McGraw-Hill, New York.
Hoffman, R. W. (1966). *In* "Physics of Thin Films" (G. Hass and R. E. Thun, eds.), Vol. 3. Academic Press, New York.
Hoffman, R. W. (1974). *In* "Physics of Nonmetallic Thin Films" (H. S. Dupuy and A. Cachard, eds.). Plenum, New York.
Huang, H.-C. W., Basavaiah, S., Kircher, C. J., Harris, E. P., Murakami, M., Klepner, S. P., and Greiner, J. H. (1981). *IEEE Trans. Electron Devices* ED-27, 1979.
Kelly, A., and Nicholson, R. B. (1963). *Prog. Mat. Sci.* **10**, 149.
Kinosita, K. (1972). *Thin Solid Films* **12**, 17.
Kircher, C. J., and Murakami, M. (1980). *Science* **208**, 944.
Kocks, U. F., Argon, A. S., and Ashby, M. F. (1974). *Prog. Mat. Sci.* **19**, 85.
Kroner, E. (1961). *Phys. Status Solidi* **1**, 3.
Kuan, T. S., and Murakami, M. (1982). *Metall. Trans. A* **13A**, 383.
Lahiri, S. K. (1970). *J. Appl. Phys.* **41**, 3172.
Lahiri, S. K. (1975). *J. Appl. Phys.* **46**, 2791.

Lahiri, S. K., and Wells, O. C. (1969). *Appl. Phys. Lett.* **15,** 234.

Matthews, J. W. (1975). *In* "Epitaxial Growth" (J. W. Matthews, ed.). Academic Press, New York.

Matthews, J. W., Kircher, C. J., and Drake, R. E. (1977). *Thin Solid Films* **42,** 69.

Mehrer, H., and Seeger, A. (1972). *Cryst. Lattice Defects* **3,** 1.

Menter, J. W., and Pashley, D. W. (1959). *In* "Structure and Properties of Thin Films" (C. A. Neugebauer, J. D. Newkirk, and D. A. Vermilyea, eds.). Wiley, New York.

Murakami, M. (1978a). *Acta Metall.* **26,** 175.

Murakami, M. (1978b). *Thin Solid Films* **55,** 101.

Murakami, M. (1979). *Thin Solid Films* **59,** 105.

Murakami, M. (1981). *J. Appl. Phys.* **52,** 1309.

Murakami, M. (1982). *J. Appl. Phys.* **53,** 3560.

Murakami, M., and Chaudhari, P. (1977). *Thin Solid Films* **46,** 109.

Murakami, M., and Kuan, T. S. (1980). *Thin Solid Films* **66,** 381.

Murakami, M., Angilello, J., Huang, H.-C. W., Segmuller, A., and Kircher, C. J. (1979). *Thin Solid Films* **60,** 1.

Murakami, M., Kuan, T. S., and Blech, I. A. (1982). *Thin Solid Films* **89,** 165.

Nabarro, F. R. N. (1948). *In* "Report of a Conference on the Strength of Solids." Physical Society, London.

Nicholson, R. B., and Embury, J. D. (1963). *Prog. Mat. Sci.* **10,** 244.

Nye, J. I. (1972). *In* "Physical Properties of Crystals." Oxford Univ. Press, London and New York.

Ronay, M. (1979). *Philos. Mag.* **40,** 145.

Ronay, M., and Aliotta, C. F. (1980). *Philos. Mag.* **42,** 161.

Shewmon, P. (1963). *In* "Diffusion in Solids." McGraw-Hill, New York.

Taylor, G. I. (1938). *J. Inst. Met.* **62,** 307.

Vook, R. W., and Witt, F. (1965). *J. Appl. Phys.* **36,** 2169.

Waldorf, D. L., and Alers, G. A. (1962). *J. Appl. Phys.* **33,** 3266.

Witt, F., and Vook, R. W. (1968). *J. Appl. Phys.* **39,** 2773.

Witt, F., and Vook, R. W. (1969). *J. Appl. Phys.* **40,** 709.

Zeyfang, R. (1971). *Solid State Electron.* **14,** 1035.

Part III

Variation of Composition of Thin Films

6

Ion Beam Modification of Thin Films

J. M. POATE

Bell Laboratories
Murray Hill, New Jersey

I. Introduction

Ion beams are now extensively used in science and technology to modify the surface layers of solids. Their most important application is in the implantation doping of semiconductors. The constraints of semiconductor technology, such as precise spatial control, are well matched by ion-beam technology. The range and doses of implanted atoms can, for example, be controlled with considerable accuracy. In fact, ion-beam technology gives us the opportunity to tailor or modify solid-state environments on the atomic scale.

In this chapter, first the way in which the impinging atom gives energy to the solid will be reviewed. Some of the atom's energy is transferred to the electrons of the solid and ultimately ends up as heat, but a sizable fraction of the energy can be transferred directly to the atoms of the solid to produce damage or new structures. When this energy deposition is close to the surface, atoms can be directly ejected or sputtered from the surface, thus producing morphological and compositional changes.

Lau and Mayer (Chapter 3, this volume) discuss the amorphization of surface layers of Si by ion beams. The resulting amorphous layer is in a metastable configuration. Studies of the epitaxial recrystallization of these layers have considerably advanced our understanding of solid-phase epitaxy. There are two reasons why ion implantation is such an apposite technique for producing amorphous layers for the study of epitaxial regrowth processes: (1) the layers are free of impurities and voids and (2) the interface between the amorphous layer and underlying single substrate is very clean. Later in this chapter we will discuss recent experiments on the rapid heating and liquid-phase epitaxy of ion-implanted amorphous layers, from which we have been able to deduce some of the thermodynamic parameters of amorphous Si.

In recent years unique metastable phases have been produced in metals by ion implantation. We will review some of the phases produced in Cu. Because of sputtering limitations, these implanted metastable alloys are usually fairly dilute. Recent developments of ion-beam mixing techniques, however, have permitted the study of phases over the complete concentration range of the phase diagram. The concept underlying ion-beam mixing is to deposit thin films of the materials of interest and then mix or react them at the interface by the collision cascade generated, for example, by an inert gas atom. We will present examples of novel metallic and intermetallic phases produced by ion-beam mixing.

Many books (Mayer *et al.*, 1970; Dearnaley *et al.*, 1973; and Hirvonen, 1980) and conference proceedings (Eisen and Chadderton, 1971; Carter *et al.*, 1976; Chernow *et al.*, 1977; Gyulai *et al.*, 1980; and Preece and Hirvonen, 1980) are devoted to the ion implantation modification of materials. In this article we will concentrate on thin-film applications.

II. Range and Energy Deposition

One of the main parameters of interest in ion-beam studies is the range of the incident ion. The range is determined by electronic and nuclear (or atomic) stopping processes. Calculations (Lindhard *et al.*, 1963) of the ranges of ions in solids are in quite good agreement with measurements. Several tabulations (Gibbons *et al.*, 1975; Smith, 1977) of these calculations have been published. Figure 1 shows the projected ranges of As in Si and Au as a function of incident energy. The crosshatched areas represent the standard deviations in the range. The figure illustrates several salient features of ion penetration. The ranges are quite shallow over the presently accessible energy ranges; in fact, the ranges coincide nicely with the thicknesses of many thin-film structures of interest. The standard deviations in the ranges are large because, for most heavy ion–target combinations, nuclear stopping predominates and the path of the ion through the solid can resemble a random walk process.

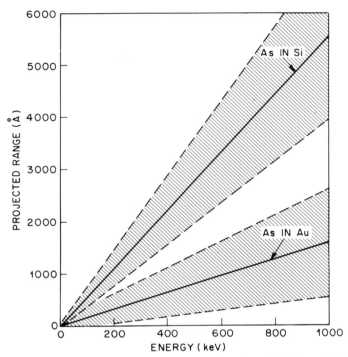

Fig. 1. Range and straggling of As in Au and Si (Smith, 1977). The solid lines are the projected ranges and the crosshatched areas are the straggling.

Greater ranges can be achieved by the use of lighter ions. Figure 2 shows the calculated range profile of N in iron (Dearnaley, 1980). The dashed curve shows the damage distribution or target atom displacement frequency. At a depth of 1000 Å each atom will be displaced up to 50 times by the bombardment. The damage curve can be calculated from a knowledge of the energy loss process (Thompson, 1969). In the Kinchin–Pease formalism, the total number of displacements ν is given, to first approximation, by $\nu = E_N/2E_d$, where E_N is the total energy deposited in nuclear processes and E_d is the displacement energy.

Of course the number of defects observed after implantation or bombardment are not necessarily related in any straightforward fashion to the number of atoms displaced. In a metal, for example, each host atom can be displaced many times and the lattice can still retain its basic structural integrity after the implantation. This resistance to damage is due to the lack of directionality of the metallic bond and the fact that damage anneals out easily. The situation is different for covalent semiconductors, such as Si, which can be made amorphous relatively easily by ion bombardment.

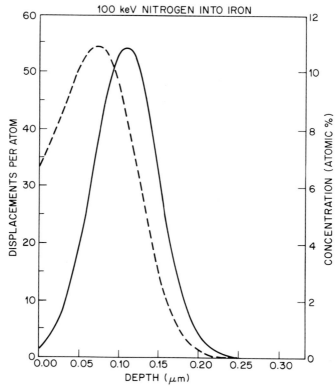

Fig. 2. Range distribution (solid curve) and target atom displacement frequency (dashed curve) for 100-keV nitrogen ions implanted in Fe to a dose of 10^{17} cm^{-2}. (From Dearnaley, 1980.)

The tetrahedral bonding is still essentially maintained but the atoms are assembled in a metastable amorphous network.

III. Sputtering-Induced Compositional Changes

One of the more noticeable effects of energy deposition from ion bombardment is sputtering—the process by which an incident beam of energetic particles removes surface atoms. Surface morphologies can be changed markedly by sputtering. In fact, the eroded surface can have the appearance of a surface which has been chemically etched.

Measurements of the sputtering yields of monoelemental targets under carefully controlled conditions have shown good agreement with theoretical

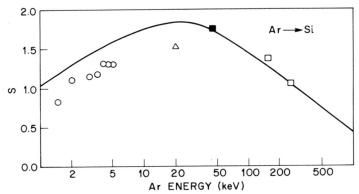

Fig. 3. Sputtering of Si by Ar. The curve is from Sigmund (1969) and the data are from Andersen (1974) and Poate *et al.* (1976).

predictions (Andersen, 1974). The agreement between theory and experiment is shown in Fig. 3, which shows the sputtering yield of Si (S is the number of atoms removed per incident ion) as a function of Ar ion energy. The calculations are based upon the collision cascade concept of sputtering (Sigmund, 1969). The incident ion makes multiple collisions with target atoms, which in turn collide with other target atoms, generating a collision cascade. Momentum can thus be returned to the surface atoms and, as a result, those atoms which obtain sufficient energy to overcome the surface binding energy will be sputtered. Consequently, the sputtering yield is proportional to the amount of energy deposited in atomic motion and is inversely proportional to the surface binding energy.

It has long been recognized that the sputtering of alloys or compounds can produce surface layers whose compositions are different than the starting material (Liau and Mayer, 1980). We have (Poate *et al.*, 1976; Liau *et al.*, 1978) observed in studies of metal alloys, silicides, compound semiconductors, and oxides that the surface layer becomes enriched in the heavier element. Some of these results are summarized in Table I. These compositional changes can be large and extend over hundreds of angstroms when energetic ion beams are used for the sputtering.

Thin-film silicides are useful model systems for studying alloy sputtering phenomena. They can be produced with well-defined stoichiometry and a high degree of purity. In our measurements we measured the surface compositional changes using Rutherford backscattering. Figure 4 shows the depth profiles (Liau *et al.*, 1978) of a PtSi film after sputtering with an 80-keV Ar ion beam. The composition has changed to a depth of nearly 800 Å and the surface composition is Pt_2Si. The depth resolution in these measurements is about 100 Å. The surface composition can be obtained

TABLE I

STEADY-STATE SURFACE COMPOSITIONS OF
SPUTTERED ALLOYS AND COMPOUNDS[a]

Materials studied	Enriched components	Surface composition
$Au_{0.2}Ag$	Au	$Au_{0.24}Ag$
$Au_{0.3}Cu$	Au	$Au_{0.33}Cu$
Au_2Al	Au	$Au_{3.8}Al$
$AuAl_2$	Au	$Au_{1.3}Al_2$
Pt_2Si	Pt	$Pt_{3.5}Si$
$PtSi$	Pt	$Pt_{2.1}Si$
$NiSi$	Ni	$Ni_{1.6}Si$
GaP	Ga	$Ga_{1.5}P$
Ta_2O_5	Ta	$Ta_{4.6}O_5$

[a] From Liau and Mayer (1980).

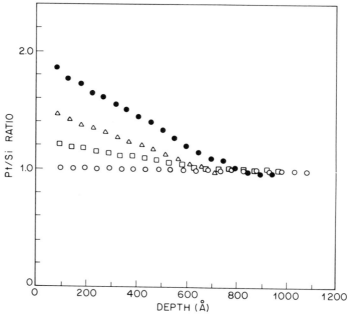

Fig. 4. Depth profiles of Pt/Si concentration ratios for 80-keV Ar sputtering of PtSi samples: (○) unsputtered; (□) 0.22; (△) 0.68; (●) 1.56×10^{17} cm^{-2}. (From Liau *et al.*, 1978.)

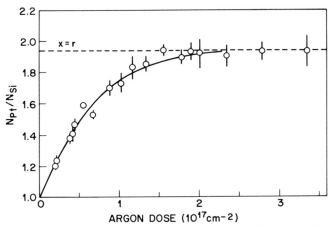

Fig. 5. Surface Pt–Si concentration N_{Pt}/N_{Si} as a function of 80-keV Ar dose. The solid curve is the calculated line for the process. (From Liau *et al.*, 1978.)

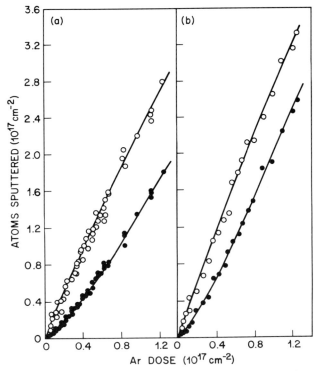

Fig. 6. Numbers of Si ($\bigcirc$) and Pt ($\bullet$) atoms sputtered from PtSi samples at (a) 80 and (b) 40 keV. (From Liau *et al.*, 1978.)

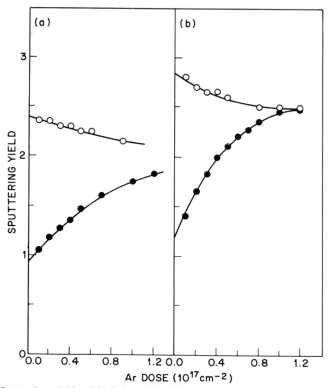

Fig. 7. Sputtering yields of Si (○) and Pt (●) atoms sputtered from PtSi at energies of (a) 80 and (b) 40 keV. (From Liau *et al.*, 1978.)

by extrapolation to the surface. Figure 5 shows the surface composition as a function of incident Ar ion dose. The surface composition approaches a steady-state value of Pt_2Si after doses of about 1.5×10^{17} cm^{-2}. Other measurements were made with 10-, 20-, and 40-keV Ar ions, and the depth of the Pt enrichment was found to be related to the Ar energy but the steady-state enrichment was independent of Ar energy.

From these measurements and other considerations, one can build a plausible *ad hoc* model of the alloy sputtering process (Liau *et al.*, 1978). At steady state the actual number of Si atoms sputtered off must equal the number of sputtered Pt. However, the initial sputering yield of Si is higher than that of Pt. As sputtering continues, the sputtering yields approach equality as the surface becomes enriched in Pt. Measurements of the number of Pt and Si atoms sputtered off the surface do, in fact, show this behavior. Figure 6 shows the actual number of atoms sputtered as a function of Ar dose and Fig. 7 shows the derivative of these curves. The derivative curves give the sputtering yields S.

Although we do not know the microscopic details of the sputter enrichment process, such as diffusion across the enriched layer, we can make the model quantitative. The excess Pt atoms in the sputtered sample are equated to the excess Si atoms sputtered from the sample. We then require that the ratio of the sputtering yields be equal to the ratio of the surface concentrations times the preferential sputtering parameter r, which is the ratio of the probability that a Si atom will be sputtered to that of a Pt atom. The solid curve in Fig. 5 is the calculated surface composition using the experimentally determined value of $S = 1.94$.

It is evident from the preceding discussion that gross changes can take place in surface compositions due to sputtering. We have discussed the PtSi case because it illustrates many of the features of the process.

IV. Implanted Metastable Phases

A. *Amorphous Silicon*

One of the earliest observations of ion implantation (Mayer *et al.*, 1970) was that Si could be amorphized to depths somewhat greater than the range of the incident heavy ion. This ability to produce amorphous Si layers in a clean and controllable fashion has been used in several ways to investigate epitaxial crystallization (Chapter 3, this volume). What else has implantation told us about the structural properties of Si or Si alloys? Because of the semiconductor's propensity for damage, it is not generally possible to implant an atom into an undamaged lattice and observe unique equilibrium or metastable configurations. Instead, implantation is used simply as a technique for introducing dopants into damaged or amorphous Si and then, in a typical experiment, the lattice site location is observed following some annealing procedure. It should be emphasized that this capability of implantation of introducing dopants into a solid without any of the usual alloying or thermodynamic constraints is quite unique.

In recent experiments (Baeri *et al.*, 1980), we have used some of these unique features of ion implantation and pulsed annealing to determine thermodynamic properties of amorphous Si. The fact that amorphous Si is in a higher free energy state than the crystalline state led Bagley and Chen (1979) and Spaepen and Turnbull (1979) to make some interesting predictions regarding the thermodynamic properties of amorphous and crystalline Si. They estimated the melting temperatures and enthalpies of melting of amorphous Si and Ge to be approximately 25% lower than the crystalline values. The advent of nanosecond pulsed heating techniques such as laser or electron beam irradiation (Ferris *et al.*, 1979; White and Peercy, 1980) has made it possible to investigate this behavior. Conventional furnace annealing does not permit examination of these predicted phenomena because recrystallization of the amorphous phase will easily occur in the solid phase at elevated temperatures.

Pulses of electron were used to heat the surface layers because the coupling between the incident beam and the irradiated sample is independent of the physical state (amorphous, crystalline, or liquid) of the semiconductor. The concept of the measurement of the enthalpy of melting is illustrated in Fig. 8. Two identical sets of Si wafers are implanted with As

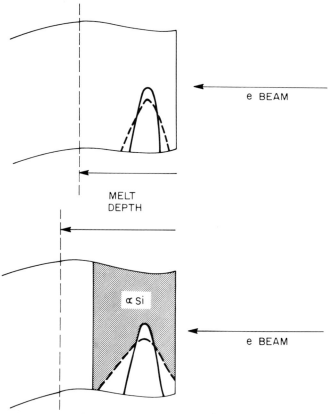

Fig. 8. Schematic of different melt depths, and As diffusion, for amorphous and crystalline Si.

diffusion markers to precisely the same range. The wafers are annealed in a furnace to restore complete crystallinity. One set of wafers is then amorphized by implantation. The amorphous and crystalline surfaces of the sets of wafers are then irradiated with pulses of electrons of 50-nsec pulse width. The electron energy is sufficiently high so that the depth of melt is greater than the amorphous thickness ($\sim$2000 Å). Measurement of the As diffusion profiles after solidification should therefore give the extent of the melt times. Diffusion in the liquid need only be considered since the As liquid-state diffusivities (2×10^{-4} cm²/s) are eight orders of magnitude higher than the highest solid-state diffusivity and the high quench rates exclude measurable diffusion in the solid. The higher free energies of the amorphous Si samples should therefore produce longer melt times, compared to the crystalline samples, and consequently broader diffusion profiles.

This difference in diffusion profiles is precisely what we observe experimentally, as shown in the backscattering measurements of Fig. 9. Once

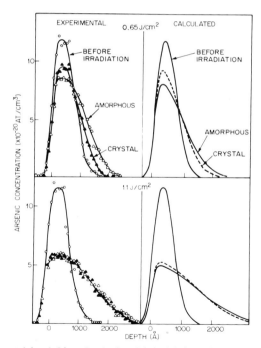

Fig. 9. Experimental (on left) and calculated (on right) As depth profiles for the initially crystalline and amorphized samples after electron irradiation of 0.65 (upper) and 1.1 (lower) J/cm², respectively. (From Baeri *et al.*, 1980.)

we assume that the specific heats are independent of the state of the Si (a plausible first-order assumption), we can compute the differences in enthalpies of melting of amorphous and crystalline Si. This is done by calculating the As diffusion profiles, assuming we know the pertinent thermodynamic parameters of crystalline Si. The right-hand side of Fig. 9 shows such calculations. We calculate the difference in enthalpies of melting to be 570 ± 60 J/g; the error arises from the fits to the backscattering spectra. We do not know the energy reproducibility of the electron beam to better than 10%. We therefore conclude that the enthalpy of melting of amorphous Si is 1220 ± 150 J/g, which should be compared with the crystalline enthalpy of melting of 1790 J/g.

In these experiments, as the melt penetrates the amorphous layer to the underlying crystal, the value we obtain for the differences in enthalpy will be independent of the actual melting temperature of amorphous Si. If the input energy is not sufficient to melt the surface amorphous layer and a part of the underlying crystal, the resulting melting and crystallization phenomena will be crucially dependent upon the actual melting temperature of amorphous Si. In this energy regime we, in fact, observe unusual recrystallization behavior. In the range 0.42–0.5 J/cm², epitaxial regrowth occurs with the interface moving 500–1000 Å. The epitaxial inner layer is highly defective and the outer layer consists of large-grain polycrystallites. Figure 10 shows a TEM micrograph of a cross-sectioned sample. Figure 10a shows the 1900-Å amorphous Si layer (A). Figure 10b shows the unusual layered regrowth at 0.5 J/cm². The epitaxial layer (B) is highly defective with a high density of microtwins. The outer Si layer (C) consisted of large-grain polycrystallites. Figure 10c for the 0.55-J/cm² irradiation shows complete recrystallization (D) with some defects at the interface.

These structures are indicative of crystallization of a greatly undercooled melt, with recrystallization occurring from both the single crystal interface and random nucleation centers at the free surface. These competitive processes produce the layered structures. The energy threshold of 0.42 J/cm² corresponds to a melting temperature of 1170 K, which should be compared with the single-crystal value of 1685 K. This melting temperature of 1170 K is lower than the proposed value of 1350 K of Bagley and Chen. Because of energy uncertainties in the energy of the electron beam, the temperature threshold cannot be estimated to greater accuracy than 100 K. Nevertheless, experiment and theory indicate that the melting temperature of amorphous Si is considerably smaller than that of crystalline Si.

B. Metals

The motivation for the early experiments on implantation into metals appears to have come predominantly from the fields of impurity hyperfine

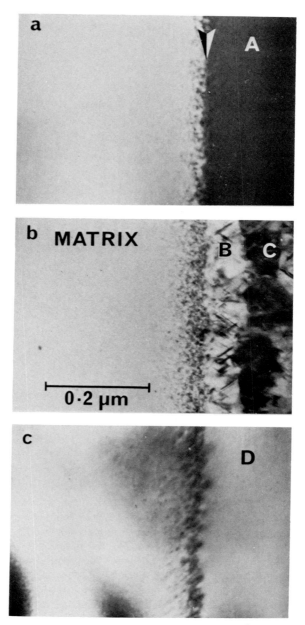

Fig. 10. TEM micrographs of cross-sectioned samples. (a) 1900-Å amorphous layer before irradiation. (b) Irradiation of 0.4 J/cm². Note epitaxial growth from original interface to polycrystalline boundary. (c) Irradiation of 0.55 J/cm². (From Baeri *et al.*, 1980.)

interactions and channeling (de Waard and Feldman, 1974). With hind-
sight, it is obvious that the interaction between these communities, while
stimulating lattice site location measurements, led to some interesting bot-
tlenecks in the development of implantation metallurgy. For example, de
Waard and Feldman in their 1974 review emphasize the point that, up to
then, there were no examples of implantations giving 100% substitutionality
(i.e., complete solubility). This lack of solubility was not all that surprising
since the systems studied were rather bizarre (e.g., Br implanted in Fe,
studied by Alexander et al., 1974) in terms of conventional alloys. When
more conventional binary alloys were studied (e.g., Au in Cu) complete
substitutionality was observed (Poate et al., 1974).

Further studies of implantation into Be, Cu, Fe, and Ni showed that
both equilibrium and metastable phases could be produced by requisite
choice of alloying species and dose. This subject has been reviewed in detail
elsewhere (Borders, 1979; Myers, 1980; Poate and Cullis, 1980; Kaufmann
and Buene, 1981). Here we will discuss some of the salient features of
metastable alloy formation by ion implantation.

In 1959, Duwez, Willens, and Klement (Duwez et al., 1960) developed
the first rapid quenching techniques (splat cooling) and were able to produce a complete series of Ag–Cu solid solutions. Figure 11 shows the
channeling angular distributions for Ag implanted into Cu as a function
of concentrations (Poate et al., 1977). The maximum concentration of Ag
that could be implanted was 16.6 at. %. At this concentration the Ag is
completely substitutional even though the Cu lattice is considerably damaged. The maximum equilibrium concentration of Ag in Cu is 4.9 at. %.
The implanted Ag is clearly in a metastable configuration.

This metastability is demonstrated by the TEM diffraction patterns
(Cullis et al., 1978) in Fig. 12 for the sample with 8 at. % Ag implanted
in Cu. The as-implanted Cu specimen exhibited high-quality single-crystal
diffraction poles. The diffraction pattern also exhibited weak subsidiary
spots (A) due to epitaxial Cu_2O and very small amounts of oriented metallic
Ag (B) present within the Cu matrix, although the lattice parameter of
this Ag was reduced by about 1% from its equilibrium value. When the
sample was annealed at 400°C for 15 min, the Cu_2O diffraction spots
disappeared. Moreover the diffraction patterns (Fig. 12b) exhibited extremely strong Ag spots (D) and when the corresponding Cu matrix spots
were excited, pronounced double diffraction effects (E) were also evident.
The Ag precipitates had dimensions on the order of 200 Å with their lattices
parallel to that of the Cu matrix.

During the course of these studies, another interesting facet of implantation metastability was discovered. It was found (Cullis et al., 1976) that
W and Ta were substitutional in Cu when implanted at low concentrations

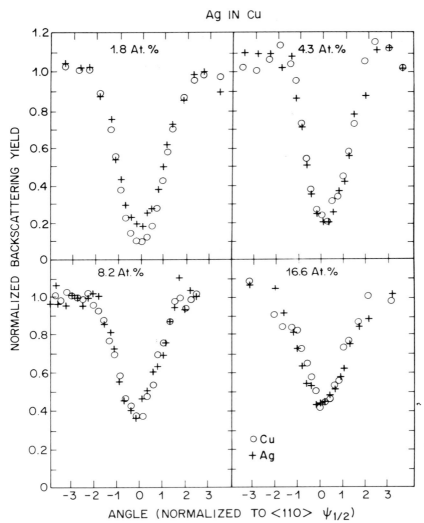

Fig. 11. Channeling angular scans of Ag implanted in Cu as a function of concentration: (a) 1.8, (b) 4.3, (c) 8.2, (d) 16.6 at. %; (○) Cu, (+) Ag. (From Poate *et al.*, 1977.)

of <1 at. %, although these elements, at equilibrium, are immiscible in Cu in both the solid and liquid phases. However, at higher implantation concentrations (≳10 at. %), amorphous surface alloys are formed (Cullis *et al.*, 1976, 1977, 1978). Amorphous alloys have also been produced by implantation of B or P into Fe, Co, and Ni polycrystalline foils (Ali *et al.*, 1978). The subject of amorphous alloy formation by implantation has re-

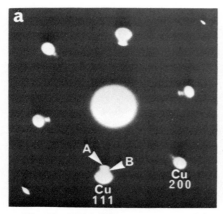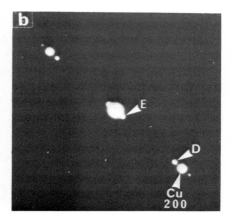

Fig. 12. TEM diffraction patterns: (a) As-implanted Ag in Cu at concentrations of 8 at. %. Note well-defined Cu pole pattern with weak subsidiary spots arising from small amounts of crystalline Cu_2O (A) and Ag (B). (b) Sample following annealing at 400°C for 15 min. Note strong metallic Ag spots (D) and double diffraction (E). (From Cullis *et al.*, 1978.)

cently been reviewed by Grant (1978, 1981). There are clear similarities between the concentrated metastable alloys produced by implantation and the more conventional rapid quenching techniques.

V. Ion-Beam-Induced Reactions of Metal Films

There is much interest in high-dose implantation, as indicated by the extensive publications in the field (Gyulai *et al.*, 1980; Hirvonen, 1980). The major limitations of this technique, as discussed previously, are the sputtering limitations on concentration and the rather shallow implantation ranges. These limitations are well illustrated by the Ag–Cu experiment described in the previous section, where the maximum attainable Ag concentrations were 16.6 at. % over a depth of some 500 Å.

One of the more exciting developments in ion-beam and thin-film science in recent years has been the reaction and interdiffusion of thin-film structures by energetic ion beams. The emergence of ion-beam mixing techniques is largely due to J. W. Mayer, B. Y. Tsaur, and their colleagues at the California Institute of Technology (Tsaur, 1980a, b; Mayer *et al.*, 1981). The concept behind this technique is to deposit the materials of interest in the form of thin films and then to react the films using the collision cascades generated by a heavy ion. It turns out in many cases that this process is remarkably efficient and the number of mixed atoms can greatly exceed the number of bombarding atoms. In this technique, concentrations are not limited by sputtering and one of the fundamental limitations of implantation can, therefore, be circumvented.

The potentialities of the technique are demonstrated by the reaction of Ag–Cu films (Tsaur *et al.*, 1980). Figure 13 shows the backscattering spectra of a series of Ag–Cu alloys produced by ion-beam mixing. Multiple layers of Ag and Cu (~ 200 Å thick) were first deposited on SiO_2 and the thicknesses were adjusted so that the average film composition varied between $Ag_{20}Cu_{80}$ and $Ag_{80}Cu_{20}$. The films were then mixed with 300-keV Xe at a dose of 2×10^{15} cm^{-2}. During bombardment, the sample was held at liquid nitrogen temperatures. X-ray examination of the films following bombardment showed a single-phase fcc structure without any elemental

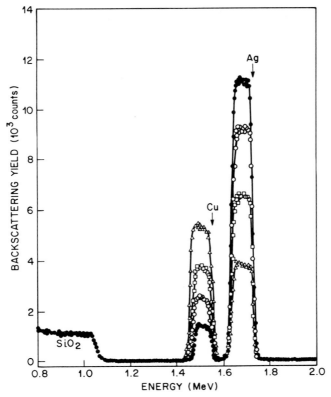

Fig. 13. Rutherford backscattering spectra of metastable solid solutions of Ag–Cu (~ 1000 Å thick) formed by ion-beam mixing with a 300-keV Xe beam at a dose of 2×10^{15} cm^{-2}. ($\triangle$) $Ag_{20}Cu_{80}$, ($\square$) $Ag_{40}Cu_{60}$, ($\bigcirc$) $Ag_{60}Cu_{40}$, ($\bullet$) $Ag_{80}Cu_{20}$. Sample at room temperature. (From Tsaur *et al.*, 1980.)

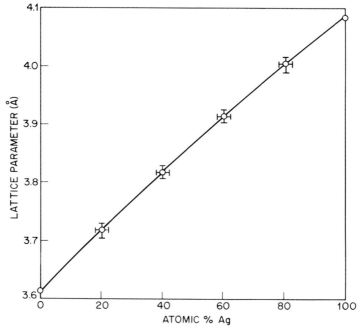

Fig. 14. Lattice parameters as a function of composition for Ag–Cu solid solutions formed by ion-beam mixing. (From Tsaur *et al.*, 1980.)

Ag or Cu reflections. The lattice parameter of this metastable solid solution is shown in Fig. 14. The maximum deviation from linearity (Vegard's law for ideal solid solution) is about 1%. These measurements of the lattice parameters of the Ag–Cu solutions produced by mixing agree with the splat cooling results of Duwez *et al.*, (1960).

One of the first demonstrations of the ion-beam mixing phenomenon was the formation of Pd and Pt silicides (van der Weg *et al.*, 1974; Poate and Tisone, 1974). More recent measurements by Mayer and colleagues on the silicide reactions have helped elucidate some of the mechanisms of ion-beam mixing. Figure 15 shows the backscattering spectra of the reacted zone progressing through a Ni film evaporated on Si. The reacted zone consists, in fact, of the Ni_2Si phase, which is the first phase to form under usual thermal annealing. The thickness of the silicide phase increases with the square root of the ion dose.

The amount of mixing or reaction as a function of temperature for Cr films on Si is shown in Fig. 16. The mixing is fairly insensitive to temperature below room temperature. But above room temperature the reaction increases very rapidly with temperature. This division into athermal

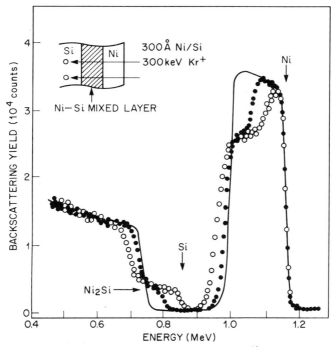

Fig. 15. Formation of Ni_2Si by ion-beam mixing: ($\bullet$) 2×10^{15}, ($\circ$) 8×10^{15} cm^{-2}. (From Tsaur, 1980b.)

and temperature-activated regimes can be explained in terms of the different driving forces. In the athermal regime the mixing is dominated by dynamic collision processes such as recoil mixing. The dynamic processes depend mainly on the efficiency of the nuclear stopping (i.e., on ion energy and mass) and should be fairly insensitive to temperature. In the high-temperature regime, however, chemical driving forces and enhanced diffusion become dominant. Discrete phases can thus be formed. The interaction between the cascade processes and temperature of the local solid-state environment is clearly synergistic.

The efficiency of the mixing process depends on the density of the collision cascade (i.e., nuclear stopping) as illustrated in Fig. 17, which shows the number (Q_{Si}) of intermixed Si atoms/cm^2 versus the square root of the Ar, Kr, or Xe ion dose for 450-Å-thick Pt films on Si for 300-keV bombardment at LN_2 temperatures. The square root dependence suggests a diffusion-like process. Mayer *et al.* (1981) argue that because dose is proportional to time, an effective diffusion coefficient ($D_{eff} \propto Q^2/t$) can be defined which is proportional to the square of the slope for each straight

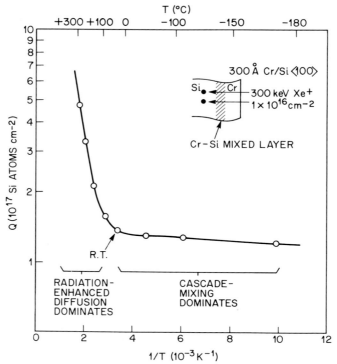

Fig. 16. The number of Si atoms, Q, contained in the Cr–Si mixed layers versus reciprocal implantation temperature. (From Mayer *et al.*, 1981.)

line shown in Fig. 17. The ratio of the D_{eff}'s for Xe, Kr, and Ar, respectively, is 7.3:4.4:1, which is very close to the ratio of the average nuclear energy loss.

Figures 18–20 show schematically the classes of thin-film reactions studied by Mayer *et al.* (1981). The phases formed by ion-beam mixing are compared to the equilibrium phases. Several patterns emerge from the studies of ion-induced compound formation shown in Fig. 18. The first phase formed, M_2Si, is the same for both thermal annealing and ion-induced reactions. After the metal has been consumed, the M_2Si phase transforms to MSi for both Ni and Pt on thermal annealing. However, amorphous structures are formed by bombardment. For Pd silicides, the Pd_2Si is stable up to 700°C under thermal annealing, whereas PdSi is formed by ion-beam mixing. No clear pattern exists for the Ni, Pd, or Pt reactions with Al.

The propensity of the ion-beam mixing technique for forming a metastable solid solution is shown in Fig. 19. Complete series of solid solutions

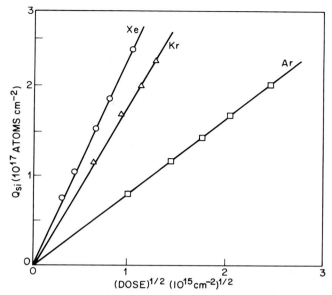

Fig. 17. Number of intermixed Si atoms, Q, as a function of the square root of Ar, Kr, or Xe ion dose. (From Tsaur, 1980a.)

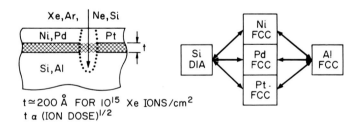

SYSTEM	THERMAL	ION BEAM (Xe AT R.T.)
Ni/Si	$Ni_2Si \longrightarrow NiSi$	$Ni_2Si \longrightarrow$ AMORPHOUS Ni–Si
Pd/Si	Pd_2Si (STABLE)	$Pd_2Si \longrightarrow Pd\,Si$
Pt/Si	$Pt_2Si \longrightarrow PtSi$	$Pt_2Si \longrightarrow$ AMORPHOUS Pt–Si
Ni/Al	Al_3Ni	Al_3Ni
Pd/Al	Al_3Pd	Al_3Pd_2
Pt/Al	Al_4Pt	Al_2Pt

Fig. 18. Ion-induced compound formation in thin-film structures of Ni, Pd, or Pt in contact with Si or Al. $t \simeq 200$ Å for 10^{15} Xe ions/cm²; $t \propto$ (ion dose)$^{1/2}$. (From Mayer *et al.*, 1981.)

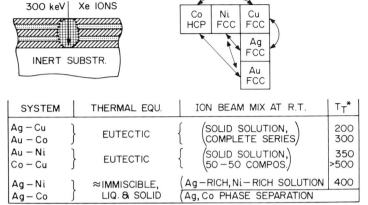

Fig. 19. Ion-induced metastable phase formation for Ag–Cu, Au–Co, Au–Ni, Ag–Ni, and Ag–Co multilayered structures on most substrates. T_T is the transition temperature (in degrees Centigrade) for the transition metastable → equilibrium. (From Mayer *et al.*, 1981.)

have been produced for Ag–Cu, Au–Co, Au–Ni, and Co–Cu thin-film systems. These systems show miscibility gaps in the solid under equilibrium conditions. It was not possible to form complete series of solid solutions in the Ag–Ni and Ag–Co thin-film systems. The equilibrium phase dia-

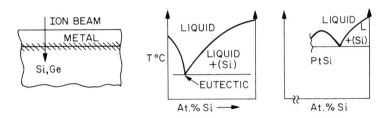

SYSTEM	EUTECTIC		ION BEAM MIXING
	T_{eut} (°C)	COMP., At. %	
Au – Si	370	18.6 (Si)	Au$_{71}$Si$_{29}$ AMORPHOUS
Ag – Si	855	13.2 (Si)	LIMITED MIXING
Au – Ge	356	27.0 (Ge)	Au$_{50}$Ge$_{50}$
Al – Ge	424	30.3 (Ge)	LIMITED MIXING
PtSi – Si	980	67.5 (Si)	AMORPHOUS → Pt$_2$Si$_3$
PdSi – Si	970	57.0 (Si)	LIMITED MIXING

Fig. 20. Ion-induced reactions in metal–semiconductor eutectic systems. (From Mayer *et al.*, 1981.)

grams for both these systems indicate a miscibility gap in the liquid. Novel metastable phases (Fig. 20) have been observed in the Au–Si (Tsaur and Mayer, 1981) and Au–Ge (Lau *et al.*, 1981) systems. Similarly, the heat treatment of ion-beam-mixed PtSi–Si samples results in the formation of novel metastable phases of Pt_2Si_3 and Pt_4Si_9 (Tsaur *et al.*, 1981). However, it does not appear possible at present to predict from the equilibrium phase diagrams which systems will show metastable phase formation.

Ion-beam mixing is a powerful new tool for the formation of metastable and equilibrium thin-film structures. Compositions can be controlled accurately by depositing films of different thickness. The mechanism of the mixing process are not fully understood, but the fact that mixing essentially occurs in the solid phase means that the process is very controllable. In many ways the technique is more versatile than either direct high-dose implantation or the melt–quench techniques.

References

Alexander, R. B., Callaghan, P. T., and Poate, J. M. (1974). *Phys. Rev. B* **9**, 3022.

Ali, A., Grant, W. A., and Grundy, P. J. (1978). *Philos. Mag.* **37B**, 353.

Andersen, H. H. (1974). *In* "Physics of Ionized Gases 1974" (V. Vujnovic, ed.). Inst. of Physics, University of Zagreb, Yugoslavia.

Baeri, P., Foti, G., Poate, J. M., and Cullis, A. G. (1980). *Phys. Rev. Lett.* **45**, 2036.

Bagley, B. G., and Chen, H. S. (1979) *In* "Laser–Solid Interactions and Laser Processing–1978" (S. D. Ferris, A. J. Leamy, and J. M. Poate, eds.), p. 97. (AIP Conf. Proc. No. 50).

Borders, J. A. (1979). *Annu. Rev. Mat. Sci.* **9**, 313.

Carter, G., Colligon, J. J., and Grant, W. A., eds. (1976). "Applications of Ion Beams to Materials, 1975." Conf. Series No. 28, Inst. of Physics, London.

Chernow, F., Borders, J. A., and Brice, D. K., eds. (1977). "Ion Implantation in Semiconductors, 1976." Plenum, New York.

Cullis, A. G., Poate, J. M., and Borders, J. A. (1976). *Appl. Phys. Lett.* **28**, 316.

Cullis, A. G., Borders, J. A., Hirvonen, J. K., and Poate, J. M. (1977). *Inst. Phys. Conf. Ser.* **36**, 181.

Cullis, A. G., Borders, J. A., Hirvonen, J. K., and Poate, J. M. (1978). *Philos. Mag.* **37**, 615.

Dearnaley, G. (1980). *In* "Ion Implantation Metallurgy" (C. M. Preece and J. K. Hirovnen, eds.). A. I. M. E.

Dearnaley, G., Freeman, J. A., Nelson, R. S., and Stephen, J. (1973). "Ion Implantation." North-Holland Publ., Amsterdam.

de Waard, H., and Feldman, L. C. (1974). *In* "Application of Ion Beam to Metals" (S. T. Picraux, E. P. EerNisse, and F. L. Vook, eds.), p. 317. Plenum, New York.

Duwez, P., Willens, R. H., and Klement, W., Jr. (1960). *J. Appl. Phys.* **31**, 1136.

Eisen, F., and Chadderton, L. T., eds. (1971). "Ion Implantation." Gordon & Breach, New York.

Ferris, S. D., Leamy, A. J., and Poate, J. M., eds. (1979). "Laser–Solid Interactions and Laser Processing–1978." (AIP Conf. Proc. No. 50, 1979).

Gibbons, J. F., Johnson, W. S., and Mylroie, S. W. (1975). "Projecting Range Statistics," 2nd Ed. Aalstead, New York.

Grant, W. A. (1978). *J. Vac. Sci. Technol.* **15,** 1644.

Grant, W. A. (1981). *Nucl. Instrum. Methods* **182/183,** 809.

Gyulai, J., Lohner, T., and Pasztor, E., eds. (1980). *Proc. Int. Conf. Ion Beam Modif. Mat.* Vol. III.

Hirvonen, J. K., ed. (1980). *Treatise Mater. Sci. Technol.* **18.**

Kaufmann, E. N., and Buene, L. (1981). *Nucl. Instrum. Methods* **182/183,** 327.

Lau, S. S., Tsaur, B. Y., von Allmeir, M., Mayer, J. W., Stritzker, B., White, C. W., and Appleton, B. R. (1981). *Nucl. Instrum. Methods* (in press).

Liau, Z. L., and Mayer, J. W. (1980). *Treatise Mater. Sci. Technol.* **18,** Ch. 2.

Liau, Z. L., Mayer, J. W., Brown, W. L., and Poate, J. M. (1978). *J. Appl. Phys.* **49,** 5295.

Lindhard, J., Scharff, M., and Schiott, H. E. (1963). *Mat. Fys. Medd. Dan. Vidensk Selsk.* **33,** 1–42.

Mayer, J. W., Ericksson, L., and Davies, J. A. (1970). "Ion Implantation in Semiconductors, Silicon, and Germanium." Academic Press, New York.

Mayer, J. W., Tsaur, B. Y., Lau, S. S., and Hung, L.-S. (1981). *Nucl. Instrum. Methods* **182/183,** 1.

Myers, S. M. (1980). *Treatise Mater. Sci. Technol.* **18,** Ch. 3.

Poate, J. M., and Cullis, A. G. (1980). *Treatise Mater. Sci. Technol.* **18,** Ch. 4.

Poate, J. M., and Tisone, T. C. (1974). *Appl. Phys. Lett.* **24,** 391.

Poate, J. M., DeBonte, W. J., Augustyniak, W. M., and Borders, J. A. (1974). *Appl. Phys. Lett.* **25,** 698.

Poate, J. M., Brown, W. L., Homer, R., Augustyniak, W. M., Mayer, J. W., Tu, K. V., and van der Weg, W. F. (1976). *Nucl. Instrum. Methods* **132,** 345.

Poate, J. M., Borders, J. A., Cullis, A. G., and Hirvonen, J. K. (1977). *Appl. Phys. Lett.* **30,** 365.

Preece, C. M., and Hirvonen, J. K., eds. (1980). "Ion Implantation Metallurgy." A.I.M.E.

Sigmund, P. (1969). *Phys. Rev.* **184,** 383.

Smith, B. (1977). "Ion Implantation Range Data for Si and Ge Device Technologies." Research Studies Press, P. O. Box 92, Forest Grove, Oregon, 97116.

Spaepen F., Turnbull, D. (1979). *In* "Laser–Solid Interactions and Laser Processing" (S. D. Ferris, A. J. Leamy, and J. M. Poate, eds.), p. 73. (AIP Conf. Proc. No. 50).

Thompson, M. W. (1969). "Defects and Radiation Damage in Metals." Cambridge Univ. Press, London and New York.

Tsaur, B. Y., (1980a). *In* "Thin Film Interfaces and Interactions" (J. F. E. Baglin, and J. M. Poate, eds.), E.C.S. Proceedings, Vol. 80-2, p. 205.

Tsaur, B. Y., (1980b). Ph.D. thesis, California Institute of Technology.

Tsaur, B. Y., and Mayer, J. W. (1981). *Philos. Mag* **A43,** 345.

Tsaur, B. Y., Lau, S. S., and Mayer, J. W. (1980). *Appl. Phys. Lett.* **36,** 823.

Tsaur, B. Y., Mayer, J. W., and Tu, K. N. (1980). *J. Appl. Phys.* **51,** 5326.

van der Weg, W. F., Sigurd, D., and Mayer, J. W. (1974). *In* "Applications of Ion Beams to Metals" (S. T. Picraux, E. P. EerNisse, and F. L. Vook, eds.), p. 209. Plenum, New York.

White, C. W., and Peercy, P. S., eds. (1980). "Laser and Electron Beam Processing of Materials." Academic Press, New York.

7

Thin Alloy Films for Metallization in Microelectronic Devices

K. N. TU

IBM Thomas J. Watson Research Center
Yorktown Heights, New York

I. Introduction

As the microelectronic industry enters the era of very large-scale integration of circuits, submicron structure is a subject of considerable current scientific research. The so-called "submicron structure" is the measure of lateral and vertical dimensions of circuit units such as contacts, gates, and interconnecting lines made mostly of metallic films on semiconductors. In submicron structure research the question most often asked, aside from

237

how to make them, is: What are the future materials problems in these submicron thin-film structures? While it is not at all difficult to project a few problems, the question can best be answered first by recognizing which of the present problems in microelectronics might persist into the future, then by looking at which of the problems that have been solved might haunt us again, and finally by asking what new problems might arise? Taking this approach, we can identify the problems in a more systematic way. Also, to project the future problems from a solid ground with generality, we must grasp the basic character of thin-film structures rather than focus on only a few special features of one or two unique cases. Moreover, we must assume some degree of continuity in the design of. device structure and similarity in processing steps of fabrication. For readers who are unfamiliar with the subject of microelectronics, the introductory articles on circuit design, processes of manufacturing, device performance, etc. published in the September 1977 issue of *Scientific American* would be very helpful.

The structure of any microelectronic device can be broadly divided into two parts: the semiconductor or the chip itself and the module or the packaging which physically holds the chip and electrically connects the chip to the outside. In fabrication, in addition to processing the chip and the packaging, we must join these two parts together. Hence, materials problems are expected to occur in processing the chip, in packaging, and in joining. Metallurgical degradation is important in these areas since metals are commonly used in all three of them. These problems worsen in submicron devices due to dimensional shrinkage, not just on the chip, but also on packaging and joining. Yet, the aforementioned submicron structures are used on the chip alone; therefore, this chapter will focus on thin-film problems on the chip and will not discuss packaging and joining problems.

In Section II, part of the structure of an actual device will be illustrated in order to point out several crucial thin-film problems in present devices, i.e., interdiffusion between layered thin films, electromigration along thin-film lines, and thin-film contacts to Si. Kinetic instability is one feature common to these problems.

In most thin-film multilayered structures used in present devices, each layer is typically a pure metal film. When several of them are stacked together by sequential deposition, the structure is unstable, so interdiffusion and reactions will occur between neighboring layers (Poate *et al.*, 1978). We must improve the stability of thin-film multilayered structures for submicron device application. In this chapter, it will be demonstrated that the use of alloys seems to combat the instability problem. In fact, alloy films of $Ti_{30}W_{70}$ (Ghate *et al.*, 1978) are known to be good diffusion barriers, Al–4% Cu films (d'Heurle and Rosenberg, 1973; d'Heurle and Ho, 1978) offer better resistance to electromigration than pure Al films, and alloy films of Pt–Si (Eizenberg *et al.*, 1981) can be used to make shallow silicide contacts to silicon. These examples show that alloy films are becoming useful in devices. Although we may be able to explain the workings of these alloys, it is clear that the concepts behind each of them may be different simply because the problems are different. Hence, the use of alloyed films in microelectronics merits a review. Since our understanding of the behavior of these alloys in the device is still incomplete due to limited usage, it is not possible to conduct a wide survey here. Rather the goal of this chapter is to illustrate both the nature of the metallurgical problems for present and future devices and the common concept of using alloys to solve these problems because it is anticipated that the use of thin-alloy films in future microelectronic devices will increase. In addition, an understanding of the problem and its solution based on thermodynamics and kinetics will be attempted in Section III. In Section IV, the specific application of the alloy concept to shallow silicide contact formation will be reviewed. Finally, a conclusion is given in Section V.

II. Metallurgical Degradation in Microelectronic Devices

A. A Typical Multilayered Thin-Film Structure

In Fig. 1, the top view of a computer device is presented. Such a device can be found in IBM 370 series computers (see the cover of *Think*, Jan./ Feb. 1978). The device is the building block of both the central processing unit and the memory unit of these computers, in which hundreds of these devices, each sealed by a metallic cap, are arrayed on boards to form a system. The device was made by joining a Si chip (the dark piece at the center of Fig. 1), with dimensions 2×2 mm, to a ceramic substrate (the larger white piece with a spider pattern), with dimensions 1×1 cm. The spider pattern comprises a set of electrodes connecting the chip to pins, which are for plugging into circuit boards. The joining of chip to substrate is achieved by soft solder joints (Totta and Sopher, 1969). The solder joints can be seen better in Fig. 2, which is a schematic cross-sectional diagram of the device. The solder joints provide both physical support and outside electrical connections to the chip. It is clear from the diagram that the device is built by using the so-called "flip chip" arrangement; the bottom side of the chip is the active side which contains circuits.

An enlarged view of the interfacial metallization between the chip and

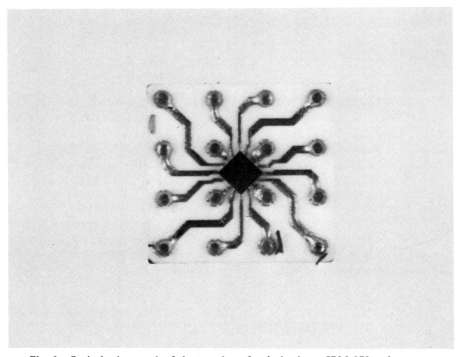

Fig. 1. Optical micrograph of the top view of a device in an IBM 370 series computer. The Si chip in the center is 2 × 2 mm and the ceramic pad is 1 cm² in area.

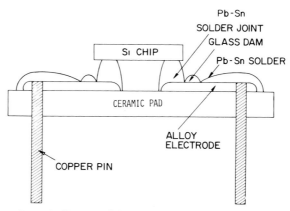

Fig. 2. A schematic diagram of the cross section of the device shown in Fig. 1.

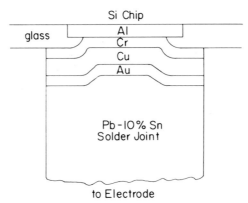

Fig. 3. An enlarged view showing a multilayered thin-film structure of Al/Cr/Cu/Au between the Si and the solder joint.

the solder joint is shown in Fig. 3 in order to illustrate the complexity of the thin-film technology used in such simple devices. Between the Si and Pb–Sn solder, there are four layers of thin films: Al/Cr/Cu/Au. In order to understand the reasons for building such a complicated structure and the problems arising from this structure, we need to discuss the function of each layer. The Al was used both as an electrical contact to the Si and as an interconnecting line between circuit elements on the Si. Since the surface of Al is easily oxidized and difficult to solder by Pb–Sn alloy, the Cu layer is introduced for soldering purposes due to the fast Cu–Sn reaction. However, Cu has poor adhesion on oxidized Al and SiO_2 surfaces. Moreover, when molten Pb–Sn consumes all of the Cu, it tends to dewet on the Al surface. So, the Cr was introduced as a glue layer between the Al and SiO_2 and to prevent the molten solder from dewetting. The surface of the Cu needs protection against corrosion because a corroded Cu surface does not solder well. Therefore, the Au was introduced as a surface passivation layer. Since Au reacts rapidly with both Pb and Sn, it will not hinder the solder–Cu reaction. In the solder–Cu reaction, a molten solder consumes Cu very rapidly. Since the amount of Cu is limited, a Pb-rich Pb–Sn alloy, instead of a eutectic alloy, is used in order to achieve a fast but limited reaction because Pb forms neither a compound nor an extended solid solution with Cu. From the above, we see that the four-layer structure was needed to fulfill functions of contact, adhesion, soldering, and passivation. The structure seems clumsy and was the object of criticism for two reasons: (1) it is not in thermodynamic equilibrium, and (2) each function requires an additional step of deposition to build up the multilayered structure. To simplify the structure is a challenge.

B. Interdiffusion and Diffusion Barrier

The most common problem with this kind of multilayered structure is instability. The driving force of instability is chemical nonequilibrium between sequentially deposited layers. Consequently, the demand for chemical equilibrium drives interdiffusion and reaction between layers. This, however, will not be a problem if the kinetic process cannot respond fast enough to the driving force. But the kinetics of these reactions has been found to be much faster in films than in bulk samples, and the kinetic rate in films becomes significant even at low temperatures. This is due to the nature of the fine-grained microstructure of evaporated thin films and the fast atomic kinetic processes along grain boundaries and interfaces. For example, in a noble metal such as Cu the lattice self-diffusivity at 200°C is about 10^{-21} cm^2/s on the basis of an activation energy of 2.1 eV (Butrymowicz et al., 1977), but its large-angle grain boundary self-diffusivity at the same temperature is only 10^{-10} cm^2/s. Therefore, at temperatures below 200°C the lattice diffusion can be regarded as negligible within a period of a few days, but not the grain boundary diffusion. Furthermore, the grain size in a noble metal film deposited by e beam onto room-temperature fused-quartz substrates is about 500 Å (Tu and Berry, 1972). For such a grain size, about 1% of the atoms in the film are located in the grain boundary regions. Using the above numbers, we can show that at 200°C the flow of materials through grain boundaries is eight orders of magnitude greater than that through the bulk, and the difference increases with decreasing temperature. Similarly, we can show that a temperature close to 200°C is sufficient for the Cu as shown in Fig. 2 to diffuse rapidly through the Cr along its grain boundaries (Baglin et al., 1974) and to change the interfacial adhesion at the Cr–SiO$_2$ interface. Also, the Cu can diffuse through the Au (Borders, 1973) and form an oxide layer on the Au surface, preventing soldering reaction. Hence, in the thin-film literature we find publications on interdiffusion and reaction in bilayer thin films of Cu–Cr, Cu–Au, Cu–Sn (Tu, 1973), and Cu–Al (Wildman et al., 1975). Cu–Al has been of great interest because of the concern about electromigration in pure Al and Al–Cu alloy films. We should emphasize here that thin-film interdiffusion is not only affected by microstructure such as grain size, but also by the chemical nature of the binary system involved. Indeed, Cu–Cr, Cu–Au, and Cu–Al represent binary systems which are immiscible, are miscible, and show compound formation, respectively. The Cu–Sn system is also unique in the sense that it involves interstitial diffusion of Cu in Sn; these two elements react spontaneously at room temperature (Tu, 1973). Clearly, the nature of kinetics is different from one system to another.

The question arises whether interdiffusion in thin films can be understood from the literature about interdiffusion in bulk samples. The answer is that our understanding is enhanced very little. It turns out that because of the very short distance of diffusion in thin-film samples, especially in the case of compound formation, we typically find the growth of a single compound phase in thin films (Tu and Mayer, 1978; Ottaviani *et al.*, 1980), rather than the simultaneous growth of two or more phases as in bulk samples. Which compound will grow first and which will grow next is generally not well understood and bulk interdiffusion is not helpful in answering these questions. In fact, what is needed in the area of interdiffusion is a means of bridging the gap between thin-film and bulk studies (Gosele and Tu, 1982).

Another unique feature of low-temperature interdiffusion in fine-grained thin films is the diffusion along moving grain boundaries. When grain boundaries move with solute atoms, they allow a new dimension of intermixing rather than merely acting as stationary short-circuit paths for fast mass transport of the solute atoms (see Section III, C) (Tu, 1977; Cahn *et al.*, 1979).

To stop or to reduce interdiffusion between fine-grained thin films, the most common method is to interpose a diffusion barrier (Nicolet, 1978; Nicolet and Bartur, 1981), which is itself a thin film. To be effective, a diffusion barrier must have a slow permeation rate. A single crystal film is expected to be a good diffusion barrier, yet it is not practical. In practice, a partially oxidized refractory metal film, a conductive oxide or a nitride phase such as TiN (Wittmer, 1980; Wittmer *et al.*, 1981), or a metallic amorphous phase with a high crystallization temperature can be used. These films will slow down interdiffusion kinetically. They are kinetic barriers, meaning that the barrier and its neighboring films are generally not in thermodynamic equilibrium.

C. *Electromigration*

In the above, we have emphasized the diffusion normal to the films. Diffusion along the films or between their interfaces is also of concern. In the structure shown in Fig. 3, it was found that electromigration had occurred along the Al film, resulting in open circuits. The electromigration can be retarded by adding a few atomic percent of Cu into the Al. To be effective, the Cu addition must go specifically to grain boundaries and interfaces in the Al film but not to the interior of Al grains. This is because electromigration at low temperature ($\sim 100°C$) in Al films occurs mainly along grain boundaries, and any addition of Cu into Al grains will raise line resistance. For the latter reason, to have a low line resistance, we should alloy the grain boundaries but not the grains, so the method of adding Cu to Al is rather crucial. Instead of codepositing Al and Cu simultaneously to form an alloy, Al and Cu were evaporated consecutively using a single e gun in a bilayer structure such as Al/Cu or a sandwich structure such as Al/Cu/Al. This was followed by low-temperature annealing to drive Cu into Al grain boundaries and to form Al–Cu compounds in the Al grain boundaries and Al–Cu interfaces. The Al–Cu films prepared in this way show good resistance to electromigration at temperatures around 100°C and under a current density up to 10^5 A/cm². Figure 4 shows an x-ray spectrum of Al$_2$Cu formation in a bilayer Al–Cu film annealed at 180°C for 5 hr.

To appreciate the effect of Cu addition in reducing electromigration in Al, readers are referred to review articles devoted to this subject (d'Heurle and Rosenberg, 1973; d'Heurle and Ho, 1978). Briefly speaking, the diffusional flux J, driven by electromigration, can be given by

$$J = Cv$$
$$= CMF \tag{1}$$
$$= C(D/kT)eZ^*\rho j$$

where C is the concentration; v, the drift velocity; M, the mobility ($=D/kT$); F, the driving force ($=eZ^*E = eZ^*\rho j$); D, the diffusivity; e, the electrical charge; Z^*, the effective charge number (Huntington, 1975); ρ, the

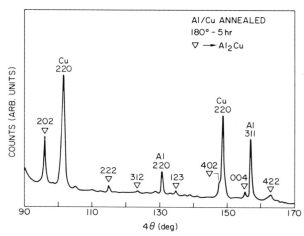

Fig. 4. Glancing-incidence Seeman–Bohlin x-ray diffraction spectrum of Al$_2$Cu formation in a bilayer Al/Cu film annealed at 180°C for 5 hr.

resistivity; j, the current density; and kT has the usual meaning. For the case of electromigration along grain boundaries, the flux J_b is modified by a dimensionless term of δ/d, where δ and d are effective grain boundary width and grain size, respectively. We have

$$J_b = C_b(\delta D_b/dkT)eZ_b^* \rho j \qquad (2)$$

According to Eq. (2), we see that at a constant current density, the grain boundary diffusional flux due to electromigration in a thin-film line can be reduced by reducing the grain boundary diffusivity D_b or the grain boundary effective charge number Z_b^*, or by increasing the grain size d. Considering the effect of grain size, it is impractical to try to deposit single-crystal thin-film lines, yet a thin-film line of bamboo-type microstructure (Kinsborn, 1980) has been tested and found to be effective in resisting low-temperature electromigration. Considering the effect of D_b and Z_b^*, we note that in fine-grained Al or Al–Cu alloy films, a measurement of electromigration flux alone will generally not show whether the improvement by Cu addition is due to reducing D_b or Z_b^* since their product is measured, so an additional independent measurement of either δD_b or Z_b^* is needed in order to unravel them. The beneficial effect of alloying Cu to Al grain boundaries results from reduction of the grain boundary diffusivity of Al by increasing its activation energy of diffusion.

On the other hand, since the failure mode of electromigration in a thin-film line is the propagation of a localized opening across the film due to flux divergence, one approach to resist this mode of failure is to spread out flux divergence by using a stable film of very fine grains (Ghate, 1981), and another approach is to stop the propagation of the opening in a way similar to stopping crack propagation along grain boundaries. As shown in the following, the latter can be achieved by the use of a diffusion barrier.

If a thicker Cu is used in the Al/Cu/Al sandwich structure, a continuous Al_2Cu compound can be formed as the middle layer by low-temperature annealing, which because of its higher resistance will carry less current in the sandwich structure Al(Cu)/Al$_2$Cu/Al(Cu). Hence this middle layer will not fail by electromigration and its integrity can be maintained, providing physical and electrical continuity even if the top and bottom Al(Cu) layers fail locally. The middle layer behaves like a diffusion barrier in preventing openings from running across the entire film. In order to have a middle layer more rugged than Al_2Cu, transition metals which form compounds with Al at a higher temperature, but dissolve very little in Al, can replace the Cu layer (Howard et al., 1976, 1978).

Because of line resistance, it is clear that any alloy film with a high electrical resistance will not be a good solution to the problem of electromigration. Hence, a codeposited high-concentration alloy film cannot be used as an interconnecting line unless the line resistance can be reduced subsequently by precipitation annealing. So far, the effective ways to prevent thin-film electromigration are to alloy (or to dope) grain boundaries rather than grains and to add a sandwiched diffusion barrier with high electrical resistance and low atomic diffusivity. However, these solutions do not guarantee that there will be no electromigration problems in the future. We also note that the sandwich films are easy to produce on a flat surface, but are not necessarily so on a stepped surface.

D. Schottky and Ohmic Contacts to Silicon

In the structure shown in Fig. 3, the Al film serves two purposes: it is an interconnecting line and a contact. We have discussed the problem of electromigration when the Al film is an interconnecting line. Now we shall discuss the problem that arises in its role as a contact, i.e., the problem of "Al penetration" at the Al–Si interface (Rosenberg et al., 1978). Briefly, the problem is the formation of pits in the Si and the filling of the pits by Al, so that the Al penetrates into the Si. If the penetration is deep, it can short the p–n junction below the contact. Pit formation occurs during annealing at 400°C for 30 min, which is required for the Al to contact the Si intimately by decomposing or dissolving the native oxide on Si. At this temperature, Al can dissolve about 0.1 at. % of the Si. The dissolution unfortunately does not take place uniformly over the entire contact area; instead it attacks Si regions around the edges and through pinholes in the oxide. When the annealing is over and the structure returns to room temperature, some Si precipitates epitaxially on the substrate doped heavily with Al and some growth occurs primarily along Al grain boundaries, forming mesas on the substrate. The consequences of both the dissolution and precipitation are undesirable: the dissolution shorts a shallow junction, and the precipitation produces p-type Si and spots of high electrical field at the contact (Reith and Schick, 1974). For this reason, silicides such as PtSi have been used to replace Al as contact materials. Provided that the native oxide is not unusually thick, silicides of near-noble metals are able to form rather uniformly without pits over the entire contact area at a relatively low temperature (Tu and Mayer, 1978). The uniformity is due to a large driving force under compound formation, unlike dissolution, which has a smaller driving force, and is therefore sensitive to defect regions and tends to occur faster at pinholes and edges.

Whereas silicides have replaced Al as contact material, Al is still used as interconnection metallization for low electrical resistance. Figure 5 shows schematic diagrams of silicide contacts in both bipolar and MOSFET

(a)

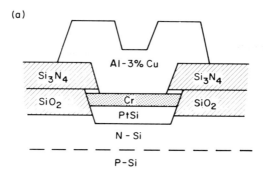

(b)

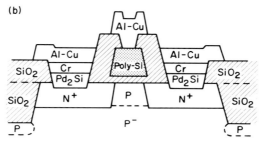

Fig. 5. Schematic diagrams of silicide contacts in (a) bipolar and (b) MOSFET configurations.

configurations. In the FET structure, the silicide is used as ohmic contacts to heavily doped source and drain regions. In a way, the silicide can be regarded as a "diffusion barrier" between Al and Si since it serves no additional function than that served by the original Al ohmic contact. Ironically, Al reacts with silicides such as PtSi and Pd_2Si, and at 400°C it is able to penetrate through the silicide to reach Si and repeat the penetration problem. Therefore, another diffusion barrier is needed to protect the "diffusion barrier," i.e., the silicide. Usually a partially oxidized Cr is used, as shown in Fig. 5. Obviously, if we can find a silicide with a low line resistance, the silicide can be applied like the original Al as interconnection, gate (Crowder and Zirinsky, 1979; Sinha, 1981), and contact metallizations, resulting in a simpler structure. Or we would prefer a thin-film structure wherein the interconnection and contact metallizations are at equilibrium with each other, so no additional diffusion barrier is needed. Such an equilibrium structure will be discussed in Section III.

In the bipolar structure, rectifying contacts are used with both high and low Schottky barriers. Silicide contacts offer a considerable advantage here since their barrier height has been shown to vary from 0.93 (Ohdomari *et al.*, 1978) to 0.37 eV on *n*-Si (Tu *et al.*, 1981), so a wide selection is possible. Schottky barrier height has a first-order effect on contact resistance, since the current transport across the contact under an applied voltage is governed by the barrier height on the basis of the thermionic emission theory. Therefore, a low-Schottky-barrier silicide phase is important in its applications as an ohmic contact.

To conclude this section, we recall that interdiffusion, electromigration, and contact problems were discussed because they will survive into the era of very large-scale integration. Obviously, we have neglected many other problems in metallization, such as corrosion and cooling. In addition, to increase circuit density on a chip, multilayers of interconnecting lines will be needed. This will introduce additional problems at interfaces between conductors and insulators and also at vias where conductors are connected (Vossen, 1981). Moreover, compatibility with joining and packaging must be taken into account also.

III.   Near-Equilibrium Multilayered Thin-Film Structure

A.   *Why Consider Thin Alloy Films?*

Multilayered thin-film structures are used in microelectronic devices because they serve multiple purposes. This has been illustrated in Fig. 3. Often, in order to reduce interdiffusion and/or reaction in such a layered structure, additional layers of thin films were introduced as diffusion barriers. This was illustrated in Fig. 5, where the silicide was introduced to prevent Al–Si interaction and the Cr was introduced to prevent Al–silicide interaction. Although this kind of diffusion barrier has often been successful, nevertheless, it possesses a fundamental shortcoming that the multilayered thin-film structure as prepared is not at thermodynamic equilibrium. It relies on sluggish kinetics to achieve the effect of a barrier, i.e., to extend the time to fail by slowing down the rate. In fact, structures of Al/Cr/PtSi/Si are known to fail; it is only a matter of temperature and time. Therefore, this kind of diffusion barrier has always worried the user because of its lack of long-term reliability in the device.

The essential problem of layered thin films is that thermodynamics demands interdiffusion and/or reaction between neighboring layers, so that they experience a driving force to react. The interdiffusion and/or reaction will stop eventually when the system reaches equilibrium, but the problem is that the intermediate states, or even the end state, will be unacceptable to device performance. In these circumstances, the best we can do is not to prevent interfacial reaction from occurring, but to try to let it happen in a way which is advantageous to our purpose, which means that we should induce a guided or controlled interfacial reaction. The concept of a guided interfacial reaction entails that it finish quickly and result in the formation of an equilibrium (or near-equilibrium as a matter of actual practice) multilayered thin-film structure which is stable and desirable. The concept is unconventional because all diffusion barriers to date have been introduced to stop or slow down the interfacial reaction, rather than to encourage it.

Equilibrium is reached when the forces and torques involved are in balance. In a chemical reaction, equilibrium ($\Delta G = 0$) is reached when the driving force of the reaction is balanced by the force of a counterreaction. The crucial question is how to build a counterreaction force into our thin-film reaction. This can be achieved by alloying.

B. Thermodynamics of Dealloying

To illustrate the concept of alloying and the design of an alloy into the reaction, we shall use the thin-film reactions between Pb and Au, Pd, and Ag, and their alloys as examples (Tu and Chance, 1975). Bimetallic thin-film samples of Pb/Au, Pb/Pd, and Pb/Ag were first prepared by e-beam deposition onto room-temperature fused-quartz substrates and then annealed at room temperature and higher temperatures up to 250°C. After annealing, the reaction in the samples was monitored by x-ray diffraction. It was found that Pb reacted with Au and Pd, forming Pb_2Au and Pb_2Pd, respectively, even at room temperature. No compound formation in Pb/Ag was detected up to 250°C. This is not surprising since Pb–Ag is a eutectic binary system. Their reactions (unbalanced) are as follows:

$$2Pb + Au \xrightarrow[R.T.]{} Pb_2Au$$

$$2Pb + Pd \xrightarrow[R.T.]{} Pb_2Pd \qquad (3)$$

$$Pb + Ag \xrightarrow[250°C—1\ hr]{} \text{no compound}$$

where R.T. is room temperature. It appears that Au and Pd react similarly with Pb. Then, we alloy Au with Ag to form $Au_{20}Ag_{80}$ solid solution by annealing a bimetallic film of 200-nm-thick Au on 800-nm-thick Ag on fused quartz at 600°C for 24 hr. The alloy was found to be homogeneous by Rutherford backscattering spectroscopy. In the same way, we also prepared a $Pd_{20}Ag_{80}$ alloy film. These two alloy films were then coated with a 500-nm-thick Pb film and annealed at 250°C for 24 hr. We found Pb_2Pd formation again, but no Pb_2Au could be detected:

$$Pb + Au_{20}Ag_{80} \xrightarrow[250°C—24\ hr]{} \text{no compound}$$

$$Pb + Pd_{20}Ag_{80} \xrightarrow[250°C—24\ hr]{} Pb_2Pd + Ag(Pd)$$

$$(4)$$

Comparing reactions (3) to reactions (4), we see that Au and Pd behave differently after alloying with Ag. To explain the difference, the free energy change of these reactions must be studied. First, we recall that in forming a stable alloy, the free energy of the system is lowered. This is demonstrated by free energy curves of both Ag–Au and Ag–Pd alloys (Hultgren *et al.*, 1973) in Fig. 6. When the composition of an alloy is changed its free energy changes, increasing or decreasing depending on composition. The free energy change equals the slope of the curve times the compositional change. The two arrows in Fig. 6 show that when Au is depleted from a Au-rich Ag–Au alloy, the free energy decreases, whereas when Au is depleted from an Ag-rich Ag–Au alloy, the free energy increases. In the former case, a reaction which involves Au depletion will be enhanced by the free energy decrease, whereas in the latter case, the same reaction will be retarded by the free energy increase. In other words, the free energy increase exerts a counterreaction force against Au depletion in Ag-rich Ag–Au alloys. The counterreaction force will vary with composition as the slope of the free energy curve increases when the composition becomes increasingly enriched in Ag. Consider the reactions of Pb with a Ag-rich $Ag_{80}Pd_{20}$ alloy:

$$2\delta Pb + Ag_{80}Pd_{20} \rightarrow \delta Pb_2Pd + Ag_{80}Pd_{20-\delta}$$

$$(1/\delta)(Ag_{80}Pd_{20} - Ag_{80}Pd_{20-\delta}) \rightarrow Pb_2Pd - 2Pb$$

$$(5)$$

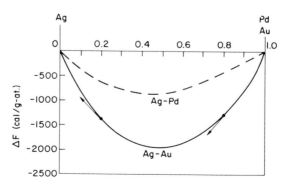

Fig. 6. Free energy curves of Ag–Au and Ag–Pd alloys. The arrows indicate the change in free energy due to the depletion of Au from a Ag-rich and a Au-rich alloy.

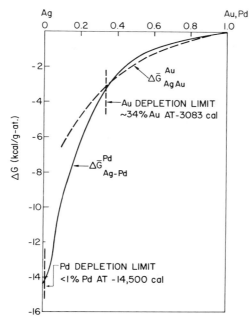

Fig. 7. Partial molar free energy curves of Ag–Au and Ag–Pd alloys. The vertical dashed lines indicate the alloy compositions below which no more Au or Pd can be depleted by the reaction with Pb.

and express them in terms of free energy:

$$\Delta \bar{G}_{Ag-Pd}^{Pd} > G_{Pd_2Pd} - 2G_{Pb} \tag{6}$$

where $\Delta \bar{G}_{Ag-Pd}^{Pd}$, G_{Pb_2Pd}, and G_{Pd} are the partial molar free energy of Pd in Ag–Pd alloy and the formation energies of Pb_2Pd and Pb per mole, respectively. The inequality dictates the condition for reaction to proceed. The reaction will stop when two sides are equal. Similarly, for a Ag-rich $Ag_{80}Au_{20}$ alloy to react with Pb,

$$\Delta \bar{G}_{Ag-Au}^{Au} > G_{Pb_2Au} - 2G_{Pb} \tag{7}$$

These terms are temperature dependent, but the partial molar free energy term depends much more on composition. In Fig. 7, the partial molar free energy of Au in Ag–Au alloy at 200°C, covering the entire solid solution range, is shown by the dashed curve and the same for Pd in Ag–Pd alloy at 250°C by the solid curve (Tu and Chance, 1975). Data for these curves were obtained from the literature (Hultgren *et al.*, 1973), where high-temperature data for $\Delta \bar{G}$ of Ag–Au and Ag–Pd alloys are given. At 200°C, the term $G_{Pd_2Au} - 2G_{Pb}$ has been calculated to be -3.083 cal/mol (Kelley, 1960) and at 250°C, the term $G_{Pb_2Pd} - 2G_{Pb}$ has been calculated to be -14.5 cal/mol. Two vertical lines are drawn in Fig. 7, with one crossing $\Delta \bar{G}_{AgAu}^{Au}$ at -3.083 kcal/mol and another crossing $\Delta \bar{G}_{AgPd}^{Pd}$ at -14.5 kcal/mol. These vertical lines indicate that reactions will occur to their right but not to their left. For example, any Ag–Au alloy containing more than 34 at. % Au will react with Pb at 200°C, forming Pb_2Au, and the reaction will stop when the Au concentration is reduced to 34 at. %. Likewise, Pb will react with most Ag–Pd alloys at 250°C, forming Pb_2Pd, until the Pd concentration approaches 1 at. %. These calculated results agree very well with x-ray measurements, as indicated by reactions (4). No reaction has been observed between Pb and the $Ag_{80}Au_{20}$ alloy due to the fact that the alloy is thermodynamically stable with Pb. The main difference between the Pb/Ag–Au and Pb/Ag–Pd reactions is that the compound Pb_2Pd has a much higher formation energy, so the driving force is greater and Pd can be depleted out. Although Ag–Au alloy is itself more stable than Ag–Pd (see Fig. 6), this fact is not crucial to the depletion reaction since it is the slope of the free energy curve that is relevant. Nevertheless, the slope of a more stable alloy tends to be steeper.

To conclude this section, it should be noted that we have shown how to achieve a self-limiting interfacial reaction by introducing a counterreaction force using alloying. Often, we prefer to have some but not a great deal of interfacial reaction in order to achieve bonding, so a self-limiting reaction is desirable. Taking Ag–Au alloy as an example, if Pb contacts an Ag–Au alloy containing less than 34 at. % Au, no compound formation will occur, which may result in a poor contact. If more than 34 at. % Au is added to the alloy, a limited Pb_2Au formation can occur at their interface, which achieves the bonding.

C. Kinetics of Dealloying

Although the above thermodynamic consideration can explain the driving force and end states of the reaction, the kinetic path is nevertheless unspecified. The fact that Pd atoms can be depleted from Ag–Pd alloys at 250°C is quite surprising considering the slow lattice diffusion in the alloy. (Rowland and Nachtneb, 1963; Peterson, 1963). To illustrate this point, we shall contrast dealloying (unmixing) with alloying (mixing) of Ag and Pd using thin-film samples (Tu, 1977). In homogenizing a bilayer film of Ag and Pd, we found that a heat treatment at 250°C for 24 hr did not achieve homogenization as measured by x-ray diffraction (see the spectrum in Fig. 8b). Figure 8a shows the spectrum of the as-deposited films. How-

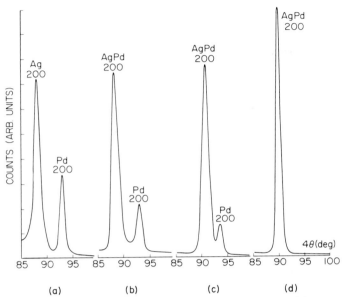

Fig. 8. Seeman–Bohlin x-ray diffraction spectra of various stages of homogenization of a bilayer film structure of 8000-Å-thick Ag and 2000-Å-thick Pd: (a) as-deposited, (b) annealed at 200°C for 24 hr, (c) annealed at 450°C for ½ hr, (d) annealed at 450°C for 4 hr.

ever, the Pd 200 reflection has shown a decrease in intensity after the annealing, indicating that some Pd has diffused away. Also there are some changes in the Ag 200 reflection and in the background level between the two. The profile of the Ag reflection has broadened asymmetrically toward the Pd, which also indicates that some interdiffusion of Pd into Ag has taken place, but it was far from achieving homogenization.

When the annealing temperature was increased to 450°C, a substantial mixing of Ag and Pd occurred. This is shown in Fig. 8c by the x-ray spectrum of a sample annealed for 30 min at 450°C. The reflection of Ag has increased in intensity, broadened, and shifted toward that of Pd. On the other hand, the reflection of Pd shows very little change except for a large decrease in intensity. All of this indicates that the homogenization proceeds by the diffusion of Pd into Ag. The peak position of Ag in Fig. 8c corresponds to about 14 at. % Pd in Ag. When the annealing at 450°C was extended to 4 hr, a nearly complete homogenization of the bimetallic film was achieved. This is shown in Fig. 8d, where the reflection now corresponds to the 200 of the Ag–20 at. % Pd alloy (Rao and Rao, 1964).

The high temperature needed to homogenize the film is not unexpected on the basis of bulk diffusion coefficients in concentrated AgPd alloys, which have an activation energy of 43.7 kcal/mol for Ag and 57.2 kcal/ mol for Pd. When extrapolated to 200°C, the diffusion coefficients are about 10^{-21}–10^{-26} cm^2/s, which indicates that in a period of 10^5 s the lattice diffusion is negligible. Thus, it is obvious that a complete homogenization dependent on mixing by lattice diffusion cannot be achieved at 200°C in a reasonable period of time even in fine-grained thin films of Ag and Pd. If it is true that mixing of Ag and Pd cannot take place by lattice diffusion at 200°C within a reasonable period of time, we expect the same is also true for unmixing a homogenized Ag–Pd alloy thin film. However, we found that Pd atoms can be depleted from a homogenized Ag–Pd alloy at 200°C by the Pb reaction. Clearly, the kinetics of unmixing of Pd from Ag cannot be explained by lattice diffusion.

Much of the low-temperature kinetics in fine-grained thin films, including permeation and electromigration, has been explained on the basis of grain boundary diffusion. We find it difficult to explain the unmixing by grain boundary diffusion since it requires that Pd atoms within a grain go to grain boundaries. If this occurs by lattice diffusion, it again becomes very slow. To overcome this difficulty, a new low-temperature kinetics process in fine-grained thin films has been introduced, i.e., moving grain boundaries (Tu, 1977). A moving grain boundary can sweep through a grain to deplete its solute atoms without invoking lattice diffusion. Similarly, it can embed solute atoms into a grain without lattice diffusion, i.e., alloying.

Figure 9a shows a two-dimensional sketch of the atomic structure of a moving grain boundary of large angle. Its position is indicated by the horizontal dotted line and its direction of motion by the arrow. The vertical dotted line indicates a stationary grain boundary. Assuming that the shaded circles are Pd and the open circles are Ag, those Pd in close proximity to boundaries can diffuse away along the boundaries. As the moving grain boundary migrates upward, it will meet more Pd atoms and enable them to diffuse away, resulting in the removal of Pd atoms from the alloy.

Now, if we assume that the horizontal grain boundary is stationary and the vertical one is moving and also that the grain above the horizontal boundary is pure Pd, as shown in Fig. 9b, alloying of Pd into an Ag grain below can take place by the diffusion of Pd along the moving grain boundary. An alloyed region is formed behind the moving grain boundary without lattice diffusion.

In the case of dealloying, experiments of depletion of Pd from an alloy of Ag$_{80}$Pd$_{20}$ in the temperature range 160–200°C were studied by x-ray diffraction. The alloy was a 1-μm-thick film and was homogenized at 600°C for 24 hr before a 500-nm-thick Pb film was deposited and annealed. The reaction products were a compound of Pb$_2$Pd and an Ag phase nearly Pd-free. Figure 10 shows a sequence of four x-ray spectra of a sample before

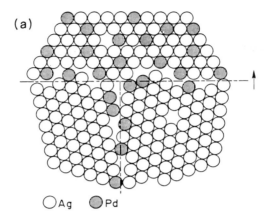

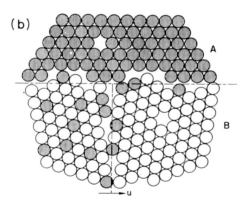

Fig. 9. A two-dimensional sketch of the atomic structure of a moving interface: (a) dealloying by a moving horizontal grain boundary; (b) alloying by a moving vertical grain boundary.

and after the reaction at 200°C for 20, 40, and 80 min. The spectra cover a selected portion of the x-ray run containing the alloy 200 reflection, the Ag 200 reflection, and two of the Pb_2Pd reflections. These spectra have been scaled by plotting all of the alloy 200 reflections to the same height, allowing easy comparison among them.

When the alloy 200 reflection is separated from the Ag reflection, it shows neither shape nor position changes. This means that during the

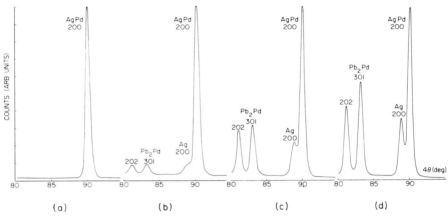

Fig. 10. Sequential x-ray spectra at various stages of reaction between Pb and AgPd alloy at 200°C: no heat treatment (a); annealed at 200°C for 20 min (b), 40 min (c), and 80 min (d).

reaction, the unreacted AgPd alloy keeps the sample composition the same as before the reaction. It also means that if the Ag forms as a neighboring layer to the AgPd, their interface must be sharp, i.e., there is no gradual concentration change between them.

The amount of Ag phase formed during the reaction can be measured by the integrated intensity of its reflections. The intensity is plotted in Fig. 11 as a function of annealing time and temperature. Its time dependence is found to be linear rather than parabolic. The activation energy of the reaction, assuming a linear reaction rate, is about 21 ± 2 kcal/mol. The

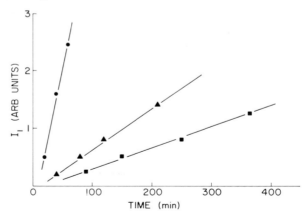

Fig. 11. Growth rate of the Ag layer in the Pb/AgPd reaction as measured by its relative intensity change at: (●) 200°C, (▲) 180°C, (■) 160°C.

morphology of the reacted phases has not been studied. Since the rate is rather linear, the reacted Ag phase is likely to have a layered structure in the thin-film sample. It was shown in the above that the formation of Pb_2Pd in the alloy is accompanied by the growth of an Ag layer. If the growth of the Ag can be regarded simply as a migration of the interface between Ag and AgPd at the expense of the latter, the migration will then serve the following processes simultaneously: the grain growth of Ag and the dealloying of AgPd. The atomic movement during the migration of the interface (see Fig. 9) into the alloy involves the jumping of individual Ag atoms across the interface from the alloy side to the Ag side. This is simply a reorientation process (the same as grain growth) for the Ag atoms because the main structural difference across the interface is a change of crystallographic orientation. The Pd atoms, on the other hand, could do the same as the Ag atoms, but could also diffuse away along the interface and the grain boundary, reaching the Pb to form Pb_2Pd. Obviously, this is a low-energy kinetic path which Pd atoms follow in order to free themselves from the Ag. In other words, although the Pd atoms in the lattice of the alloy can be regarded as frozen and unable to jump to the interface, the low-temperature reaction can occur by the migration of the interface to Pd atoms, and it requires no lattice diffusion of Pd. The driving force for the migration of the interface is the gain in free energy in forming the compound Pb_2Pd, and this driving force is countered by the reaction force from dealloying. In the following, an analytical kinetic model is developed based on this physical picture of a moving interface. The Ag layer is assumed to be continuous and to have a columnar grain structure with grain size S. In Fig. 12, the cross-sectional view of such a layer is shown. The columnar grains are approximated by cylinders, and conventional cylindrical coordinates r and y are used. The AgPd layer is on top of the Ag layer and has a Pd concentration C_0. The Pd concentration in the Ag layer is

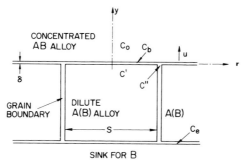

Fig. 12. A schematic diagram of the cross section of a Ag thin-film layer during its growth in a cylindrical coordinate system.

C'. The interface between the Ag and AgPd has a Pd concentration of C_b, an effective width of δ, and a steady velocity u in the upward direction. Furthermore, C_b is assumed to be constant across the interface. Therefore, the continuity equation in the moving interface takes the following form:

$$D_b\delta\left(\frac{d^2C_b}{dr^2} + \frac{1}{r}\frac{dC_b}{dr}\right) + u(C_0 - C') = 0 \tag{8}$$

where D_b is the diffusivity of Pd atoms along the interface. We note that Eq. (8) is analogous to the one-dimensional diffusion equation in Cartesian coordinates developed by Cahn to describe cellular precipitations (Turnbull, 1955; Cahn, 1959). Let

$$k = C'/C_b \quad \text{and} \quad \alpha^2 = ukS^2/D_b\delta \tag{9}$$

where k can be regarded as a segregation coefficient, and α is a convenient parameter. The solution of Eq. (8) is

$$C' = C_0 + AI_0(\alpha r/S) + BK_0(\alpha r/S) \tag{10}$$

where A and B are constants to be determined by boundary conditions, I_0 and K_0 are the modified Bessel functions of zeroth order of the first and second kind, respectively. With the following boundary conditions:

$$dC_b/dr = 0 \quad \text{at} \quad r = 0$$

$$C' = C'' > C_e \quad \text{at} \quad r = S/2$$

where C'' satisfies the inequality $C_0 > C'' > C_e$ and C_e is the equilibrium Pd concentration in the interface, the solution which describes the concentration profile of C'' along the moving interface is

$$\frac{(C' - C_0)}{(C'' - C_0)} = \frac{I_0(r\alpha/S)}{I_0(\alpha/2)} \tag{11}$$

We note that C'' is still arbitrary in Eq. (11) but will be fixed when the diffusion equation along the grain boundary is solved. From Eq. (11), we see that α is an important parameter in the solution. If we rewrite the expression for α given in Eq. (9), we obtain

$$u = (\alpha^2/k)(D_b\delta/S^2) \tag{12}$$

The growth rate u is proportional to $D_b\delta$, but inversely proportional to S^2. By measuring u and S, we can make an estimate of D_b. Typically, the thin-film reaction at 200°C was found to finish in 48 hr. With a 1-μm-thick AgPd film, the reaction rate $u \approx 5.8 \times 10^{-10}$ cm/s. Taking $S = 300$ nm and $\delta = 0.5$ nm, we obtain $D_b \approx 2 \times 10^{-11}$ cm^2/s. Since there are no direct measurements of interface or grain boundary diffusion in AgPd alloy, the only comparison that can be made here is to use the measured activation energy 21 ± 2 kcal/mol of the reaction. The activation energy will give a value 10^{-10} cm^2/s at 200°C, which is close to that estimated from the model. The essence of the model is that there are no high-activation-energy kinetic steps involved in the migration of the interface, i.e., the diffusion of Pd along the interface and the grain boundaries, and the reaction of Pd and Pb to form Pb$_2$Pd compound. No analysis of the diffusion along Ag grain boundaries and compound formation is given here since the rate-limiting step of the reaction is assumed to be the one that frees Pd from the alloy by the migration of the interface. The grain boundary diffusion may become rate-limiting when the thickness of the Ag layer is much larger than its grain size, where the reaction rate will be parabolic. Compound formation of Pb$_2$Pd is known to take place at room temperature in bimetallic thin-film couples of Pb and Pd (Tu and Rosenberg, 1974). Thus, its activation energy of growth must be low and the compound formation cannot be a rate-limiting step in the Pb/AgPd reaction.

In the case of alloying by a moving grain boundary, experiments of alloying of Cu into Au in a bilayer thin-film structure at temperatures as low as 160°C have been conducted by combining conventional and scanning transmission electron microscopy (STEM) (Cahn *et al.*, 1979). Alloyed regions produced by the migration of a grain boundary in the Au film after etching off the remaining Cu have been observed by conventional TEM. The Cu concentration in the alloyed region has been measured by STEM using energy dispersive analysis. The STEM results confirmed that alloying had taken place only in those regions experiencing grain boundary migration.

In passing, we note that there is now a class of phase transformations which can be induced by grain boundary migration, including grain growth, ordering (Tu, 1980), alloying (Cahn *et al.*, 1979), dealloying (Tu, 1977), cellular precipitation (Turnbull, 1955; Tu and Turnbull, 1967), and dissolution (Tu and Turnbull, 1971). They occur at low-temperature regions where lattice diffusion via vacancy mechanisms becomes negligible. In fine-grained thin films, such a kinetic process should not be overlooked.

D. Near-Equilibrium Multilayered Structures Produced by the Dealloying Reaction

In Sections III,B and C, we have discussed the thermodynamics and kinetics of a self-limiting reaction. In this section, we shall apply this reaction to form a near-equilibrium multilayered thin-film structure. We start by extending the bilayer structure to a sandwich structure, e.g., from Pb/AgPd to Pb/AgPd/Pb or AgPd/Pb/AgPd. Obviously we can regard the sandwich structures as the bilayer structure together with its mirror image. Hence, depletion of Pd by Pb in Pb/AgPd/Pb will be self-limiting as in Pb/AgPd, and we expect eventually to achieve an equilibrium multilayered structure of $Pb/Pb_2Pd/Ag(Pd)/Pb_2Pd/Pb$, provided there is sufficient Pb on both sides.

Although the Pb/AgPd/Pb sandwich films may seem useless, we note that it has the structure suitable for interconnecting lines: the Pb can be used to carry electric current, and the alloy and its compound layers serve as diffusion barrier layers that resist failure caused by electromigration or stress relaxation. Since Pb is not a good normal conductor, we can replace it by Al or Au. However, the alloy layer might have to be changed also since both Ag and Pd can react with Al to form compounds. Following the dealloying scheme discussed in Sections III,B and C, we can incorporate CuBe alloy in a Al/CuBe/Al structure. Also, we can use high-melting-point refractory metals such as W and Ta alloyed with Cu or near-noble metals to achieve the same results. Although W and Ta can react with Al to form compounds, this occurs at a higher temperature ($\sim 400°C$) than the reaction between Al and Cu ($\sim 200°C$) or between Al and Pd ($\sim 250°C$). Therefore, upon annealing a sandwich structure such as Al/CuBe/Al and Al/PdW/Al at around 250°C, a selective reaction can occur between Al and Cu and between Al and Pd, respectively. The latter is similar to the reaction in PdW/Si (Olowolafe *et al.*, 1979), wherein annealing at 400°C produces Pd_2Si but not WSi_2.

Since we can use PdW alloy for both Al and Si, we can prepare the Al/PdW/Si structure which will lead to the multilayered structure $Al/Al_xPd_y/W(Pd)/Pd_2Si/Si$ after annealing at 200–400°C. Such a structure can be used to contact Si, i.e., the Pd_2Si layer can serve as a Schottky or ohmic contact and the W(Pd) and Al_xPd_y compound layers can serve as diffusion barrier layers between the Al and Pd_2Si. Greater detail about using alloys to make such a contact will be given in Section IV.

In the above, we have extended a simple structure of Pb/AgPd to make a complicated structure of Al/PdW/Si on the basis of the concept of dealloying. To reduce the concept to a practical device, more studies are needed. We must specify the composition of the PdW alloy used and understand the difference in reaction between Al/PdW and PdW/Si. However, we should emphasize that the composition of the alloy need not be constant and can be varied across its thickness. In other words, we can "phase-in" an alloy layer between Al and Si such as $Al/Pd_{80}W_{20} \cdots Pd_{20}W_{80}/Si$ rather than deposit a constant composition layer such as Al/

$Pd_{50}W_{50}/Si$. The "phase-in" of graded composition is a unique feature of thin alloy films.

IV. Applications of Thin Alloy Films in Forming Shallow Silicide Contacts

A. *Contacts in Shallow Junction Devices*

Research and development work on small device structures is being actively pursued at present due to the increasing demand for tiny circuit elements on microelectronic devices. In designing a small contact in a device, we cannot reduce its lateral dimensions without reducing its vertical dimension (Tu, 1981). Although the inability to shrink lateral dimensions will undoubtedly limit circuit density per unit area, the same is also true for the reduction in vertical dimension due to scaling. The nature of scaling is illustrated in Fig. 13, which is a simple schematic diagram of a silicide contact with Si showing that as the lateral dimension of a contact approaches 1 μm, the vertical dimension of the $p-n$ junction and the depth of contact in a bipolar configuration will be about 250 and 20 nm, respectively. In other words, a shallow junction requires a shallow contact; otherwise a deeper contact not only brings itself too close to the junction but also causes an unwanted sidewise reaction (see Fig. 13). For instance, a 0.1-μm-deep silicide contact will extend about 0.1 μm sidewise, which, as a consequence, enlarges the contact area. Such an enlargement for a

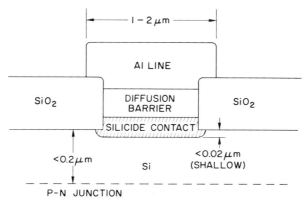

Fig. 13. Schematic diagram of the cross-sectional view of a shallow silicide contact on a shallow junction.

1-μm contact is not insignificant: $\sim$20%. Furthermore, an extended side-wise reaction in the source and drain areas in an FET configuration might also change the length of the channel. The sidewise reaction is yet another example of our concern as device dimensions become small. Shallow con-tacts may also be needed in solar cells made of large-grain or amorphous Si thin films.

The depth of a contact is measured by the amount of Si consumed from the substrate in forming the contact. To control the depth means to control the reaction at the metal–Si interface, including its rate, product, and extent, so that a uniform and limited interfacial reaction can be achieved. A limited interfacial reaction will reduce the sidewise reaction. Near-noble metals are known to react easily with Si to form silicides at low temper-atures (Tu and Mayer, 1978), hence it is difficult to prevent silicide for-mation in the presence of free near-noble metals on Si upon annealing. Consequently, a layer of Pt, e.g., will consume an equal amount of Si, forming PtSi. Refractory metals also form silicides, but they require a much higher temperature (Tu and Mayer, 1978), so it is possible to keep a metal such as W on Si to 600°C without silicide formation, i.e., without consuming Si, provided that no dissolution of Si by W has taken place. Typically, such a nonreactive contact always shows a wide spread in its electrical and mechanical properties, which is unacceptable for a high-performance device. For this reason, a reactive contact which is uniform and limited is most desirable.

In addition to controlling interfacial reaction, we would also like to control electrical contact properties, such as Schottky barrier height. More-over, it would be ideal if we could tailor the barrier at will. Regarding the electrical contact property, there are two points worth mentioning. First, the control of contact properties and the control of contact reaction are inseparable. Specifically, "formation of the Schottky barrier" is related to "formation of the silicide" in silicide–Si contacts. Electronic equilibrium across a contact which defines a Schottky barrier must be considered in conjunction with chemical equilibrium across the contact (Ottaviani et al., 1980). Second, the Schottky barrier of silicides on Si exists over a very wide range from 0.93 to 0.37 eV, and its value depends on the chosen contact material (Tu et al., 1981) (see Fig. 14) rather than on a specific pinning mechanism.

In the following, we shall survey ways to produce shallow silicide con-tacts of depth $\approx$0.01 μm and to correlate them with their Schottky behavior. Both high- (0.85–0.75 eV) and low- (0.5–0.4 eV) Schottky-bar-rier-height contacts will be discussed. Shallow ohmic contacts can be made on heavily doped Si using the same approach, so they will not be discussed here.

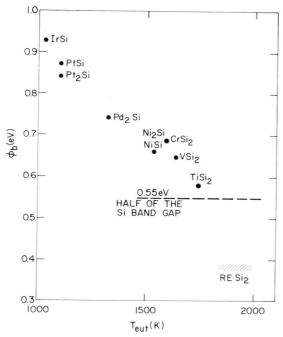

Fig. 14. Plot of Schottky barrier height against eutectic temperature of transition and rare-earth metal silicides. The barrier heights were measured at room temperature using 1- to 16-mil-diameter diodes on $\sim$200-μm-thick n-Si by the I–V technique. The metallic films were e-beam-deposited in 10^{-7}–10^{-8} Torr onto the diodes, which were cleaned by buffered HF, deionized water, and dry N_2 just before deposition.

B. Ways to Make Shallow Silicide Contacts by Using Alloys

We assume a reactive interface between the contact metal and Si, so that the native oxide can be broken by interfacial reaction for an intimate contact to Si. We further assume silicide formation at the interface, so our primary concern is to limit the silicide reaction. Three approaches to limiting the silicide reaction will be discussed in the following.

First, we can supply Si from outside for the silicide reaction so that the consumption of Si from the substrate will be reduced. Variations of this approach are shown in Fig. 15. Figure 15a shows a bilayer thin-film structure of Si and metal before contact formation. The structure can be made using a single e-gun evaporation; and the metal layer should have a thickness more than sufficient to consume all the deposited Si and be able to penetrate the interface between the deposited Si and the substrate. Figure

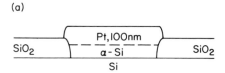

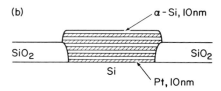

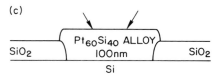

Fig. 15. Schematic diagrams of (a) a double layer of Si and a metallic film, (b) a multilayered structure of alternating Si and metal films, and (c) a codeposited metal–Si alloy film for shallow silicide contact formation.

15b shows a multilayered structure of Si and metal (Tsaur *et al.*, 1981). The structure again can be made using a single *e* gun, and the first deposited layer is preferably the metal. The thickness of each alternating layer can be 2–20 nm and the total thickness is about 100 nm. Figure 15c shows a codeposited, metal–Si alloy film using a dual-*e*-gun system. The alloy film should contain a certain amount of excess metal for reaction with the substrate. For example, if a contact of PtSi is expected, the Pt–Si alloy film should contain more than 50 at. % Pt. It is clear that the amount of Si to be consumed from the substrate can be estimated by the thickness and composition of the alloy film. More detail about using codeposited metal–Si alloy films to produce shallow Pd_2Si (Kritzinger and Tu, 1981; Eizenberg *et al.*, 1981) and PtSi (Eizenberg *et al.*, 1980) contacts will be presented in the next section.

It is conceivable that if a ultra-high-vacuum system and an oxide-free Si substrate are used and if we can deposit an epitaxial layer of silicide by either codeposition, sputtering, or molecular beam, we can achieve the "shallowest" contact. A high-resolution lattice imaging (Foell *et al.*, 1981) of an atomically flat interface between an epitaxial $NiSi_2$ and (100) Si is shown in Fig. 16. Unfortunately, the example was not obtained by deposition but rather by reacting a Ni film on Si at 800°C; nevertheless, it shows the epitaxial relationship between the silicide and Si.

The second approach is to choose a silicide-forming metal such as A which has the Schottky barrier height required and alloy it with an element B which forms no silicides. The reasoning behind this approach is illustrated in Fig. 17. The alloy dilutes the contact reaction, here we can control the amount of Si consumed from the substrate by controlling the alloy film thickness, alloy composition, and composition of the selected silicide. The element B must fulfill two criteria: it must be able to form a solid solution with A and not be able to form a silicide. The latter limits B to those elements which either form no compound with Si, such as Au, Al, and Ag, or are completely miscible with Si, such as Si itself and Ge. These choices are hardly desirable except for the Si just discussed. The criterion for

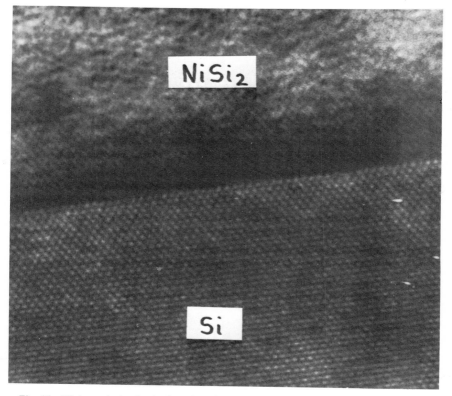

Fig. 16. High-resolution lattice imaging of a cross section of the epitaxial interface between NiSi$_2$ and (100) Si.

(a)

(b)

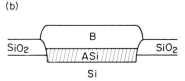

Fig. 17. Schematic diagrams of an alloy AB used to control silicide formation, where A and B form silicide and no silicide, respectively. The amount of Si consumed by the reaction can be predetermined by the thickness of the alloy film, alloy composition, and silicide composition. (a) Before contact reaction and (b) after contact reaction, during which a phase separation into a two-layer structure occurs.

forming a solid solution with A depends on the element A chosen. If A = Pd, those elements with form a solid solution with Pd can be found in a Darken–Gurry plot (Darken and Gurry, 1953) of electronegativity versus atomic radius (see Fig. 18). The arbitrary circle around Pd includes, more or less, those elements, such as Pt, W, Cr, and V, which tend to form a

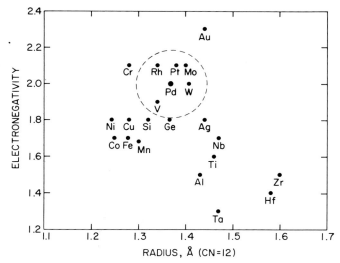

Fig. 18. Darken–Gurry plot of electronegativity versus atomic radius for most metals and semiconductors.

solid solution with Pd to some degree. The solubility can be checked using their binary phase diagrams (Moffatt, 1976). Yet, all these metals form silicides and seem useless for our purpose. However, earlier studies of silicide formation (Tu and Mayer, 1978) showed that near-noble metals differ greatly from refractory metals in their kinetics of silicide formation. Table I summarizes these differences in silicide formation kinetics. Specifically, Pd can form Pd_2Si with Si substrate upon room-temperature deposition, whereas W will not form WSi_2 with Si until the annealing temperature reaches above 600°C. Therefore, we expect that an alloy of Pd–W will form Pd_2Si preferentially on Si provided that the annealing temperature is around 400°C. This means that we can achieve the same alloying effect by relaxing the criterion of no silicide formation by B. As long as B does not form silicide at a given temperature, it will satisfy the requirements. More detail about the use of codeposited near-noble and refractory metals to produce shallow Pd_2Si and PtSi contacts will be presented in the next section. A variation of this approach is to prepare A and B in layered structures as shown in Fig. 15a and b with the A next to the Si. In these structures, a properly selected B may compete with Si in reacting with A, resulting in a reduction of Si consumption from the substrate, otherwise A will be depleted from the phase.

The third approach is to find a silicide which is very rich in metal and is stable on Si. A metal-rich silicide such as Pd_5Si definitely consumes much less Si than Pd_2Si in formation, but how to form such a silicide on Si and keep it stable pose challenging obstacles. We might also try ternary silicides such as Ni_3Ti_2Si and Ni_3V_6Si (Pearson, 1972), but in addition to the aforementioned obstacles, we do not know the Schottky barrier heights of these silicides.

The above approaches all rely on silicide formation to break through the native oxide in achieving an intimate silicide–silicon contact. However, whether a shallow contact must use silicide or not is questionable. It may

TABLE I

COMPARISON BETWEEN NEAR-NOBLE METAL SILICIDE AND REFRACTORY METAL SILICIDE

Kinetics	Near-noble metal	Refractory metal
First phase formation	M_2Si	MSi_2
Formation temperature	~200°C	~600°C
Growth rate	$x^2 \approx T$	$x \approx T$
Activation energy of growth	1.1–1.5 eV	>2.5 eV
Dominant diffusion species	Metal	Si
Mechanism of metal diffusion in Si	Interstitial	Substitution

be unnecessary provided that we can find a metal which can dissolve the native oxide uniformly over the entire contact, yet does not react with the underlying Si substrate. Such a metal must be an excellent getter for oxygen but must not form silicide or dissolve an appreciable amount of Si, or alternatively it might be acceptable if it forms silicide only at very high temperatures as discussed earlier. Al would be an ideal contact metal were it not for its nonuniform dissolution of Si and the problem of Al penetration. The same might apply for the use of pure refractory metal rather than refractory metal silicide as the contact to Si. So far, the only known metal which seems to satisfy our requirements is $Ti_{80}W_{20}$ alloy (Babcock and Tu, 1982), which will be discussed in Section IV,D.

C. Shallow Silicide Contacts with High Schottky Barrier

We review here the use of Pt–Si and Pd–Si alloys and also Pt–refractory metal and Pd–refractory metal alloys in making shallow PtSi and Pd_2Si contacts on n-Si. PtSi and Pd_2Si obtained by reacting pure Pt and Pd on Si have Schottky barrier heights of 0.87 and 0.74 eV, respectively.

1. Pd–Si AND Pt–Si ALLOYS

A series of e-beam codeposited alloy films of Pt–Si (Eizenberg et al., 1981) with composition stepping from $Pt_{75}Si_{25}$, to $Pt_{67}Si_{33}$, to $Pt_{55}Si_{45}$, to $Pt_{50}Si_{50}$, and of Pd–Si with composition stepping from $Pd_{80}Si_{20}$ (Kritzinger and Tu, 1981), to $Pd_{75}Si_{25}$, to $Pd_{71}Si_{29}$, to $Pd_{67}Si_{33}$ (Eizenberg et al., 1981), have been prepared on n-Si for a systematic study of shallow silicide contact formation as a function of alloy composition and heat treatment. In these two series, the first alloy studied was $Pd_{80}Si_{20}$, which was chosen because it is a homogeneous amorphous alloy and is expected to produce a homogeneous contact over the entire contact area. Upon annealing above 175°C, the amorphous alloys reacts with Si to form Pd_2Si. The Schottky barrier height increased with annealing time until it reached 0.74 eV— the value of Pd_2Si. In comparison to pure Pd, the alloy $Pd_{80}Si_{20}$ consumed 50% less substrate Si in forming Pd_2Si. A further reduction in consumption can be achieved by using alloys containing more Si. These alloys were no longer homogeneous and were embedded with grains of Pd_2Si in the as-deposited state, and the amount of Pd_2Si increased with Si content. We found that the inhomogeneity did not affect the final outcome after annealing, i.e., they all showed a Schottky barrier height similar to that of Pd_2Si—0.73–0.74 eV (see Fig. 19). We note that except for the amorphous alloy, the other alloys showed a higher Schottky barrier height in the as-

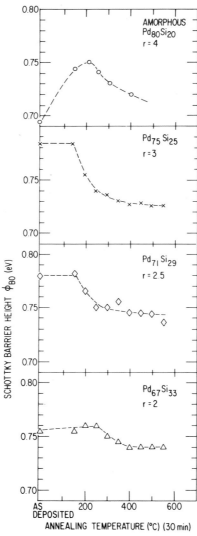

Fig. 19. Schottky barrier height of various Pd–Si alloys on *n*-Si as a function of isochronal (30 min) annealing temperature.

deposited state, which can be attributed to the nonconductive areas in the contact due to patches of interfacial oxide or deposited Si. As Pd_2Si formation increased with annealing, these nonconductive areas decreased and the measured Schottky barrier height returned to the value of Pd_2Si. These results show that although interfacial reaction may not occur uniformly, a uniform contact can still be obtained if we have a single phase making contact with Si over the entire contact area. It was found that a high substrate temperature during alloy film deposition enhances the formation of a uniform contact, which seems critical in using alloys of the limiting composition $Pd_{67}Si_{33}$.

Results of similar studies using Pt–Si alloys are shown in Fig. 20. They are more complicated due to sequential formation of Pt_2Si and PtSi. In Fig. 21 a cross-sectional transmission electron micrograph of a $Pt_{67}Si_{33}$ alloy on Si after 30 min at 350°C is shown. The layer between Si and the original film–substrate interface, where the string of dots of high contrast appears, is about 20 nm thick, which means that the contact depth is about 10 nm.

2. REFRACTORY METAL–Pt (OR Pd) ALLOYS

The general behavior of the contact reaction between the Si substrate and a set of alloys consisting of a refractory metal (W, V, Cr) and a near-noble metal (Pt, Pd, Ni) has been investigated (Ottaviani et al., 1980). The unique feature common to these alloys is that phase separation which occurs during alloy reaction with Si leads to a two-layer structure on Si: the layer next to Si is a silicide of a near-noble metal (PtSi or Pd_2Si) and the outer layer is a refractory metal or a refractory metal silicide. It appears that the near-noble metal has been leached out to react preferentially with Si, forming a silicide layer that separates the remaining refractory metal and Si. The refractory layer is a metal layer when the reaction temperature is low ($\sim 400°C$), yet it becomes a refractory metal silicide layer when the temperature is above 700°C.

The phenomenon of phase separation is illustrated in Fig. 22, which shows Rutherford backscattering spectra (RBS) using 2.3-MeV $^4He^+$ ions for a $Pd_{80}W_{20}$ alloy before and after 20-min annealing at 400°C (Ohdomari et al., 1979). After the annealing, the signal of Pd and the signal of W parted company. Whereas the Pd signal was extended to lower-energy channels joining the Si in forming Pd_2Si, the W signal grew at the higher end. The growth of the W signal indicates the depletion of Pd, so the layer becomes more concentrated in W. Combining these changes, we obtain a two-layer structure formed by annealing (see Fig. 22b). We note that the

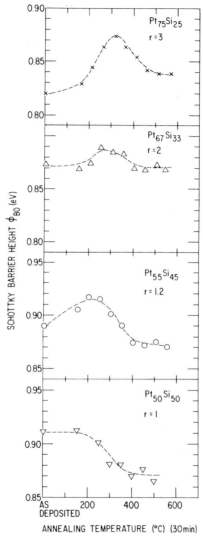

Fig. 20. Schottky barrier height of various Pt–Si alloys on *n*-Si as a function of isochronal (30 min) annealing temperature.

outer W layer was not completely free of Pd and still contained several atomic percent of Pd. This can be explained by the thermodynamic principles treated in Section III,B.

When the alloy was annealed at higher temperatures, the outer refractory

Fig. 21. Cross-sectional transmission electron micrograph of a $Pt_{67}Si_{33}$ film on Si after annealing at 350°C for 30 min. The string of light dots indicates the original film–substrate interface. The reacted layer between Si and the original interface is about 20 nm thick.

metal layer was converted to a refractory metal silicide. This is illustrated in Fig. 23, where RBS of a $Pd_{15}Cr_{85}$ alloy before and after an annealing at 800°C are shown (Ottaviani *et al.*, 1980). The outer layer is $CrSi_2$ containing some Pd_2Si. The formation of a refractory metal silicide is undesirable for shallow contacts since it defeats the purpose of the alloy approach and consumes more Si from the substrate. However, the high-

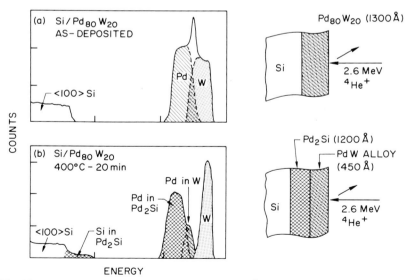

Fig. 22. Rutherford backscattering spectra of a 1000-Å-thick $Pd_{80}W_{20}$ alloy before (a) and after (b) annealing at 400°C for 20 min on Si.

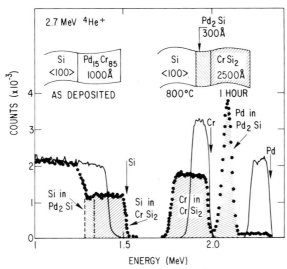

Fig. 23. Rutherford backscattering spectra of a 1000-Å-thick $Pd_{15}Cr_{85}$ alloy before and after annealing at 800°C for 1 hr on Si, using 2.7-MeV $^4He^+$.

temperature annealing results confirmed that no ternary compound forms in these alloys, contrary to alloys of Ni–Pt (Finstad and Nicolet, 1979) and Ti–W (Harris et al., 1976). That no ternary compounds were formed was also confirmed by x-ray diffraction.

Other features of interest in these alloys are the effects of alloying on silicide formation temperature and the first silicide phase formed upon annealing. In general, we observed an increase in formation temperature of near-noble metal silicide and a decrease in formation temperature of refractory metal silicide in these alloys. A typical example is Pd–W alloys. We know that Pd_2Si forms most easily and, in fact, forms during room-temperature deposition of Pd on Si (Buckley and Moss, 1972), yet, on the other hand, WSi_2 has the highest formation temperature reported to date (Locker and Capio, 1973). By alloying them together, their silicide formation temperature has been altered. Figure 24 shows a schematic map of silicide formation temperature as a function of composition for the Pd–W system (Eizenberg and Tu, 1982). It appears similar to a phase diagram but is not since formation temperature is not a temperature of equilibrium. The map consists of three regions corresponding to no silicide, one silicide, and two silicides. The shaded area is the area of special interest to us for shallow silicide contact formation.

The first silicide phase formation in the contact reaction between Si and transition metals has been observed to be quite regular. It has always been

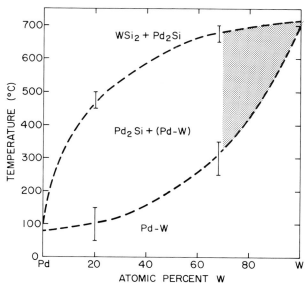

Fig. 24. A schematic map of silicide formation temperature as a function of composition for the Pd–W system.

Pt$_2$Si, Pd$_2$Si, or Ni$_2$Si in the cases of near-noble metals. Alloying of ≥ 10 at. % refractory metals has produced PtSi (Tu *et al.*, 1980) as the first phase formed, while Pd$_2$Si remains unchanged. At present, the explanation of this change is unclear and whether it is correlated to the change in formation temperature is unknown. Whether the first phase for refractory metals will also change by alloying is also unclear.

The phenomenon of phase separation into a two-layer structure is of some technical importance because the inner layer can be used as the contact and the outer layer as the diffusion barrier, hence it deserves more analysis. We shall not discuss thermodynamics and the kinetic process of the reaction between Si and WPd alloy here; the reader is referred to the discussion of the reaction between Pb and AgPd alloy given in Section III. We note that it is the two-layer structure rather than phase separation itself that is of technical interest, because otherwise a mixed two-phase structure resulting from phase separation at the contact is undesirable from the viewpoint of reliable contact applications. We believe that a layered product is obtained because the kinetic reaction rate between Si and near-noble metals is much faster than that between Si and refractory metals at low temperatures and also because of the planar surface of Si wafers.

This can be illustrated by the resultant phase reversal (Mayer *et al.*, 1979) in the annealing of bilayer films on Si, i.e., Pd/V/Si. The interfacial reaction between the Pd and V competes with that between the V and the Si. At temperatures up to 500°C, no silicide formation between V and Si can occur, so the reaction between Pd and V dominates, producing Pd–V compounds and their solid solutions. The reaction continues until it reaches the Si and at that moment Pd starts to react with the Si, forming Pd_2Si. As a consequence, V is displaced backward and phase reversal occurs, i.e., Pd and V swap positions before and after the reaction. The final two-layer structure is similar to the reaction between Si and a codeposited Pd–V alloy.

The Schottky barrier heights and their thermal stabilities for several shallow silicide contacts made of near-noble and refractory metal alloys such as Pd–W, Pt–W (Eizenberg *et al.*, 1980), Pt–Cr (Tu *et al.*, 1980), and Pd–V (Mayer *et al.*, 1979) have been reported. In Fig. 25, we show the Schottky barrier heights of Pd and Pd–W alloys on Si as a function of isochronal annealing temperature and deposition temperature. The data for Pt and Pt–W alloys are shown in Fig. 26. These figures show that barrier heights approaching those of Pd_2Si and PtSi were obtained for these alloys. Specifically, by maintaining a substrate temperature of 100°C during the deposition of W-rich $Pd_{20}W_{80}$ alloys, the Schottky contact of Pd_2Si on Si can be obtained without annealing. Similarly, a substrate temperature of 300°C enables the formation of the Schottky contact of PtSi on Si during the deposition of W-rich $Pt_{20}W_{80}$ alloys. However, the PtSi contacts tend to degrade after annealings beyond 550°C for unknown reasons.

The thermal stability of alloy contacts in the presence of Al has been investigated for both $Pd_{80}W_{20}$ (Olowolafe *et al.*, 1979) and $Pt_{10}Cr_{90}$ (Tu *et al.*, 1980) alloys. These alloys were first reacted with Si, producing a two-layer structure of contact and its diffusion barrier. Then deposition of Al took place, followed by postannealing. We found that the barrier height of the Pd_2Si contact was stable up to a 500°C annealing for 1 hr and that of PtSi was stable up to a 450°C annealing for 1 hr.

A brief comparison of the two approaches, using Si alloys versus using transition metal alloys, concludes this section. The use of Si alloys is simple because a binary system is involved, and it is possible to produce an extremely shallow silicide contact. The use of transition metal alloys is more complicated because it creates a ternary system, yet it is possible to produce a near-equilibrium layered thin-film structure of interconnection and contact on Si. No patterning procedure has been considered here. If patterning can be accomplished by a lift-off step, both types of alloys can be used in device fabrication.

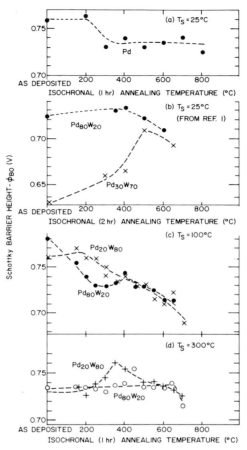

Fig. 25. Schottky barrier height of Pd and Pd–W alloys on Si as a function of isochronal annealing temperatures: (a) Pd deposited at 25°C; (b) alloys deposited at 25°C; (c) 100°C; and (d) 300°C.

D. Shallow Silicide Contacts with Low Schottky Barrier

There have been very few reports on low-Schottky-barrier contacts with *n*-Si, let alone shallow ones. According to Fig. 14, contacts with *n*-Si that have a barrier height lower than half of the band gap of Si include rare-earth metal disilicides (Tu *et al.*, 1981) and Ti (Andrews, 1974). To make a shallow contact using rare-earth disilicides, we can follow the two approaches described in the previous section, namely, by alloying rare-earth metals with Si or with refractory metals. The latter is still workable since

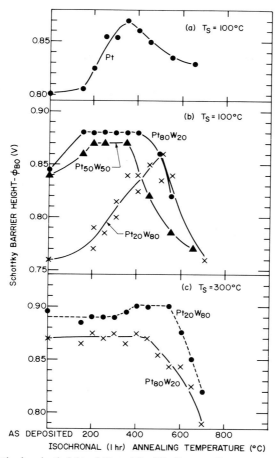

Fig. 26. Schottky barrier height of Pt and Pt–W alloys on Si as a function of isochronal (1 hr) annealing temperatures: (a) Pt deposited at 100°C; (b) alloys deposited at 100°C and (c) 300°C.

the formation temperature of rare-earth disilicides (Baglin *et al.*, 1980; Thompson *et al.*, 1981) has been measured to be ∼400°C, which is about 200°C lower than that of refractory metal disilicides.

During the study of rare-earth disilicide contacts, we have experienced two difficulties: rapid oxidation of rare-earth metals and the need for computing fitting to calculate the value of low barrier heights on *n*-Si due to the large current at low applied voltage. To overcome the first difficulty, we have used a passivation coating. The best coating we found was a bilayer of Pt/W on the rare-earth metal. Any oxygen which has permeated the

Pt will be gettered by the W, and W does not react with rare-earth metals even at 700°C. To confirm computer-obtained values, we have both *p*- and *n*-Si on n^+-Si wafers.

For shallow contact formation, we prepared samples of $V/Gd_{20}V_{80}$ and $V/Gd_{80}V_{20}$ on both *n*- and *p*-Si for reaction and barrier height measurements as a function of annealing (Thompson *et al.*, 1981). Since V has been selected as the alloying element, it was used as the passivation coating in these cases. Figure 27 shows the Schottky barrier height of Gd–V alloys on Si as a function of isochronal (1 hr) annealing temperature. At 400–500°C, both alloys have the same Schottky barrier height. Similar behavior in Er–V alloys has also been observed (Thompson and Tu, 1982). The use of rare-earth metal and Si alloy to produce low-barrier-height shallow contact has not been reported yet.

Another theme of low-barrier-height shallow contact formation is to choose a metal that can break down native oxide on Si without forming any silicides in order to produce a metal–silicon contact rather than a silicide–silicon contact. As mentioned in Section II, Al meets the reaction requirements, yet it cannot be used because of the high Schottky barrier height and the "Al-penetration" problem. Ti will also break down native SiO_2 and establish a low Schottky barrier height (0.52 eV). Unfortunately, Ti forms a sequence of silicides causing the measured barrier height to scatter between 0.5 and 0.6 eV, and to be sensitive to processing steps. The scattering is attributable to nonuniform formation of silicides at the in-

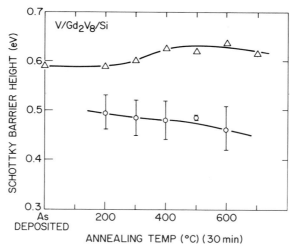

Fig. 27. Schottky barrier height of Gd–V alloys on Si ($V/Gd_2V_8/Si$) as a function of isochronal (½ hr) annealing temperatures: ($\triangle$) *p*-Si, (○) *n*-Si.

terface. Since the Schottky barrier height for $TiSi_2$ has been measured to be 0.58 eV and for other Ti-silicides most likely exceeds that of Ti, fabrication of a stable and reproducible low-barrier-height contact requires no Ti-silicide formation at the interface. One way to achieve this is to stabilize Ti against silicide formation by alloying it with a high-melting-point refractory metal (see Fig. 24).

Alloys of composition $Ti_{80}W_{20}$, $Ti_{40}W_{60}$, and $Ti_{20}W_{80}$ have been prepared by dual-e-gun codeposition onto Si for reaction and Schottky barrier height measurements. These alloys are deposited as a single bcc phase, and their thermal stability increases with W content. Figure 28 shows the Schottky barrier height measured for $Ti_{80}W_{20}$ alloy and for Ti for comparison (Babcock and Tu, 1982). The Schottky barrier height of the alloy is stable with small scatter at about 0.53 eV at a temperature close to 500°C, and both RBS and x-ray diffraction detected no silicide formation in the alloy. Alloys of higher W content are undesirable due to poor adhesion properties, which are attributable to high stress and/or a Ti content insufficient to break the native oxide in a uniform manner. We note that $Ti_{30}W_{70}$ alloy (Nowicki et al., 1978) is well known for its use as a diffusion barrier between Al

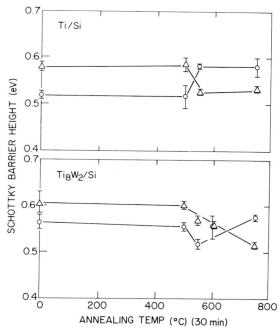

Fig. 28. Schottky barrier height of Ti and $Ti_{80}W_{20}$ alloys on Si as a function of isochronal (½ hr) annealing temperatures: (△) p-Si, (○) n-Si.

and PtSi. In this application, it is generally believed that Ti can increase the corrosion resistance of W and improve W as a diffusion barrier by a preferential oxidation along grain boundaries of W. Also the alloy can be chemically etched.

V. Conclusion

We have stressed in this chapter the advantages of using thin alloy films as metallization in microelectronic devices. As the design of microelectronic circuitry demands an increasingly higher density per unit area, eventually the use of a stack of pure metal films as metallization will not satisfy the requirements. Alloying is in fact a very old method of improving and tailoring the properties of a metal; an example at hand is the use of steel instead of iron. Hence, it is fair to expect greater use of alloy films with unique and wide applications in advanced microelectronic devices.

Alloying affects not only the composition but also the microstructure in films. The latter has been completely ignored here, but the correlation of microstructure with alloy composition and properties will be of great interest.

Also, we have not mentioned the preparation of thin alloy films. Many techniques such as *e*-gun codeposition or sputtering can be used for the preparation of thin alloy films, and it is by no means trivial that a thin alloy film can be made repeatedly of the same quality. The influences of deposition parameters such as the level of vacuum, rate of deposition, substrate surface, and temperature on the alloy film being prepared are still subjects which demand more study.

Among the many properties of alloy films, we have concentrated on the free energy change and low-temperature kinetics in dealloying, and we have illustrated their application in obtaining a near-equilibrium multilayered structure which can be used in shallow-contact metallization. Clearly, there are other applications. Also, many properties of alloy films were not covered here. These are exciting areas in which much more study can be anticipated in the future.

Acknowledgment

The author is grateful to his colleagues at IBM in Yorktown, East Fishkill, and Endicott for simulating interactions during study of the subjects covered in this chapter, to his collaborators whose contributions have made this chapter possible, and to the Central Scientific Service Laboratory at Yorktown for preparing various kinds of alloy films.

References

Andrews, J. M. (1974). *J. Vac. Sci. Technol.* **11**, 972.

Babcock, S., and Tu, K. N. (1982). *J. Appl. Phys.* (in press).

Baglin, J. E. E., Brusic, V., Alessandrini, E., and Ziegler, J. F. (1974). *In* "Application of Ion Beams to Metals" (S. T. Picraux, E. P. EerNisse, and F. L. Vook, eds.), p. 169. Plenum, New York.

Baglin, J. E. E., d'Heurle, F. M., and Petersson, C. S. (1980). *Appl. Phys. Lett.* **36**, 594.

Borders, J. A. (1973). *Thin Solid Films* **19**, 359.

Buckley, W. D., and Moss, S. C. (1972). *Solid State Electron.* **15**, 1331.

Butrymowicz, D. G., Manning, J. R., and Read, M. E. (1977). "Diffusion Rate Data and Mass Transport Phenomena for Copper Systems." National Bureau of Standards, Washington, D.C.

Cahn, J. W. (1959). *Acta Metall.* **7**, 18.

Cahn, J. W., Pan, J. D., and Balluffi, R. W. (1979). *Scr. Metall.* **13**, 503.

Crowder, B. L., and Zirinsky, S. (1979). *IEEE Trans. Electron Devices* **26**, 369.

Darken, L. S., and Gurry, R. W. (1953). "Physical Chemistry of Metals." McGraw-Hill, New York.

Eizenberg, M., and Tu, K. N. (1982). *J. Appl. Phys.* **53**, 1577.

Eizenberg, M., Ottaviani, G., and Tu, K. N. (1980). *Appl. Phys. Lett.* **37**, 87.

Eizenberg, M., Foell, H., and Tu, K. N. (1981). *J. Appl. Phys.* **52**, 861.

Finstad, T. G., and Nicolet, M.-A. (1979). *J. Appl. Phys.* **50**, 303.

Foell, H., Ho, P. S., and Tu, K. N. (1982). *Phil. Mag.* **A45**, 32.

Ghate, P. B. (1981). *Thin Solid Films* **83**, 195.

Ghate, P. B., Blair, J. C., Fuller, C. B., and McGuire, G. E. (1978). *Thin Solid Films* **53**, 117.

Gosele, U., and Tu, K. N. (1982). *J. Appl. Phys.* **53**, 3252.

Harris, J. M., Lau, S. S., Nicolet, M.-A., and Nowicki, R. S. (1976). *J. Electrochem. Soc.* **123**, 120.

d'Heurle, F. M., and Ho, P. S. (1978). *In* "Thin Films—Interdiffusion and Reactions" (J. M. Poate, K. N. Tu, and J. W. Mayer, eds.), Ch. 8. Wiley (Interscience), New York.

d'Heurle, F. M., and Rosenberg, R. (1973). *In* "Physics in Thin Films" (G. Hass, M. Francombe, and R. Hoffman, eds.), Vol. 7. Academic Press, New York.

Howard, J. K., Lever, R. F., Smith, P. J., and Ho, P. S. (1976). *J. Vac. Sci. Technol.* **13**, 68.

Howard, J. K., White, J. F., and Ho, P. S. (1978). *J. Appl. Phys.* **49**, 4083.

Hultgren, R., Desai, P. D., Hawkins, D. T., Gleiser, M., Kelley, K. K., and Wagman, D. D. (1973). "Selected Values of the Thermodynamic Properties of the Alloys." Am. Soc. for Metals, Metal Park, Ohio.

Huntington, H. B. (1975). *In* "Diffusion in Solids—Recent Developments" (A. S. Nowick and J. J. Burton, eds.). Academic Press, New York.

Kelley, K. K. (1960). "Contributions to the Data on Theoretical Metallurgy," Bull. No. 584. Bureau of Mines, Washington, D.C.

Kinsborn, E. (1980). *Appl. Phys. Lett.* **36**, 968.

Kritzinger, S., and Tu, K. N. (1981). *J. Appl. Phys.* **52**, 305.

Locker, L. D., and Capio, C. D. (1973). *J. Appl. Phys.* **44**, 4366.

Mayer, J. W., Lau, S. S., and Tu, K. N. (1979). *J. Appl. Phys.* **50**, 5855.

Moffatt, H. B. (1976). "Binary Phase Diagram Handbook." General Electric, New York.

Nicolet, M.-A. (1978). *Thin Solid Films* **52**, 415.

Nicolet, M.-A., and Bartur, M. (1981). *J. Vac. Sci. Technol.* **19,** 786.

Nowicki, R. S., Harris, J. M., Nicolet, M.-A., and Mitchell, I. V. (1978). *Thin Solid Films* **53,** 195.

Ohdomari, I., Tu, K. N., d'Heurle, F. M., Kuan, T. S., and Petersson, S. (1978). *Appl. Phys. Lett.* **33,** 1028.

Olowolafe, J. O., Tu, K. N., and Angilello, J. (1979). *J. Appl. Phys.* **50,** 6316.

Ottaviani, G., Tu, K. N., Mayer, J. W., and Tsaur, B. Y. (1980). *Appl. Phys. Lett.* **36,** 331.

Pearson, W. B. (1972). "The Crystal Chemistry and Physics of Metals and Alloys." Wiley (Interscience), New York.

Peterson, N. L. (1963). *Phys. Rev. B* **132,** 2472.

Poate, J. M., Tu, K. N., and Mayer, J. W., eds. (1978). "Thin Films—Interdiffusion and Reactions." Wiley (Interscience), New York.

Rao, C. N., and Rao, K. K. (1964). *Can. J. Phys.* **42,** 1336.

Reith, T. M., and Schick, J. D. (1974). *Appl. Phys. Lett.* **25,** 524.

Rosenberg, R., Sullivan, M. J., and Howard, J. K. (1978). *In* "Thin Films—Interdiffusion and Reactions" (J. M. Poate, K. N. Tu, and J. M. Mayer, eds.), Ch. 2. Wiley (Interscience), New York.

Rowland, R. L., and Nachtneb, N. H. (1963). *J. Phys. Chem.* **67,** 2817.

Sinha, A. K. (1981). *J. Vac. Sci. Technol.* **19,** 778.

Thompson, R. D., Eizenberg, M., and Tu, K. N. (1981). *J. Appl. Phys.* **52,** 6763.

Thompson, R. D., and Tu, K. N. (1982). *J. Appl. Phys.* **53,** 4285.

Totta, P. A., and Sopher, R. P. (1969). *IBM J. Res. Dev.* **13,** 226.

Tsaur, B. Y., Silversmith, D. J., Mountain, R. W., Hung, L. S., Lau, S. S., and Sheng, T. T. (1981). *J. Appl. Phys.* **52,** 5243.

Tu, K. N. (1973). *Acta Metall.* **21,** 347.

Tu, K. N. (1977). *J. Appl. Phys.* **48,** 3400.

Tu, K. N. (1980). *Scr. Metall.* **14,** 603.

Tu, K. N. (1981). *J. Vac. Sci. Technol.* **19,** 766.

Tu, K. N., and Berry, B. S. (1972). *J. Appl. Phys.* **43,** 3283.

Tu, K. N., and Chance, D. A. (1975). *J. Appl. Phys.* **46,** 3229.

Tu, K. N., and Mayer, J. W. (1978). *In* "Thin Films—Interdiffusion and Reactions" (J. M. Poate, K. N. Tu, and J. W. Mayer, eds.), Ch. 10. Wiley (Interscience), New York.

Tu, K. N., and Rosenberg, R. (1974). *Jpn. J. Appl. Phys. Suppl.* **2** (Pt. 1), 633.

Tu, K. N., and Turnbull, D. (1967). *Acta Metall.* **15,** 369.

Tu, K. N., and Turnbull, D. (1971). *Metall. Trans.* **2,** 2509.

Tu, K. N., Hammer, W. H., and Olowolafe, J. O. (1980). *J. Appl. Phys.* **51,** 1663.

Tu, K. N., Thompson, R. D., and Tsaur, B. Y. (1981). *Appl. Phys. Lett.* **38,** 626.

Turnbull, D. (1955). *Acta Metall.* **3,** 55.

Vossen, J. L. (1981). *J. Vac. Sci. Technol.* **19,** 761.

Wildman, H. S., Howard, J. K., and Ho, P. S. (1975). *J. Vac. Sci. Technol.* **12,** 75.

Wittmer, M. (1980). *Appl. Phys. Lett.* **36,** 456.

Wittmer, M., Noser, J., and Melchior, H. (1981). *J. Appl. Phys.* **52,** 6659.

Part IV

Variation of Pattern
of Thin Films

8

Fabrication and Physical Properties
of Ultrasmall Structures

R. B. LAIBOWITZ and A. N. BROERS

IBM Thomas J. Watson Research Center
Yorktown Heights, New York

I. Introduction

In order to fabricate and study the properties of thin-film structures with linewidths (size) in the sub-0.1-μm range, many different and new techniques are required. This is especially true if a measurement of the electrical characteristics of the sample is the desired result. The study of the physical properties of samples of such restricted size opens up new areas of scientific inquiry into both the behavior of materials and the development of the new techniques. In addition, practical applications such as new devices and high densities and speeds are also of great interest. Contact to the sub-0.1-μm sample (nanostructure) must be provided and care taken to insure the sample integrity throughout the processing and measurement. Such electrical measurements require regular geometrical patterning, and nanostructure fabrication requires the extensive use of both optical and electron-beam lithographic techniques. Optical lithography can easily generate patterns with linewidths of a few microns, whereas conventional electron-beam lithography is usable in the 0.1–0.25 μm range. To get to smaller sizes, special techniques are generally required which employ very thin resist (Broers, 1981; Molzen *et al.*, 1980) layers, such as contamination lithography, or thin substrates (Broers *et al.*, 1976; Broers and Laibowitz, 1978). Shadowing of the vapor-deposited metal on preformed edges has also been used to produce samples with these dimensions (Feuer and Prober, 1980). In this article we shall only describe the results using contamination processes which have given fine lines with dimensions as small as 8 nm (Broers *et al.*, 1976). These studies have also led to highly sensitive superconducting quantum interference devices (SQUIDs) (Voss *et al.*, 1980). The device aspects of the nanostructures will be described in Section III.

In addition to the results on the devices, we shall also discuss recent results on the minimum metallic conductivity in such fine lines, and more generally the problem of measuring and studying resistance and superconductivity in nanostructures. Such studies have led us to experiments in variable thickness bridges (nanobridges), which exhibit a variety of Josephson effects. The samples to be described have dimensions that can easily be on the order of the grain size in the polycrystalline film from which the nanostructure is made. This can influence the physical properties and also affect edge definition and film growth. Amorphous or single crystal films would not have such problems, at least not to as great an extent. These concepts will be described in Section III.

II. Fabrication

A. *STEM and Window Substrates*

During the fabrication of a fine line with a width of about 10 nm and an approximately square cross section, it is essential to be able to view the sample at several stages. Most scanning electron microscopy (SEM) does not have the required resolution and transmission electron microscopy (TEM) must be used to view the details of the fine-line structure. As the line gets broader and thicker the use of SEM becomes important. In our work we have used scanning transmission electron microscopy (STEM) with a focus spot of a few angstroms to generate the fine-line pattern and to examine *in situ* the size and structure of the line (Broers *et al.*, 1978).

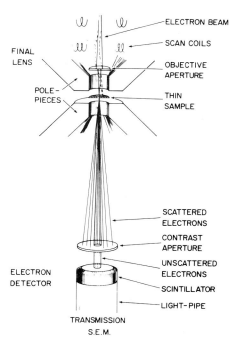

Fig. 1. Schematic of a scanning transmission electron microscope showing the position of the thin sample between the pole pieces of the microscope. The detection system for the transmitted electrons is also shown.

Such a system is shown in Fig. 1. In order to utilize transmitted electrons, a thin substrate is required and thus the nanostructures to be described are generally fabricated on thin membranes or windows as shown in Fig. 2. These window substrates are formed by preferentially etching the window pattern in coated silicon wafers. The preferred coatings generally consisted

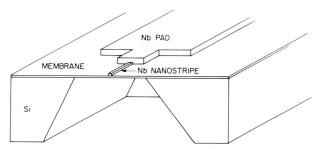

Fig. 2. Schematic of window structure for use in the scanning transmission electron microscope. An example of a fine line is shown which is fabricated on a thin membrane so that the stripe material and the thin window are transparent to the electrons in the microscope.

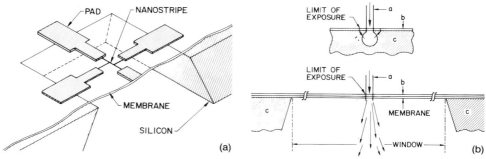

Fig. 3. (a) A view of a four-terminal nanostripe showing the four connecting pads. The pad separation which determines the length of the fine line is not to scale. (b) A schematic demonstrating the resolution improvement that is possible with a thin window which eliminates most of the backscattered electrons. This source of resolution improvement is most effective for linewidths ≲50 nm.

of silicon nitride or oxide 20–200 nm thick. Although such substrates are very convenient for microscopy, they are fragile and limit the sample yield.

However, the window substrates are also beneficial for fine-line patterning in that they reduce the number of backscattered electrons. The effect of these backscattered electrons is shown in Fig. 3, where they are shown increasing the total exposed area. The reduction of this effect by using thin membranes is shown in Fig. 3b. The resolution improvement obtained using such substrates is effective for linewidths ≲50 nm.

B. Metallization

Most of the lines and nanostructures fabricated to date have been made from metals such as Nb (Laibowitz *et al.*, 1979), Au (Broers *et al.*, 1976; Flanders and Smith, 1978), Au–Pd (Feuer and Prober, 1980; Giordano *et al.*, 1979), Al (Mayadas and Laibowitz, 1972), Sn (Broers and Laibowitz, 1978), and W–Re (Chaudhari *et al.*, 1980). The data to be discussed below are mostly on Nb, and Nb will be used as a typical example of a material from which a fine line is to be fabricated. A contact pad set is first established on a window substrate in a way that allows electrical contact to finally be made to the nanostructure. Thus, the pad geometry provides electrical contact both to the outside world and to the fine line itself. The pad separation actually determines in many cases the length of the fine line. This gap between the pads must appear over the window as shown in Fig. 4, and the pads must extend beyond the window over to the solid substrate where contact is made to the outside measuring equipment. Conventional electron-beam lithography (Chang *et al.*, 1976) is used to gen-

Fig. 4. An SEM micrograph showing the pad pattern at a magnification of 1000.

erate the pattern for the pads and separations as small as ~0.12 μm have been achieved as shown in Fig. 5. The thickness of the pad metallurgy can generally be chosen over wide limits; in the case of Nb, 60 nm was typical. Because the fine line occupies very little space along the gap edge, irregular edges were even found to be useful in that they allowed a greater choice of pad separation. Smooth edges were, of course, also possible with opti-mized development of the electron-beam resist. A second example of pad metallurgy is shown in Fig. 6, where Au has been used. The irregular pattern of the pads has resulted from grain changes during processing, e.g., the grain growth probably occurred during the bakeout at a temperature of 160°C, as required for the resist processing.

In fact, the pad edges where the fine lines are to be formed cannot be too rough or ragged in the vertical direction. Such irregularities can make

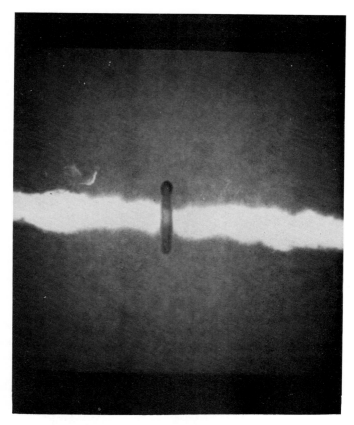

Fig. 5. A STEM micrograph of a nanobridge showing a pad separation of 0.12 μm, which is about the narrowest than can be achieved with the present techniques. The pad edges are intentionally made with the scalloped edges by overdeveloping to obtain a variety of pad separations on the same sample.

it difficult to contact the final stripe, and yet such defects are common in lift-off technology. In general, the edges are carefully examined before proceeding to the subsequent steps. This can be conveniently accomplished in TEM by tilting measurements as shown in Fig. 7. SEM imaging is often helpful in this phase of the study and an example is shown in Fig. 8. Such considerations are, of course, most important when the film from which the fine line is to be fabricated is deposited after the pad formation. This sequence is especially beneficial when it is necessary to keep the fine-line material from experiencing the bakeout process. When such considerations are not important, the pads can be put down on the nanostructure material,

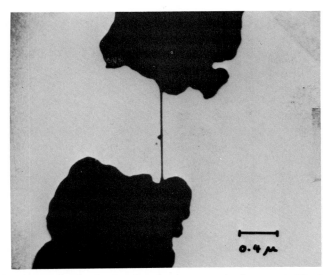

Fig. 6. A micrograph of a Au fine line showing a nearby focus spot. The finest lines of ~8-nm linewidth are generally made of Au or Au–Pd alloys.

which generally insures good contact. In addition, an Ar plasma cleaning step is generally included between the two depositions in either case. The fine-line films had thicknesses that varied from about 10 to 70 nm, although other values could have been used.

In order to form well-defined nanostructures, the grain size of the fine-line material was an important parameter. Fine-grained or amorphous films were generally preferred since these reduced the effect of the grain boundaries. W–Re and Au–Pd films were amorphous, and very smooth films and edges were obtained. The Nb films were generally polycrystalline with grain sizes of about 150 Å. An example of this type of film is shown in Fig. 9. It is out of such a film that the fine line is fabricated and in certain measurements the observed granularity is a determining factor. Some aspects of this problem will be discussed in a later section. The grain size and stability of the film can be even greater in importance in large-grain, low-melting-point materials such as Pb; an example of this type of problem is shown in Fig. 10, where actual discontinuities are observed.

C. Contamination Lithography

The lithographic process that we have primarily used to define the small structure relies on the buildup of a layer of carbonaceous material during

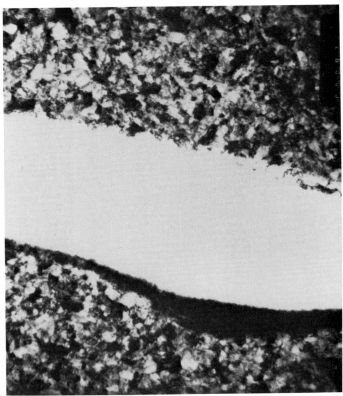

Fig. 7. A TEM micrograph taken by tilting the specimen in the beam in order to show the quality of the pad edges. The pad separation is ~0.75 μm and the upper pad edge is suitable for microfabrication, whereas the lower edge is not.

the electron-beam processing. This type of layer is familiar to electron microscope users and builds up wherever the electron beam strikes the sample. The source for this material is the background or contamination layer of oil that develops in a typical oil-pumped system. We have introduced controlled amounts of contamination, e.g., by pre-exposing the sample to the vapors above a silicone oil diffusion pump. The contamination buildup is pictured schematically in Fig. 11a. This layer of contamination is formed wherever the electron beam is scanned on the sample and it can then serve as a protective layer in a subtractive etching process. An SEM view is shown in Fig. 11b, which also shows cones of contamination that form at the end of the raster where the beam pauses each time before scanning the line. The large thicknesses of contamination possible are easily

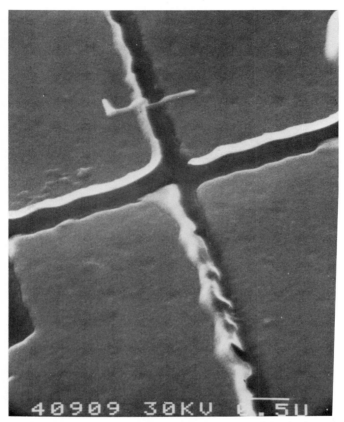

Fig. 8. An SEM micrograph showing a sample with poorly defined edges. A fine line is also shown.

seen. The etching process—in this case ion milling was used—then removes all the surrounding material except that protected by the contamination layer or the pads, which are much thicker.

The contamination layer is an amorphous film and can easily be 100 nm thick. With this type of film in place, high-resolution TEM work on the final fine line did not always reveal the grain structure of the stripe. Of course, the overall dimensions could be determined, but the granularity studies were difficult to make through this extra thickness. Continued etching was sometimes used in addition to careful work on the contaminated samples. In this way we were able to determine that at least for the Nb films the grain size and distribution were about the same in the as-deposited film and in the final fine-line structure.

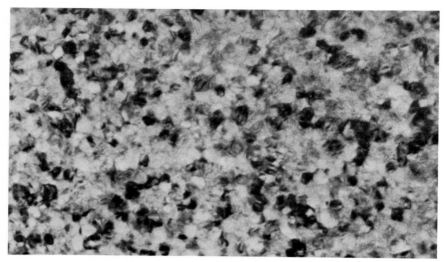

Fig. 9. A TEM micrograph showing the grain size in a 30-nm-thick Nb film. It is from this type of film that the Nb nanostripes are fabricated. The average grain size is ~15 nm.

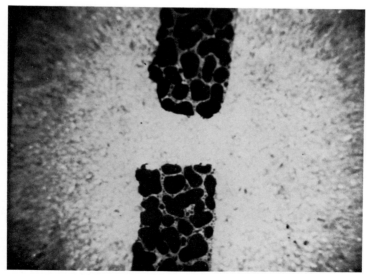

Fig. 10. A TEM micrograph of Pb pads showing the discontinuities that can result when grains grow and separate. The distance between the pads is ~4 μm.

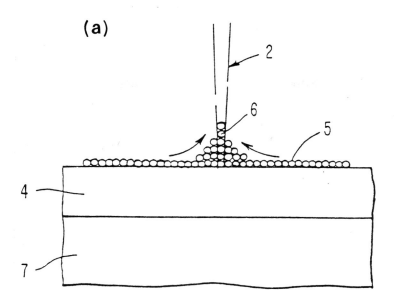

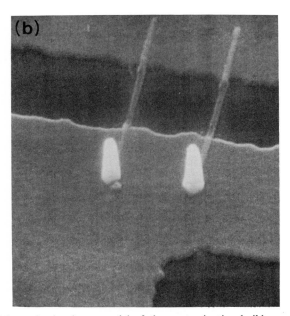

Fig. 11. (a) Schematic showing a model of the contamination buildup under electron irradiation: (7) the window (membrane), (4) the Nb film, (5, 6) the contamination material, and (2) the incident electron beam. (b) An SEM micrograph showing two fine lines in a SQUID configuration and cones of contamination at the ends of the lines where the electron beam pauses in its scanning. The pad separation is ~0.75 μm.

D. Establishing the Line Pattern

With the contamination layer in place, a variety of subtractive etching processes are available, e.g., ion milling and sputter etching. Most of our structures were made using ion milling as described by J. Harper in the work of Molzen *et al.* (1980). Typical beam currents were about 1.5 mA/cm^2 with approximately 1 kV using Ar. In this way the time to remove the background or unwanted or uncontaminated Nb material was about 35 s. The entire structure was exposed to the ion beam and again care was taken not to damage the windows during the etching procedures. It was possible with high-resistance samples to monitor the sample resistance *in situ* during the etching, but because this exposed the sample to burnout possibilities, it was not commonly practiced. The etching process was studied carefully as a function of time in order to insure that the samples were not overetched. An example of such a study can be seen in Fig. 12, which shows a series of TEM photographs made before, during, and after the required ion milling. By monitoring the unexposed Nb outside the stripe, particularly by observing the diffraction pattern, it was possible to determine when to stop the etching procedure. It was, of course, necessary to completely remove the surrounding Nb in order that the fine line would stand alone. It is also worth noting that it was possible to fabricate lines of contamination over insulating substrates. These were made in order to check that the contamination lines were completely insulating.

E. Preparation for Electrical Measurements

In order to conveniently handle the window substrates with the fine-line pattern established, the samples were fastened to alumina substrate holders which had up to 16 possible pin connections. A view of such a setup is shown in Fig. 13. The large wires (actually less than 0.025 mm in diameter) were bonded to the connecting pads ultrasonically. Occasionally, pressed contacts were tried in order to insure that problems were not encountered in the wire bonding process. In addition, SEM pictures were also used to check the samples. Throughout the fabrication procedure, good optical microscopy was necessary. The samples were then mounted in a variety of sample holders for low-temperature measurements. The sample holders generally had resistors in series with the sample leads at low temperatures in order to help protect the devices from current surges. The sample holders could deliver microwave radiation to the small structures as well as control the temperature to better than 0.2 K over a wide temperature range from room temperature to about 1.5 K. Standard electronics were used to mea-

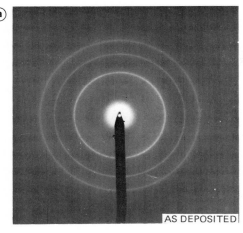

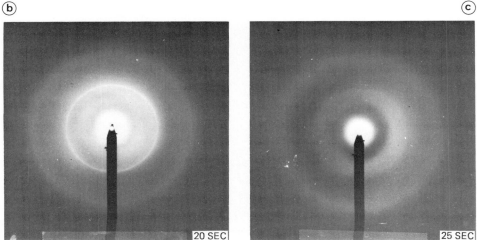

Fig. 12. A TEM study of the ion milling process wherein a transmission electron diffraction pattern is initially taken after the thin Nb film has been deposited (a). Partway through the etching (b) the amorphous pattern of the thin window is beginning to show and finally as the etching is complete (c) the diffraction pattern of the polycrystalline Nb film is gone: (a) as deposited, (b) after 20 s, (c) after 25 s.

sure the *I–V* characteristic and resistance as a function of temperature, whereas more sophisticated techniques were used to measure derivatives and noise spectra of SQUID. The entire measuring system and the cryostat containing the sample were placed in a metal-screened room in order to minimize noise and static electricity pickup.

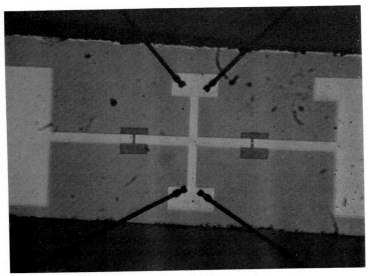

Fig. 13. A micrograph at low magnification showing a sample on a ceramic header with the connecting wires already in place. The Si chip is ~1 mm wide.

F. Concluding Remarks on Fabrication

In the preceding sections, we have described only one of many possible procedures for fabricating nanostructures; the references contain several others as indicated previously. Our process has provided us with reliable samples and was the first to actually fabricate nanostructures with line-widths of ~10 nm. More automated processes using lift-off techniques, shadowing, edge depositions, and a variety of other new ideas would be very desirable for future advances in the field of the science and technology of ultrasmall structures.

III. Physical Properties

A. Structure and Resistive Transition

The fine lines that are most interesting for physical studies have line-widths that are generally smaller than 100 nm, and in many polycrystalline films the grain size can be of the same order of magnitude. Thus, a fine line may be only one or a few grains wide and the granularity can determine, at least in part, the electrical properties (Alessandrini *et al.*, 1981) of the sample. In Fig. 9 we showed an example of a polycrystalline Nb film and in Fig. 14 we show a dark-field image of the same film. It is generally simpler to obtain the grain size from such an image. Such studies also reveal that the spread in grain size on the same sample can be quite large, with grains as small as 5 nm and as large as 30 nm appearing. For Nb, larger-grain films show a tendency to have a sharper superconducting transition (T_c) and a slightly higher T_c, impurities localized in the grain boundaries of Nb films generally lower the T_c. In the same study, we have shown that with a better vacuum during deposition, somewhat larger grains can evolve.

The actual shape (Laibowitz *et al.*, 1980b) of the superconducting transition can change according to the granularity of the fine line. A resistive transition is shown in Fig. 15; in general, the transition is not smooth but has steps as indicated. Typically two transitions are observed: the higher transition T_{co} occurs when the grains themselves become superconducting, whereas the lower T_c occurs when long-range superconductivity across the

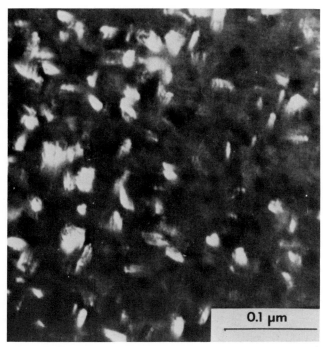

Fig. 14. Dark-field image taken by TEM to emphasize the granularity and grain size of the thin Nb films.

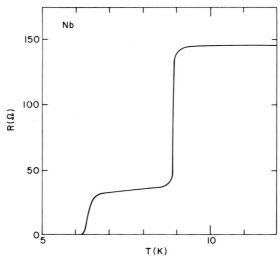

Fig. 15. A typical superconducting transition for a granular Nb nanostripe showing the two transitions as discussed in the text.

entire sample is achieved (Deutscher *et al.*, 1974). This could occur, for example, when Josephson coupling between grains is achieved. This problem has been treated analytically, and using this theory (Patton *et al.*, 1980) and the data for Nb films with resistivities in the range of 40–200 $\mu\Omega$-cm, a new term, the average intergranular resistance, can be defined and calculated. This value ranges from a few hundred ohms to >1 kΩ as the resistivity increases. Grain size and film thickness are also important in these calculations (Laibowitz *et al.*, 1980b). Amorphous films of W–Re have also been used for the fine-line studies and generally show a smoother superconducting transition; however, a complete study of the transition in amorphous samples has not been done yet. Very good edge definition is generally achieved in these amorphous films, as expected.

Such studies of the superconducting transition can be made more precise by controlling the sample geometry, which is, of course, a strong point for the present fabrication technique. As an example of this, in Fig. 16 a Nb sample with a four-terminal geometry is shown; the two extra fine lines (on the horizontal axis) can serve as voltage probes so as to limit the length of line being tested. This type of pattern eliminates problems associated with edges, contacts, and thickness changes. Using a two-terminal geometry, it is possible to have many steps in the superconducting transition; a simple two-step transition as shown previously is easily achievable with

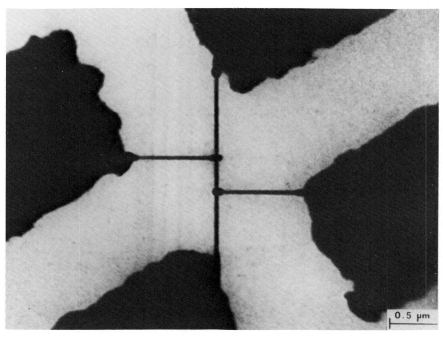

Fig. 16. A micrograph of a nanostructure in a four-terminal resistance configuration. In this case four independent connecting pads had to be fabricated over the window.

the more complex geometry. However, this structure requires making three fine lines and the yield is usually lower than for a single line.

The ability to make a fine line of superconducting material has widened the field of fluctuation effects in samples of reduced dimensionality. In a general sense, when the sample dimensions become less than or equal to some critical length, it can be expected that the phase transition will change and in a way that can be theoretically predicted, as is the case for superconducting fluctuations. The superconducting coherence length in an Al fine line (Mayadas and Laibowitz, 1972) can be as long as 1.5 μm, and thus the sample has two dimensions which are small compared to this coherence length; in this sense it is a one-dimensional conductor. The fluctuation phenomena—the observance of superconductivity above the transition temperature as an excess conductivity σ—is shown in Fig. 17; this result was the first such data obtained. Fluctuation effects have also been seen in other superconducting fine lines; the Al lines exhibit the one-dimensional fluctuations to very high temperatures relative to T_c: $\sim 4.5 T_c$.

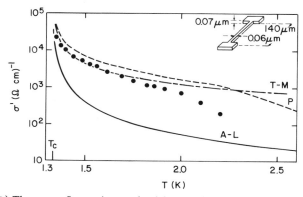

Fig. 17. (●) The excess fluctuation conductivity as a function of reduced temperature for the Al film as shown in the inset. Comparisons with some existing theories are also shown by the solid and dashed lines: A–L, Aslamov–Larkin; T–M, Thompson–Maki; P, Patton.

B. Josephson-Related Effects

Most studies of the Josephson effect have been made on tunnel junctions and have resulted in an *I–V* characteristic as shown in Fig. 18. These devices have many interesting properties and are being studied for possible application in computers due to their high switching speed and low power consumption. Other applications include high-frequency oscillators, receivers and mixers, SQUIDs, and voltage standards. Although the tunnel junction has received a great deal of attention and its fabrication is well under control, Josephson effects are also observed in samples consisting of two bulk superconductors connected by a small bridge of superconductor. If the bridge is small enough, Josephson coupling will exist across the bridge; examples of the *I–V* characteristics of typical bridges (nano-

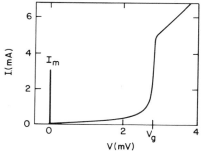

Fig. 18. *I–V* characteristics of an illustrative Josephson tunnel junction showing the zero-voltage supercurrent I_m and V_g ($=2\Delta$ for identical superconductors).

bridges) are shown in Fig. 19d–f. We will not attempt in this chapter to completely describe the Josephson effects in tunnel junctions versus nanobridges. However, it should be observed that the tunnel junction typically has a large capacitance and its quasiparticle characteristic is generally that of Giaver tunneling. In contrast, the nanobridge has no parallel plate capacitance associated with it and its voltage behavior is dominated by its metallic resistance, although ac Josephson effects can alter this to some extent. As can be seen in Figs. 18 and 19, both devices have a zero voltage supercurrent, which when exceeded causes the device to switch into the voltage state. The study of such bridges (micro or nano) has lagged behind the tunnel junction work due to previous inabilities to fabricate reproducible and reliable structures. Although this difficulty still exists to some extent, our high-resolution electron-beam techniques are capable of making very satisfactory samples. A problem with previous samples of larger size was that they typically had normal resistances of only ~0.1 Ω (Anderson and Dayem, 1964) and often showed Josephson effects only in a range of temperature (Laibowitz, 1973) close to T_c. The present nanobridges have resistances as high as 400 Ω; 50 Ω is generally easy to achieve and Josephson effects are seen over the entire temperature range below T_c.

An example of this is shown in Fig. 19, which shows the results of our study of the length dependence of a series of small Nb bridges. The I–V curve for a long sample shows that as the zero-voltage critical current is exceeded, the sample switches in several stages (phase slip centers) to the normal state. The quasiparticles generated at the phase slip centers diffuse away and an estimate of the quasiparticle diffusion length can be obtained from analysis of the I–V curves (Skocpol *et al.*, 1974). The ratio of the resistance at the first step to the total resistance is simply related to the ratio of the diffusion length to the total sample length. Such an analysis gives a quasiparticle length in the Nb films of 90 nm. In addition, an estimate of the inelastic scattering time for the quasiparticles of 13 ps was also derived (Laibowitz *et al.*, 1979), in good agreement with theoretical calculations. As the samples become shorter, fewer of these intermediate states are seen until the sample becomes about one diffusion length long. Similar phase slip measurements have been made in fine lines of W–Re in connection with studies of the maximum metallic conductivity (Chaudhari and Habermeier, 1980b). This subject will be discussed more fully below under localization effects; the diffusion length in these samples was shown to be ~45 nm.

Also shown in Fig. 19 is the response of the sample to microwave radiation at 36 GHz. As is commonly seen in the Nb nanobridges, the I–V characteristic shows the well-known ac Josephson microwave-induced steps which satisfy the relation $h\nu = 2 eV$. In general, the bridges are very sen-

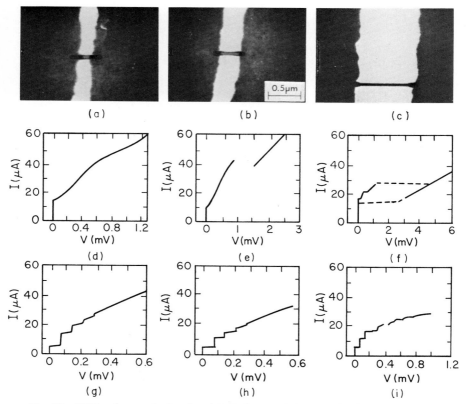

Fig. 19. TEM micrographs (a–c) and *I–V* characteristics with (d–f) and without (g–i) microwaves (36 GHz) applied for three bridges [(d) and (g) correspond to (a) and so forth]. The bridge thickness in this case is 30 nm.

sitive to microwave radiation, although in these studies the samples are simply irradiated from an open waveguide and thus an accurate determination of the sensitivity was not attempted. It is also possible to observe these steps at higher frequencies and an example of the response at 145 GHz is shown in Fig. 20. The dependence of the height of the current step on the microwave voltage can be treated theoretically and plots of both experimental and theoretical data are given in Fig. 21. It can be seen that only a limited fit to the theory has been possible; a recent extension of the theory (Gallegher and Laibowitz, unpublished results) using the well-known resistively shunted junction (RSJ) model in the two extremes, i.e., current and voltage biasing, and the parameters from the sample are shown in Fig. 21b. A better fit to the zeros of the data is obtained, but the

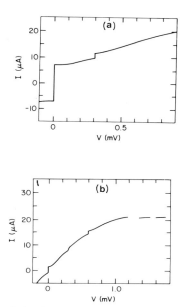

Fig. 20. An *I–V* characteristic of a Nb nanobridge exposed to 145-GHz radiation. Three or four steps can often be observed at this energy as shown in (b) which is at a much higher power level than (a). The bridge critical current is ∼7 μA.

amplitudes do not agree well. Noise in the electrical system is a possible cause of this discrepancy.

One or more Josephson devices may be put into a superconducting loop to form a SQUID. Tunnel junctions, point contacts, and bridges have been used in this regard and commercial SQUID systems are available for use as sensitive magnetic flux detectors. We have incorporated two fine lines in a superconducting loop as shown in Fig. 22 to form a dc SQUID of very small dimensions (Voss *et al.*, 1980; Laibowitz *et al.*, 1980a). These SQUIDs have been shown to be very sensitive magnetic field detectors with energy sensitivity approaching levels where quantum limitations to the sensitivity are expected. If the minimum energy resolution is given in units of energy multiplied by time, then the bridge SQUID has a value ≲*h*, Planck's constant (6.6 × 10^{-34} J s). This value is the lowest ever obtained for this type of device and among the lowest ever obtained for any device. Of course, to actually use the SQUID in a practical circuit, it must be coupled effectively to the outside world, which may add more noise to the circuitry; coupling to the bridge SQUIDs has not yet been attempted. In order to use nanobridges in a SQUID, knowledge of the critical current as a function of temperature and the control of this current using the

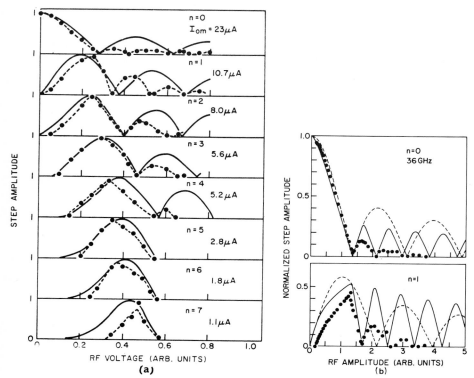

Fig. 21. (a) A plot of the microwave-induced step height as a function of the applied microwave voltage at 36 GHz. Not all data points are shown on this plot; the solid line is the Bessel function normalized to the data at zero or the lowest possible voltage. (b) Data and theory (dashed line) are shown which are similar to that in (a), but only the 0 and 1 steps are shown. Also included is a modified theory, as indicated by the solid line, which uses an analysis (Russer) based on the current-biased resistively shunted junction model with a value of $h\nu/I_cR$ of 0.3.

fabrication parameters are very important. As shown in Fig. 23, the critical current increases almost linearly with decreasing temperature, as might be expected for such long bridges. Data on bridges shorter than 0.1 μm are not yet available; of equal interest for future work will be to learn to control both the granularity and the cross-sectional area in such a way as to be able to control the final current density.

C. Localization Effects

Recently, theoretical and experimental interest (Chaudhari and Haber-meier, 1980a,b; Giordano *et al.*, 1979; Dolan and Osheroff, 1979; Thouless,

Mayadas, A. F., and Laibowitz, R. B. (1972). *Phys. Rev. Lett.* **28,** 156.

Molzen, W. W., Broers, A. N., Cuomo, J. J., Harper, J. M. E., and Laibowitz, R. B. (1980). *J. Vac. Sci. Technol.* **16,** 269.

Patton, B. R., Lamb, W., and Stroud, D. (1980). *AIP Conf. Proc.* **58,** 13.

Skocpol, W. J., Beasley, M. R., and Tinkham, M. (1974). *J. Low. Temp. Phys.* **16,** 145.

Thouless, D. J. (1980). *Phys. Rev. Lett.* **39,** 1167.

Voss, R. F., Laibowitz, R. B., and Broers, A. N. (1980). *Appl. Phys. Lett.* **37,** 656.

Contents of Previous Volumes